SMASH

SMASH

by Garson Kanin

· The Viking Press · New York ·

LIBRARY OF CONGRESS CATALOGING IN PUBLICATION DATA
Kanin, Garson, 1912–
Smash
I. Title.
PZ3.K137Sm [PS3521.A45] 813'.5'4 78–26973
ISBN 0–670–14803–2

Printed in the United States of America
Set in Videocomp Gael

ACKNOWLEDGMENTS:

William Collins + World Publishing Co., Inc.: From *Webster's New Twentieth Century Dictionary*, second edition. Copyright © 1977 by William Collins + World Publishing Co., Inc. Reprinted by permission.

Warner Bros. Music: From *Shine On, Harvest Moon*. © 1908 Warner Bros., Inc. Copyright renewed. All rights reserved. From *Tea for Two*. © 1924 Warner Bros., Inc. Copyright renewed. All rights reserved. Reprinted by permission.

"Is Hitler dead? Or alive? I don't know. But if he *is* alive, I hope he's out of town with a musical!"
—*Larry Gelbart*

NEW YORK

· I ·

I have no way of knowing if it is true for others, but for me, things seem to work out for the best.

I owe a lot of it to luck, but most of it to my brother Vartan. Our father is extremely Armenian, our mother beguilingly Irish. They met at the USO Club in San Francisco during World War II. I was born in Saint Helena, California, at 3:30 P.M., Sunday, June 17, 1951. At home, the way our family has always done it. Old Armenian joke: "I was born in Saint John's Hospital." "What's a matter, you were sick?" I am a Gemini, and although I do not believe in astrology for one minute, I check out my sign every afternoon in the *New York Post* and any magazine that carries such info when I run across it in doctors' or dentists' offices.

My father is a winemaker, a wonderful one. My mother has worked with him since their marriage. Three brothers: one older, two younger. Vartan (thirty-four), Sean (twenty-three), Keta (twenty). The two younger boys are in the business with my parents. Vartan is a high-up editor on the *San Francisco Chronicle*.

From about the time I started high school, Vartan took charge of me, quietly. He was already living away from home, and I often went down to San Francisco to spend weekends with him. Movies, plays, concerts, museums, restaurants. What a brother!

One night at Yamato's, he made it all clear. "Mariam," he said. (I hadn't become Midge yet.) "Little Mariam. I'm glad you're my sister and I'm glad you're smart."

"Not so smart. I got two B's."

"They don't mean a thing. Letters, not learning. You're smart, all right."

"O.K."

"So you'll be able to understand my plan. Listen. I want to steer your education and your career, if you should decide to have one."

"Acting," I said. "Or nursing."

"All right."

"Or airline stewardess."

"Whatever," he said. "But the main thing is—it has to be between you and me. I wouldn't want to hurt Pa's feelings—not for the world. He's a fine, sensitive man."

"I know."

"But remember, he lives in a different world, maybe even a different time—not the world or the time *you're* going to face."

"Uh-huh."

"So this summer—instead of just farting around with pimple-faces the way you did last summer, and wasting your time at the beach— I'd like to get you a job on the paper."

"Super!"

"But as soon as possible you've got to get started on shorthand and typing."

"Oh, boy! Here we go again."

"Right. And again and again—until you do it."

"I'll do it."

"And don't pout. It's one of your least attractive faces."

He had been at me for years on this subject. It was by way of being an obsession with him. His argument was that in the modern world, every young woman—or young man, for that matter—should know steno and typing, a few languages, piano playing, and some drawing, in addition to reading, writing, and arithmetic.

God, how I fought him (and the extra subjects) and God, how grateful I am that I lost.

He argued: *"Pokrig kooyr"*— Armenian for "little sister"—"we're poor, but the world is rich. The ones who train themselves, prepare for the rough battle out there, are the ones who make it in time. Abilities are like tickets—like free passes—passports, even. If you equip yourself the way I want you to—you'll always be employable —and in life, one job leads to another, and another. Look at Lucine."

(His former wife.) "Top skills. So in L.A., when we were first married and I was a cub on the *Times*, we both worked—which meant we could live twice as well. Then she got that cushy job as secretary to the head of Paramount. Next thing you know, she's assistant story editor—then into television, became a producer, and left *me*. Isn't that a beautiful, upside-down Cinderella story?"

"I think it's sad."

"*You* know what I mean, *pokrig kooyr—nothing* would have happened if she hadn't been able to make that first entrée."

"I know, I know. But how's all this going to help me be a great actress—a star? If that's what I decide to be."

"It's going to support you while you struggle."

"Maybe I won't *have* to struggle."

"*All* actresses have to struggle."

"Not all."

"You're going to need training, right? The family'll help, sure, all they can—but don't *count* on it. Count on yourself. Be resourceful, independent. Self-reliant. That's one of the tricks of life, believe me. Being on your own and working is so great for the morale and your strength—yes, health. This is turning into The Century of the Female. So be part of it, be more than the little woman. Be a *big* woman. You don't strike me as the housewife type."

As a result of all this hectoring—I am now able to take shorthand (140 wpm) and type (90 wpm)—and play the piano (good to excellent) —have Spanish and French (fluent)—and draw (fair to good).

Vartan was entirely right. My skills have led me into all kinds of life. Put me through Vassar.

After that, Vartan got me a dream job—personal secretary to the biggest female movie star in the business. Sixteen months of glamour and filmmaking and Europe and excitement. (I omit her name because I have already been hounded mercilessly by all those who want inside dope on her, especially since the recent scandalous happenings.) Then she married (her fifth) an out-and-out creep, who couldn't stand me any more than I could stand him. So I took off for New York and made it into the American Academy of Dramatic Arts, where I studied for two years and had a glorious time.

Then, after a serious and concentrated try, I gave up the idea of becoming an actress. Two off-Broadway flops; one off-off-Broadway hit; one Broadway hit; and two local TV commercials hardly seemed to be leading to stardom or even a sensible career. In addition, my innate common sense pointed out that most of my classmates at AADA had been more talented than I, and that out here in the Real World, the competition was near-devastating. One long, troubled, sleepless, soul-searching night, I decided, irrevocably, to give up the theatre and try another road. It came when I qualified for the job of Assistant to the Publisher at Doubleday. All went well and happily, but when the agency asked me to recommend someone for the Broadway job, the smell of the greasepaint became overpowering— and I took it myself. And here I am.

I started nine weeks ago, just as auditions for the principals were getting under way. Clay Botsford, the Production Supervisor, was the one who actually hired me, after an interview/test that lasted three and a half hours. The clincher may have been the piano playing (Thanks, Vartan!), in view of the fact that this *is* a musical, and the musical skill comes in handy every so often.

Clay is an angel—helpful and supportive and patient. He is about forty, I think. Crew-cut gray hair. Tall and thin and mild-mannered, but firm. Horn-rimmed glasses give him an added intellectual look. When I asked him to give me an outline of my duties—I think I used the phrase "job description"—he laughed.

"Sweetie, there's no such thing in this business. You're going to have to make it up as you go along—the way the rest of us do. You'll probably turn out to be the nerve center of the whole operation."

"How's that?"

"Well, you'll be dealing directly with every department—music, book, staging, choreography, production, notes, bulletins—so that, in a way, you'll be coordinating all the elements."

"God," I said. "I hope I can handle it."

"Of course you can," he said. "I have every confidence in you."

He was lying on the leather-covered sofa in his cramped office. I was sitting in the matching armchair beside him.

He looked at me, seriously. Blue eyes. Always a turn-on for me.

"I'm following my instinct about you," he said, "and it's seldom wrong where young women are concerned."

I crossed my legs in such a way as to make my double-knit skirt slide up neatly, and turned slightly to my left, giving him a nice under-thigh shot with intimations of Pikes Peak.

"Your main problem," he said, "will probably be adjusting to all the different personalities and temperaments. We're all nutty, of course, or we wouldn't be here."

"*I'm* not."

"Not here, or not nutty?"

"Not nutty."

"Of course you are. You leave a solid, respectable, steady, lucrative job—with fringe benefits, chance for advancement, a future—and throw in your lot with a band of mountebanks and minstrels. Why? Because you're stagestruck, and that's an indefinable affliction for which there is no known cure."

"You're wrong," I said, knowing full well that he was right as right can be.

"Basically," he said, "attach yourself to Larry Gabel. At this point, the director is the key. Everything has to flow through him. But then, later on, you'll have to make yourself available to any one of us who needs you. I imagine we'll end up tearing you to pieces."

"And then what?"

"And then I'll have to find a new Production Secretary."

"How many did you use up on your last show?"

"Six," he said.

"Six!" I said and threw my left leg over the arm of my chair. "Maybe I ought to quit while I'm winning."

He laughed, got up from the sofa, went to his desk.

My erotic acrobatics had gone for naught. I sat there, spread, feeling like a female horse's ass.

"Let's go," he said. "Got your book?"

"Yes."

He waited until I was ready before he began pacing and dictating, in a strong voice, with clear articulation and perfect speed.

"To the staff colon I am happy to inform you that we now have our Production Secretary cap P cap S in the person of Miss   paren She does not approve of Ms paren   Midge Maghakian. . . . Do you know how to spell that?"

"Yes, sir."

"Good, because I don't."

" '—does not approve of Ms paren   Midge Maghakian.' "

"Thanks . . . who I am certain will be a valuable addition to our company period   She is highly qualified with an exceptional background and comes to us highly recommended para   For the present she will be attached to Larry Gabel but understands that she will be servicing all . . . no, cut that. Sounds dirty, doesn't it?"

No reply.

". . . that she will be *assisting* all departments. . . . That's better. . . . May I suggest that all of you dictate to MM any information of common interest   As I have previously requested please put everything in writing   As they say in the business world out there colon AVO   Avoid Verbal Orders   cap A V O   paren Note to Hy Balaban colon Miss M is an expert pianist   Say thanks paren

During rehearsal hours MM will be at the director's desk phone five eight six seven eight five oh to be used only   underlined for matters of immediacy or urgency   At other times she may be reached in the theatre production office five eight six seven eight five one   Mornings probably in the main office   Her home phone is   fill that in please   not to be used in emergencies or urgencies I mean of a business comma not personal comma nature. . . . No, strike that."

"Strike what?"

"Period after 'urgencies.' I'm sorry. We tend to get playful around here. Sorry."

"No harm done."

"Thank you. End of memo."

"Read it back?"

"No, I'm sure you've got it. Let's make that form. No reading back."

"Very well."

"Memo to Art Clune colon We have lucked out on the Production-Secretary spot A ten-strike   A winner   Midge Maghakian is her name and I'm sure she will be useful to us all   In addition to her skills and talents I can assure you that you can trust her with matters of strictest confidence. . . . That's it."

• II •

I am now going to describe myself. Although I am no more than a minor character in the story I have to tell, I feel that the reader should know something about the writer. It makes for a more congenial relationship.

I have three superlative assets. (Four, really. But there is one I prefer not to go into at this time.) First, my legs. Looking at them objectively—as I often do—I consider them as good as any. They are outstanding right from the pelvic region to the toes. Thighs, knees (back *and* front), calves, ankles, feet, toes—all have been the subjects of spoken as well as unspoken praise.

I first became aware of them fourteen years ago. I had just turned twelve. I was sitting alone in a booth in Tillie and Mac's Coffee Shop in Pebble Beach, California, where my family had taken a cottage for the summer. I was waiting for Betty Winkler, my best girlfriend. We were going to ride out to Seal Rock on our bikes.

From the booth behind me, I heard my name spoken.

"Who?" asked a cracking voice.

"Midge Maghakian. That how you say it?"

"You don't say it. You *sneeze* it!"

Raucous, adolescent laughter.

They had not seen me because I was still, at that time, small. 5′ 1″. Sitting there, my feet touched the floor only when I extended my toes. I scrunched down and turned my ear to the separating partition.

"Midge. Yeah. What's about 'er?"

"You ever get a load of those gams on 'er?"

The sound of a two-note wolf whistle through teeth.

I shivered and went damp. By "gams," I assumed that the speaker meant my almost-new breasts, which were at that time a cause for daily concern. First thing each morning, last thing each night. From the day of their initial protuberance, I had begun to rub them, pull them, force them into more. Then Betty, staying over one night, had warned me against touching them at all.

"There's nothing you can do, chum," she had said solemnly. "It's like the color of your eyes. So as far as the ol' chests go, whatever you're going to have there, you'll have there. In time. Sub-nubbins, nubbins, boopers, or super-droopers."

I made her repeat the categories until I had committed them to memory.

"Where on *earth'dy'* get *that?*" I asked.

"From my dirty brother, where else?"

"He's *super!*"

"That's what *he* thinks. But listen, don't *ever* rub 'em, or even touch 'em. You've heard of breast cancer, haven't you?"

"Yes!" I was properly terrified. "But eventually," I said, *"somebody*'s going to touch 'em. I mean, isn't that part of the *foreplay*—the way it says in our book?" (We had skillfully swiped a copy of *Human Sexual Response* from Newbegins.)

"Sure," she replied uncertainly. "But *they* have to be careful, too. And also—I don't think they do foreplay every *day!*"

"Oh."

I continued to examine my treasures daily and nightly, without touching them, except when I used a tape measure. They seemed to be developing, but I could not be sure.

Now here, today, in this odd place, in these unlikely circumstances, I have learned that they had at last been *noticed.*

I touched them gently as Betty arrived, then put a finger to my lips, and indicated the next booth. Tillie brought us our customary black-and-whites and left. Betty and I whispered for five minutes.

The boys pounded out.

I told Betty what I had overheard and said I was going to tell it to my mother to prove to her that I did *so* need a bra.

Betty choked on her soda.

"Oh, you *goop!*" she spluttered. "Wait'll I *tell* everybody! What a goop! *Gams.* 'Gams,' they said. Gams are legs, not tits, you goop!"

"Gams?" I echoed. "Oh. Listen, Betty. Cool it, willya? And *don't* tell?"

"I won't," she said magnanimously.

She went on talking, but I stopped listening. My concentration was divided between my ice-cream soda and my growing understanding of the attention my lower extremities had been getting for some time. I had been aware of glances and—yes—of hard, uninhibited looks, but had assumed that my *shoes* were the objects of interest. I decided not to mention this to Betty. What I still could not fathom was why my legs—my gams—should be of interest to anyone. In the weeks that followed, I studied my legs, studied others, and began to learn how to use them.

Now, after fourteen years of practice, I am an expert. I know how to shave them and dress them and display them. I know—have learned—about skirt lengths and evening gowns (always transparent or clinging) and ankle-showing. I know when to cross them and when not. I can judge the angle and intensity of a voyeur's gaze and can supply more or less as the mood strikes me.

So I would say that my legs are probably my best feature.

My bosom comes second. Betty was right. It is all in the luck of the game. My sub-nubbins became nubbins and remained torturingly so until the summer of 1968, when (with the help of a certain amount of expert foreplay) they blossomed or burgeoned into fine, firm boopers. I felt as though I had been graduated and given a diploma. *Two* diplomas.

What a curious broad this Dame Fashion is! For years, my mother and I fought The Battle of the Bra. She would not permit me to wear one. Then, at last, yes. But now, for the past few years, she *insists* that I wear one—at least when I am at home visiting—and will not listen when I try to explain that the bra is passé for people like me. So I keep one in my bag and slip it on when I go to see her.

Otherwise, I do feature my second feature.

Last (or next to last) there are my eyes. They are large and green and piercing and, I find, powerful when I want them to be.

An art student I dated last fall told me that what made my eyes interesting was the fact that they were a "unique spectrum balance" with my light-red hair.

Which brings me to my favorite (and last) good point. I suppose having gone *this* far, I may as well continue. It is my pudendal area, which has been much admired. The silken pubic hair there is somewhat lighter than that on my head, which means that it is a sort of reddish gold. Fletcher—the art student—called it Henna until I made him cut it out. Then he said he thought it was more like Cardinal, but for some reason that embarrassed me.

One morning he said, "I was wrong. In this light, true light, it's Mandarin. Definitely."

He was so pleased to have found the answer that he kissed it.

I settled for Mandarin, although when I looked it up on the Winsor and Newton color chart and compared it, it wasn't even close. Fletcher is no longer an art student. He has switched to electronic-tape editing.

There is more to the phenomenon than the color, however. Something about the composition and dynamics of the whole region is extraordinarily decorative, even to me. The skin tint changes with the seasons: White in winter, Burnt Amber in full summer. The shape of it is unusual, as well. From my navel down to the tops of my thighs, the lines are flowing and symmetrical. At least, that is what I was told many times while I was modeling in Life Study at The Art Students League on 57th Street—a job that Fletcher got me and that finally broke us up—but that is another story entirely. Thirty dollars an hour for standing still was not bad at all, and left me plenty of time for acting classes and interviews and auditions (I was still an aspiring actress in those days, God help me). Further, it was blessedly quiet in there, and I could think. And I did.

One of the problems of living in New York is the noise. It is worse than the air. For twenty-four hours a day, one's ears and nerves and senses are assaulted by unnatural and inhuman sounds. Someone once said that Marcel Marceau, the pantomimist, was such a hit because where else could you go for two hours of quiet?

When my brother Vartan came to spend Christmas with me, we went to a bar to talk. The jukebox was going.

Vartan said, "Why don't they have one slot where you throw in a quarter and get five minutes of silence?"

Apart from the four exceptional features I have described, there really isn't a hell of a lot to me—physically, that is. I am fairly tall

(5'8"); I wear my light-red hair long, so that I can provide variety: bun, pony tail, top of head, down; I keep my weight at 118, which is neither thin nor fat—my first Jewish beau, Maxie, at the Academy, called me "zoftig." And now I know you're all waiting to hear what I think of my face. Well, it's hard to say. It changes all the time. When I'm menstruating, it gets all puffed and sort of blotchy and is generally unattractive. When I drink too much, the same. At other times, it is—what can I say?—not pretty, certainly not beautiful or handsome or striking. But wait, I think I have it—appealing. That's it. I have an open, friendly, pleasant, *appealing* face. So women seem to like it because it doesn't challenge them. And men do because it gives them an edge. Beauties are scary, a lot of guys tell me.

Anyway, about Fletcher and me and my modeling job at the ASL —the night he stubbornly made it a question of the job or him, I kept the job.

Not for long.

Professor Lowdermilk sent for me one day on a ten-minute break. He is a dizzyingly attractive, rugged, abstract painter from Maine, who teaches during half of every year and paints up there during the other half.

He asked me to sit down, offered me a cigarette, and told me he was thinking of letting me go.

"Why?" I asked, naturally.

"My dear," he said, "you are simply too unsettling to the male students."

"How?"

"There's nothing you can do about it. Nothing. That absolutely stupendous middle of you. You're *you*, that's all." He reached over, stuck his right hand inside my robe, and cupped my right breast expertly. "A model should be, you see, insofar as possible, an object. You, I'm afraid, are anything but that. You create, as the kids say, 'wild vibes.'" He smiled warmly. His adroit fingers were at work. As my nipple stiffened to his touch, he put his left hand on my belly and began to move it downward, slowly, tantalizingly.

I stood up and said, "Well, if I'm fired, I'm fired."

He stood up. There was action in the area of his fly.

"Wait a minute," he said, "not so fast. Maybe we can work something out."

"What you mean is you'd like to work something *in,*" I said, and wished to hell it had come out better, classier. He laughed hard, and that irritated me. I said, "Look, you bastard. Either I can do this job or I can't. But don't proposition me. What's one thing got to do with the other? If you'd come on straight—like a man, not like an operator —I think you'd've made it."

"You're terribly exciting," he said.

"Goodbye," I said.

"Hold it. You've got a class to finish."

"No. The middle of me is too unsettling to the male students."

"Cup of coffee?" he asked. "After all, this *is* a coffee break."

"No, thanks."

"A drink?" he asked, sort of reaching for a cabinet.

"Don't con me."

"I rescind the discharge," he said.

I had to laugh at this idiot locution. When I stopped, I said, "I quit."

"You *can't* quit."

"Watch me."

I started out.

"You've got a class to finish!" he yelled.

"No. I'm through," I said at the door. "Because you want to make a sleazy deal—like a goddam businessman. Aren't you ashamed of yourself? You're an artist. A fine artist."

"Sit down a minute."

"And if you *want* to make it a deal, Professor, it's worth more than thirty dollars an hour."

I opened the door.

"If you don't finish the class," he said, "you won't get paid."

I drew myself up and spoke from high above him with the greatest possible dignity—but the words that came out were: "Shove it."

That ended my career in modeling. But I learned a lot about life up there in Life Study.

If I had stayed with Fletcher, it would have ended badly. He is rich and spoiled and flighty. Also, he was never so much a lover as he was a performer. He always made me feel like an audience for his feats. Watch this, he seemed to say. And at the end, each time, he expected more than appreciation. He wanted applause. Goodbye, Fletcher.

And if I hadn't quit or been fired from the ASL—what? I certainly wouldn't have this fascinating, glamorous, absorbing job that I have now: Production Secretary on the biggest Broadway musical of the year, *Shine On, Harvest Moon.*

SHINE ON, HARVEST MOON
Company Bulletin
Tuesday, August 14

BULLETIN: This bulletin will be issued daily to the cast (so far) and crew and is for your use as well as mine. If you are looking for a roommate, for a used car, want to borrow money, or give away a cat, please feel free to use this means of communication with your colleagues. Please send in theatre quotes: Nora Bayes, Everleigh Club material, etc. Midge Maghakian, the editor (among other things), can be reached at 586-9191.

CASTING: We are still looking for an actor-singer to play the part of Claude Gordon. A physical resemblance to the original is desired, but not mandatory. He should be about forty or younger. The main requisites: elegance and authority. Please communicate any suggestions to Clay Botsford or Midge Maghakian.

OPEN CALL: Auditions for dancers will be held at The Imperial Theatre on Monday, August 20 from 10-1 and 2-6. The open Equity call for principals will be held at the Imperial on Tuesday, August 21 from 10-1 and 2-6. Call-backs will be Wednesday at 9:00 A.M.

SCRIPT: The final script to date is dated from July 27 through August 3. A complete First Act should be in the hands of those concerned by Wednesday evening. Also, we would greatly appreciate the return of all out-dated scripts.

OUT-OF-TOWN HOTEL RESERVATIONS: In the course of the next week, all information with regard to out-of-town hotels will be posted on the Call Board at The Imperial Theatre.

DRESSING ROOMS: Your rehearsal dressing-room assignments are posted on the bulletin board. Please note that Dressing Room #2 is the Production Office and is to be used by members of the Production Staff.

THE COMPANY YOU KEEP: CLAY BOTSFORD
(Production Supervisor)
  Born August 10, 1932, Santa Barbara, California.

Music major, USC.

First employment, NYC, Boosey-Hawkes. Night jobs playing piano in bars of Hotel Carlyle, The Drake, St. Regis.

Met Cole Porter and life began. Rehearsal pianist and musical assistant AROUND THE WORLD IN EIGHTY DAYS; KISS ME KATE; OUT OF THIS WORLD; LES GIRLS (MGM).

Into stage management for David Merrick, Alex Cohen, Theatre Guild.

No aspirations other than to be the best Production Stage Manager in the business.

DIRECTORY: Midge has sent each of you a Cast Directory and Rehearsal Schedule. There have been changes made in the latter and a new one is enclosed.

QUOTE TO REMEMBER:
> *An interviewer:* "Tell me, Monsieur Guitry, do you find acting difficult?"
> *Lucien Guitry:* "No, Madame, I find it impossible."

SHINE ON, HARVEST MOON will open at The Shubert Theatre, Boston, on October 19.

· III ·

Auditions began on Monday. There are many separate calls. Open for boy dancers. Also girl dancers. Equity calls for same. And all four for singers. Also showgirls. Then open and Equity for the remaining small parts. How do they do it? We shall see.

Monday. I am sitting here at the director's desk in the orchestra of The Imperial Theatre. It is 9:40 a.m. I am the first one here— of the company, that is. The wings are already crowded with girls, all of them in rehearsal clothes. The atmosphere is tense and anxious. It is dark here, but I am using a Penlite that Clay gave me as a present.

When I talked to Vartan over the weekend and told him about my new job, I thought he was going to come right through the damn phone. (He hasn't yelled at me like that since the summer of '70, when I totaled his Thunderbird in Big Sur.) He said it looked as though all my expensive education and training had been a complete bust, that he had thought I was finally on the track at last and that now I had not only gone off the track, but into the river, and what did I plan to do after the show opened? So I said, Look for another show; and he asked, Will that be easy? And I said, No, maybe impossible, even. And he said, I'm coming to New York. And I said, Don't you dare. I'm doing what I want to do and that's good enough for me. So he said, One final question: When this feckless nonsense is over, do you think you can get your Doubleday job back? And I said,

Probably not. He said, Look, I'll have to call you back later, I'm too upset to talk to you now.

He did call back later, and he'd cooled off some, but not much. We talked along awhile, and finally, he said, "Well, one constructive thing you might do."

"What's that?"

"Write about it. Keep a record of it. It *is* an experience, after all —and an unusual one. So cover it—as though it were a story. It'll help solidify it in your mind and give you perspective on it as part of your life."

"All right," I said. "I will."

I agreed only because I didn't want to rile him anymore. And having agreed, I must do it. That is how I am with him. No lies. Moreover he may ask to see it. But I know him so well—in fact, better than I know anyone else in the world—and what he hopes is that putting it all down, I'll see—in black and white—on the page before me, what a crock it all is. A feeling for the theatre is, after all, something abstract and unexplainable. Writing it all down might very well be a way to get rid of the ghost. If so, so be it.

They have all arrived. The auditions are about to begin. More later.

Later. I am at home after what a day. Auditions 10 to 1, then 2 to 6. Then a session—overstuffed sandwiches from Gaiety sent in, and a knock-down, drag-out until 11:15. Over thirteen hours. I have now had a bath and an omelet and a vodka and tonic, and if I thought I could sleep, I would go to bed, but I know it is no use, so I'm going to do this for a while.

Those auditions! Jenny Flagg, the choreographer, is in charge. But Larry hovering about. Jenny is a former leading dancer, but does not look it. She is overweight, a trifle blowsy. Nervous, impatient, cross. Moves beautifully. Wears slacks always. Either too much makeup or none at all, depending on her mood. She is a looker, but hard. They began with what the kids refer to as a "cattle call," and they're not far off the mark. We are going to engage eight girl dancers—*eight!* —and over a *thousand* showed up. To begin with, they lined them up a hundred at a time, in rows of ten. Jenny went up and down the rows with an assistant, Buddy Rice, saying, "Wait" every now and then, and "Sorry" all the rest of the time. The Waits moved—usually jumped or ran or danced—to one side of the stage, and the Sorrys slunk off to the other to get dressed and leave for what? Only a few musicals a year are done these days. Most of them cost over a million dollars to mount. So the opportunities are few. These kids—gypsies, they are called in the trade—have worked and studied and practiced, and all they got today was a chance to put on their rehearsal clothes and stand there like hunks of meat and be told, "Sorry"—most of them. And I thought of all the money for lessons (where did *that* come from?) and the effort and sweat and physical pain, and finally, getting good enough to enter the profession, then—one look, and a rejection. I couldn't understand it. I asked Russ Kelly, Larry's assistant, to explain. He is a small, myopic, laid-back type. Young, about twenty-five; acts old, about seventy-five. Pale, almost bald, a chain smoker. When it's quiet, you can hear his brain clicking. Still, he gets in with everyone, including me.

"Well," he said. "First off, they've got to type them out, that's all."

"But how can they tell? Maybe they're saying sorry to some of the best dancers in the bunch."

"That's not the point!" he said, fretfully. "We start with the assumption that every single one of them can dance up a storm. We *give* them that, for a start. But it's up to Jenny to decide on the *look* she wants—the size and shape and face and eyes, and so on. In this case, it's period. Nineteen-eight. Around. So there's a look. A kind of person she wants."

"I still say, how can she tell?"

"That's her *job*," he snapped. "That's her *talent*."

"I see," I said, wondering if I did.

This process took until lunchtime. Then Clay asked me to lunch with him and Larry and Russ.

Larry Gabel is impressive. He is ruggedly attractive, intense, lean, and the opposite of flaky. He is asthmatic and carries a pocket inhalant device that he uses several times a day. Usually at a crisis. Nerves. Sometimes, in the dark auditorium, one hears the sharp whoosh! whoosh! sound it makes. The most intelligent eyes I have ever seen. A disarming smile. A self-deprecating manner that only a confident, self-assured man could have. His hair and his eyes match—gray. He is forty-six. I looked it up. We went to Joe Allen's. I couldn't eat.

"Why not?" asked Clay.

"Not hungry," I said.

"Better have something," he suggested. "Nice clean chicken sandwich and a glass of milk. O.K.?"

"O.K."

"She got all emotional," said Russ (a big mouth). "That's what it is."

"No," I protested weakly.

Larry took my hand.

"We all feel it, love. But there's no other way. All we can offer is the chance—not the job. We've got eight spots, and eight thousand girls want them. Why, God only knows."

"It seems so cruel," I said. "The way, the method. I know I'm a complete outsider, but—well, God—if they'd only gotten a chance to dance a minute."

My companions laughed.

"Thousands of minutes," said Larry. "There wouldn't be time, and time costs money these days—more than we can afford. And in any case—if—I mean, even if we could—how—Oh, Christ! Now *I've* got no appetite."

"Eat it while it's hot," said Clay.

"No, I'm through."

Coffee was ordered, and Clay insisted that I eat some ice cream, so I did. I am anxious to please Clay. I'm slowly building something of a thing for him.

"What troubles *me*—" Clay began.

"What burns your ass, you mean," said Larry.

"No," said Clay, looking at me. "What troubles me is the fact that our Miss Jenny goes through all these motions, with her mind—such as it is—absolutely closed."

"You know what they say about choreographers," said Larry. "All their brains are in their feet!"

Russ laughed, too hard. A kiss-ass for fair.

Clay went on. "What *you* know and what *I* know—in fact, what we *all* know, except those damn nervous sweating hopefuls—is that she's got her sixteen spots all filled. In her head."

Larry nodded grimly, his jaw tightening. "A nice little, neat little, closed little shop."

"Right," said Russ.

Larry slammed the table so hard with the palm of his hand that the cups and saucers bounced into the air.

"—what *she* thinks!" he shouted.

The whole room was startled.

"Easy, easy," said Clay.

"Hold it down, Larry, will you?" said Russ, leaning toward him. "There's Buddy right there. Her right-hand fag."

"Yeah? Well, fuck *him*, too."

"No, thank you," said Russ. "I've made other plans."

Larry got out his inhalator, stuck it in his mouth, and pressed twice. Whoosh! Whoosh! He put it away.

"This show," he said, quietly, "is going to have one guiding intelligence, and that is going to be *me. Is* me. I don't know much in life —but I know my job. What's more, I know what my job is. That's one of the basic troubles in our business—it's full of people who know their job and damn few who know what their job is."

"That's profound, Larry," said Russ.

Clay and I exchanged a look. Larry went on.

"I respect every one of the creative elements—including her. But they're inclined to look out for Number One at all times. I'm here to provide the overview, to bring all the pieces together. Casting. Jesus, sometimes I think that's half the battle. I remember when I worked for Hal—he used to say casting could make the difference. Not the leads only, but the whole stageful. All *she* cares about—that selfish cow—is her little groupie. I'm thinking first off about the overall look—God!—the look, the feel, the atmosphere. How do you get it?"

"You start with Kurlansky," said Clay.

"I'll say!" said Larry, and brightened. "God damn. Isn't his stuff *impeccable!* What an artist."

"There's *one* guy cares about the whole show," said Clay.

"Indeed, indeed," Larry agreed. "Some of them—most, in fact— get sore at the actors for standing in front of their scenery."

"There's another thing about ol' Ivan," said Clay.

"When you walk into the Shubert in Boston a few weeks from now, what you're going to see on the stage is what you saw in his models yesterday."

Larry smiled, shook his head in admiration, and said, "Did you know he went to Chicago and photographed old buildings and details —and dug into the libraries for period stuff—not only pictures, but text, too? Christ, he knows nineteen-eight better than the people who lived in it."

"I've noticed something," I said. "Mr. Kurlansky talks about atmosphere all the time."

"You're lucky you can understand him," said Russ. "I usually get about one word out of four."

I could see that Clay was nettled, but he is a man who knows control. He looked at Russ and said, "Ivan Kurlansky doesn't need *words* to express himself. He does that with his *art*. How would you like it if you understood every word he said, but only one of four of his sets?"

"That's very funny," said Russ.

"I didn't *mean* it to be," said Clay, still steamed.

I picked up again. "What I was saying was how when I was trying to get him to do his bio for the bulletin—I could hardly get him to talk about himself. All he seemed to be interested in was the show and the story, and he got to telling me about how most of the girls in The Everleigh Club were—as he said—'statues-esque.' "

"God *damn* it!" said Larry, slamming the table again. "That's just what I God damn mean! That's the *look*—and if she thinks she's going to load me with the same bunch of ponies and hoofers she's had around for years—she's God damn demented. Sure she likes her own gang around—it makes her job easier. But that's not *my* concern."

"Don't jump the gun, Larry. You're into a whole plow routine already—"

"What does that mean?" I asked.

"Tell her," said Clay. "I'll be right back."

He went off as Larry said, "The old joke. The *old* old joke. Farmer needs to borrow a plow from his neighbor three miles away. Starts to walk over, and thinks: He'll lend it to me, I'm sure. Why wouldn't he? I lent him my tractor last spring. Yuh, but people are funny. He might claim he's using it or's going to. Well, I'll ask him when *could* he lend it to me. But what if he stalls? He won't. He might. So. On and on like this—getting himself more and more charged up—until, finally, he gets to his neighbor's house—knocks on the door—the neighbor opens it, and says: 'Why, Luke! How are you? Good to see you!' And our guy says: 'Yeah? Well, you can take your plow and stick it up your ass!' "

I laughed. Russ looked bored, or preoccupied. He kept looking over at Buddy's table—to see if there was any eavesdropping going on. Buddy kept looking over at our table—so there probably was. I can't seem to get a line on Buddy. Older than Russ—perhaps thirty. Handsome. *Too* handsome. No, not handsome at all. Beautiful. And knows it. Perfectly groomed and combed and clad. I understand that a few years ago he was thought to be one of the best young dancers in New York, with a limitless future. Then he went skiing in Aspen, broke both legs and a hip and ended his career. So now, although he can demonstrate, he cannot dance a full routine. He covers his bitter frustration with an acid, put-down, caustic air. Complicated fellow. Ambitious?

Larry spoke. "That's what Clay meant about me doing the plow routine. He's right. I apologize. These are touchy days. We're *all* edgy—worried about getting off on the wrong foot. It can happen. More coffee?"

"No, thank you."

"Well, let's bail ourselves out of here, then. Check, Joe!"

I asked, "Shouldn't I pay for my own?"

"Yes," said Larry, "you should. But this time you're not going to. Just don't make a habit of it. I can't afford it. I'm keeping nine women now."

Clay came back.

"Are we off?"

"Yes."

"Good. We'll be right on time."

Back to the theatre, and the agony of more auditions. The boy dancers this time. The drama even more heightened. The rejected boys seem to take it even worse than the girls.

The Waits (boys *and* girls) are assembled at about 4:00. There are thirteen boys and nine girls.

To my surprise, Dora Cohen, our rehearsal pianist, appears, and each one of the Waits does a chorus of a song. Some have brought their music, others give the pianist a title and a key, still others sing *a cappella.*

"I'm mixed up," I say to Clay.

"How so?"

"I thought these were the *dancers.*"

"They are," he says. "But that's how it's done these days. Later on, when we audition the singers, the picked ones'll be asked to dance. Everybody has to be able to do everything in a musical."

Larry and Jenny sat together through all this, discussing each applicant carefully. I was happily relieved.

"Look," I said to Clay. "All that noise in the restaurant. As you said —a plow routine—they seem to be doing fine."

Clay smiled. "Playing the game, love. Playing the game. Right now, they're about as sincere as a tap dancer's smile."

In time, the twenty-two were cut down to sixteen. I took names, addresses, phone numbers, agent information—preparatory to the call-backs.

Two days later. It is still going on. Open calls over. Equity calls over. Actors and actresses are auditioning, playing scenes, reading from our script, singing, performing specialties.

All morning, members of the staff have been drifting in and out. The songwriters, Mr. Clune, Cindy Sapiro (a money lady), Ivan; one afternoon SHE came in. Big fuss. She thought every audition She saw was awful, and left, saying: "You've sure got a long way to go, people."

Her husband, Val Belmonte, stays behind and makes a nuisance of himself. He has, of course, no official connection with the show—but everyone cossets him (or pretends to) because he is, after all, Husband of the Star, a standard show-business canker sore.

A perfectly remarkable girl comes on—sings beautifully, then while she is dancing, this oaf sings out, "No contrast!" Again: "Where's the contrast?" (What he means is that she faintly, very faintly, resembles his wife, The Star, in type.)

The dancing girl flushes, misses a step, but goes on gamely and splendidly.

We all applaud when she finishes. She starts off, and damned if he doesn't yell again, "Where's the contrast?"

The girl on the stage stops, looks out into the auditorium, and says, "The contrast, Mr. Belmonte, is between professionals and amateurs," and walks off.

We all feel like applauding again, but no one does.

Belmonte says, "What's a matter with *her?*"

"Nothing," says Larry. "She's marvelous."

"Not for this show, she ain't," says Belmonte. He lights a cigar and leans back, waiting for the next victim. The atmosphere is unbearable. I have a pain in my stomach, and for some reason, both my nipples have become so sensitive that I sit there, rubbing them. The lunch break, thank God.

I get out of the theatre fast, because I feel I want to have lunch by myself and calm down. No one has to tell me what a mistake it is to get emotionally involved in this damned thing. It's a job, that's all, like any other job, and as far as feeling sorry for the ones who don't make it, I have to believe that the ones with real talent are going to get there one way or another. If not this show, then another show; if not this year, then next year. I know this is Pollyanna thinking, but maybe I'm Pollyanna, who knows?

I walk around for ten minutes or so and find myself inside Joe Allen's. An empty table, and I sit at it. They don't like parties of one in there, but I can say I'm waiting for someone, and then— what of it?—the someone doesn't turn up; that happens all the time in Allen's. I order a club sandwich (a mistake) and a Coke (another mistake), and sit there wishing I had not given up smoking. I am beginning to think that only a *part* of this tension is being brought on by the events of the day after day. Another contributing factor may well be the lack of sexual expression in my life since Jean-Pierre returned to France. Of all my involvements, that was by far the most misguided. Still, looking back on it, I do not see how I could have escaped it. He was as determined as he was irresistible.

He was one of those trainees sent over to the United States and Doubleday by Hachette, the French publishing house, to observe American methods.

I met him when, in the second quarter of his planned year here, he was assigned to Editorial. This meant that he came to the twice-weekly conferences on the forty-second floor.

The first time he turned up, I did not know who he was, and I'm sure *he* did not know who *I* was, but he looked at me across the table and performed a small bow. I nodded my head, I suppose. The meeting turned into one of those rare noisy, argumentative ones, and since it was my job to write the report, I was soon too busy to do anything but tend to business. He was gone by the time I had finished.

I inquired about him, was told who he was and what he was doing.

The next day, I saw him walking up Park Avenue with an Avedon-model type, and wondered why this should trouble me. He reminded me vaguely of someone. Who?

He was trim and alive. Physically, he looked not unlike my one-time overwhelming screen passion, Gérard Philipe. He gave the impression of enjoying every moment of life. Who was he like in spirit?

Finally, it struck me. Vartan. He had the same graceful movements, the same sudden laughter.

Another editorial meeting. I was sitting in one of the chairs at the foot of the table. He sat two chairs away. The chair between us was unoccupied.

The conference droned on. Everyone seemed to be doodling, including the Frenchman. He folded his doodle and snapped it over to me. (Shades of Saint Helena High!) I opened it. A single word, in block letters: "DRINK?" I looked up at him. His attention was on the speaker at the head of the table.

Impulsively, I wrote "Yes" under the question and snapped the note back. He read it, smiled, and held up his spread fingers, indicating "Five." I nodded.

Another note: This one read: "DINNER?" I wrote under it, "Perhaps," and shot it back. He looked at it and held up eight fingers. I shrugged.

He worked a long time over his third note, consulting a pocket dictionary, with apparently no success.

He passed it to me, and I read: "FOCK??"

I wrote: "Your spelling is terrible."

He wrote back: "What matters? My focking is *formidable.*"

How right he was. For all his gross approach, he proved, in time, to be a gentleman.

He came up to my office at five, promptly, introduced himself: Jean-Pierre Duhamel, and gave me his card.

We went to The Four Seasons. There, over drinks, he told me about himself—an only son of a physician, who had disappointed his family by abandoning his medical studies for a career in publishing.

"If one cannot write," he said, "is it not a best thing to make the good life for who can?"

"Yes," I said.

He asked me where I would like to dine. What cuisine did I prefer?

"In *merveilleux* New York," he said, "you have the table of the world. Not so in Paris."

We decided, eventually, on Nippon, since we both admired Japanese food, and Nippon, which I consider the best in New York, was unknown to him.

"Good, good," he said. "It will be for me an adventure."

He walked me home, kissed my hand, and said he would return in an hour and a half, at 7:45.

At 7:15, the doorman called on the intercom.

"Flowers coming up."

An arrangement of multicolored roses and lily of the valley in a lovely vase. I was sure it was his creation, not the florist's.

At 7:45, the doorman again.

"Man down here."

"On my way."

He had held his taxi, and asked, "You prefer to ride, to walk?"

"Let's ride," I said. "I'm famished. We'll walk later."

"O.K.," he said. *"D'accord."*

He gave the driver the address of Nippon, carefully and clearly.

What is it about shoes off and sitting on the floor that loosens it all up?

Throughout the exquisite dinner, he charmed me with his manners and wit and youth and aspiration and appreciation and candor.

I was ready for him whenever he said the word.

He did not, however, say it that evening.

After dinner, we walked.

"You like to hear the jazz?" he asked.

"I don't know much about it."

"But it is American," he protested. "And *you* are American."

"Oh, yes," I said, "but I was born in fifty-one. I'm a Beatles baby. Dylan. Baez. The Rolling Stones."

"Very good, all," he said. "Yes. But come. I show you."

To Jimmy Ryan's on 54th Street, and an hour of excitement. Roy Eldridge. Ellis Larkins. Ruby Braff.

Walking again. Home.

"Would you like to come up?" I asked.

"Very much."

Brandy and coffee and shoes off again and feet up and talk.

All at once, he rose.

"I will leave you now," he said.

"Oh?"

He must have sensed the disappointment in my voice, because he said, "Is better so. Now we have met, we know each the other a little. You will think of me, I hope. I will think of you, I am sure. Soon we will know. You are not a casual girl, I can see. So is best to be sure. And for my rude note, I apologize."

I wanted to say, "I am sure." Instead, I said, "Thank you."

He kissed me, neatly and sweetly, and was gone.

Troubled sleep.

Flowers on my desk when I arrived. And a note: "I have two tickets for the theatre this evening. *A Chorus Line.* I suggest how we tear them and spend the evening together in your adorable apartment. I can cook. You are a most desirable person. Sincerely, J-P."

So it began. The first truly satisfactory relationship of my life.

We went home together that evening, and did everything together. Prepared drinks, bathed, and went to bed. He was a partner, not a predator. He took and gave pleasure. When he knew I was ready, that he had made me ready—he saw first to my comfort, then entered me—gently at first, tentatively—but as I arched to him, signaling that I needed him more deeply—he thrusted. I heard a scream. Mine. I was in pain, in transport, in ecstasy. He moved inside me easily, keeping me alive. After a timeless time, he began an insistent probing, as though there were depths in me still to be plumbed. There were, and he found them. I moved with him, up up up and out. White light. Skies. A whirling rainbow, and my body melting into thin air. As I was recovering, I felt him plunging into me, desperately. How could I help? I clung to him, giving him the inside of me, more, more, and still more—until I felt him convulse above me and sensed his heated flow within me. The paradisiac end—but no, not yet. He continued to fill me, seemingly without end. At long last, we both were still. How long before he rolled off to lie beside me, face-to-face, still joined? We kissed. Kissed again. Slept.

When I awoke, I heard sounds in the kitchen. I got out of bed, looked at the sharp red-lighted figures on the digital clock: 7:40. I brushed my hair, put on a dressing gown, and went out to the kitchen. There he stood, stark naked—stirring a stew with great concentration.

I embraced him and wondered if it was too early to fall in love.

My reverie on the subject of Jean-Pierre was interrupted by a voice:

"Hey, Midge! Can we sit here with you? The jerk was supposed to hold a table, so naturally he didn't, and we're gonna be late."

Russ. And Buddy. Was he wearing makeup?

"Of course," I said. "Help yourself."

They sat down, next to one another, not with me in the middle. Jean-Pierre would not like *this* picture, I thought.

They whispered together for a rude minute, then remembered I was at the table with them.

They ordered. Beef stew. I thought of Jean-Pierre again.

"Fasten your seat belts," said Russ. "Turbulence ahead."

"Already?" asked Buddy. "It's ahead of sked."

"My ol' faithful Larry," said Russ. "Coming on too strong again. I tell him. Does he listen? What the hell, I'm only a pipsqueak assistant, so what do *I* know?"

"I'll tell you one thing," said Buddy. "And *you* can tell *him*. Jenny's not going to take any shit this time. Excuse me, Midge. I forgot you were here."

"What makes you think I am?" I asked.

"Didn't *you* feel some of it over there today?" asked Russ, looking at me.

"Some of what?"

"The bristles. The hackles."

"No. It just looked to me as though everyone's trying to get their own way. I'm used to that."

"Yuh," said Buddy. "But who *does,* in the end? That's the 'Twenty-five-thousand-dollar Pyramid.' "

"The way I read it," said Russ, "Jenny's cucumber-cool."

"For the present," said Buddy. "This is my fifth show with her. She always starts like this. Watches the weather. Just see to it your man doesn't make it too rough or *he's* the one liable to find himself overboard. There are certain things I could say, points I could make, but I won't. Not right now."

"Why *not* right now?" asked Russ.

"Frankly?"

"Frankly."

"I don't know you well enough, either of you—to open up. Maybe someday I will."

"But maybe someday'll turn out to be too late," said Russ.

"For what?"

"To save an ass or two."

"Don't worry about that, sugar. Before the curtain goes up on this thing opening night, there're going to be a lot of asses lost. I've never seen it to fail. Have you?"

"Depends which asses. If they lose the wrong ones—it can mean the difference between smash or bomb."

"Sure—but there's only one ass I'm interested in. Mine."

"Oh, really? I thought it was mine."

As they giggled, ridiculously, I realized they had forgotten I was there. This being the case, I paid my check, left a tip, and went out.

Forty-five minutes later. I am at the desk in the middle of the auditorium again, making some calls for AC. Russ comes in, plops down beside me and asks, "What happened to *you?*"

"I left."

"I realize that, dummy. I'm not blind—just deaf and dumb. But did we say something? Or what?"

"Or what."

"Come on, Midge. Don't hassle me. We've got to be a team. You'll see. It'll be better that way."

"All right."

"Buddy thought maybe you got teed off on account of us kidding around."

"Good God, no."

"*You* know. It doesn't mean a thing around here. Anybody says anything."

"You mean nothing ever means anything."

"Well, sometimes."

"How can you tell?" I asked.

"Ah! That's it! That's the trick. That's what makes some of us go *this* way—" He pointed up. "And some go *that* way—" He pointed down.

"And which way do you think *you're* going?"

He went pale, clenched his jaws so hard that they made a sound. He looked at me, his eyes blazing.

"I don't *think*, Missy. I *know*. I—am—going—*that*—way!" His finger shot up—pointing to the ceiling, through to the sky, up to the heavens. "That way!" he repeated. Now the finger was pointing at me, as he added, "And don't you forget it!"

He got up and walked away.

Crazy boy, I thought. As matters turned out, I was wrong. Not crazy. Not crazy at all.

The auditions went on, mechanically now. I was able, between notes, to return to my thoughts of Jean-Pierre and the vicarious gratification I needed now in temporary (I hoped) celibacy.

His penis came to mind. I had seen a good many, many of them exciting, particularly in erection—but there was something unique about Jean-Pierre's—a finely sculptured, perfectly proportioned, utterly charming appendage.

I first saw it when we showered together, and my impulse was to kiss it. I did so. I went to my knees, put my hands behind him, and kissed his prick. It came to life, slowly and steadily, as I continued. The water was splashing over my head. I went on kissing it until it was strong and stiff. Jean-Pierre touched my head. I licked him, gently, but did not take him into my mouth, not yet. Better to wait, hold something back. I wanted him inside me, where soon he was to be.

Oral sex, in its many manifestations had, up to now, been something of a turn-off for me. I did not much enjoy being sucked. I found it sometimes painful, often unsatisfying, and always faintly embarrassing. As to fellatio itself, I provided it gamely when it was called for, but found it difficult and uncomfortable. The only pleasure I ever derived from it was in the knowledge that I was *giving* great pleasure.

Not so with Jean-Pierre. His organ, from the first, became a personal possession. I derived joy from the sight and touch of it. I felt power in being able to return it to erection often soon after it had been spent.

My sexual life with Jean-Pierre was indeed a new world. Up to that time, it had been characterized as a desperate act. A contest. A war? A hunger. With Jean-Pierre, it was the loveliest of games, filled with joyous delight. We smiled a great deal as we fucked, and often laughed afterward, feeling triumphant.

There were evenings of reading at home. Sometimes, we would read the same book and then discuss it deep into the night. Books were a kind of food to him.

We explored the city together: restaurants, small museums, concerts, and when we felt flush—the wondrous sounds of the Met. The months went by like days.

One Sunday afternoon. We have returned from Yankee Stadium. Yanks 8, Boston 7. (WP Hunter, 14–6; LP Tiant, 13–8.) Jean-Pierre is worn out from the excitement of the spectacle. I am exhausted as a result of trying to explain the game to him as it went along, and answering his too many questions. Two hot dogs apiece. Popcorn. Ice cream. Root beer.

At home, we tear off our clothes. And . . .

"Wake up, willya?" AC's voice. "Jesus, I wish *I* had time to daydream," he says. "Get me Ivan on the blower. You know where he is? At the shop, I think. Now!"

"*I'll* find him."

I do so, and hand the phone to AC. How to describe Art Clune? He looks like an overweight Mickey Mouse. His voice is a rasp. No wonder. He spends a third of his life on the phone. He seems brittle, frightened, suspicious. Then, all at once, he will say something astonishingly witty and comical and win you. He has a slight tic. His eyes are very small.

"Hello, Ivan. How we comin'? . . . Yeah? . . . No. . . . *No,* I said. Nothin' doin'. If I want to piss my money away, *I'll* piss it away. I don't need anybody to piss it away *for* me. . . . Sure, I know all that. I've heard all that, but these guys, you give 'em a finger, next they want your nuts. I give in on this one, next you know, he's comin' up with something else. . . . Tell 'em no; and if he don't get it, spell it for him. You know how to spell 'no'? I'll tell you. N-O. Learn it, Ivan. Y'wanna know how I got rich? I got rich saying 'no,' not 'yes.' . . . I don't *want* to think it over, Ivan. . . . Anyhow, that's not what I called you about. What I called you about is I'm having trouble— my hands full—with this Alicia character. . . . Did I say she *wasn't* good? Sure, she's good, but she wants to be the star of the show— what am I saying? *Wants* to be? She thinks she *is* the star of the

show. And, by the way, what's her beef with *you,* do y'know? . . .
Well, me neither, but she keeps hocking me day in day out about
your stuff. . . ."

He listened, saw me watching him, winked mischievously, then
wagged his head from side to side.

"What do *I* know what? Your colors, your lights—who knows—
your beard, I suppose. I said to her, 'Look, lovey, why don't you leave
kickin' to the Rockettes. . . .' The Rockettes. . . . The *Rockettes,* for
Chrissake. The Radio City Music Hall. . . . Yeah. . . . Then I tell 'er
—'Whyncha talk to *him,* not me?' She says no—she's got to play it
cool with you. . . . Listen, don't mention I said anything, y'know? The
one thing we don't need at this point is dissension. I'll try to find out
specifics about what's eatin' her, and if I do, I'll lay it on you. . . . O.K.
And listen, Ivan. One thing sure. You're my boy."

He did not hang up. Instead, he handed me the phone and said,
"Alicia."

I reached her at once and gave back the phone.

"Beautiful?" he said, dripping charm. "How we doin'? . . . Good,
good. Look I've just had forty long Russian minutes on the phone
with a no-friend of yours. . . . Ivan. Mr. Kurlansky. . . . Search me, but
he's got nothin' but beefs about your stuff. . . . That's what I told him,
I said talk to *her,* her hearing aid's workin'—but he says no, he wants
me to be the baddie. . . . I swear I don't know. Colors, mostly—and
he says a lot of the period stuff, especially the men, is all wrong. He
says maybe for England, all right, but n.g. for U.S. From the what?
. . . Oh, yeah. *American* fashion magazines. All right, I'll tell 'im he's
wrong. . . . And listen, Kiddo. You're my Kiddo. O.K.?"

He handed me the phone. "Not that I owe you any goddamn
explanations," he said. "Who the hell are *you,* anyway? But just so
you understand—the way to keep these bastards on their toes is to
let them know they're not perfect. With those two, it's like this—
whether they like each other or not personally, who knows, who
cares? But they do have respect for each other's work and stuff—so
my technique is gonna help them both, without them knowing it
even. Understand?"

"Of course."

"What else? Oh, yeah. Did Chris give you the rewrite on Scene
Three?"

"Yes, he did."

"So why didn't you give it to me? What're you savin' it for? Armenian Easter?"

"I haven't had a chance, Mr. Clune. You came in and started phoning right off."

"What's more important, for Chrissake, a phone call or a rewrite?"

I heard myself yelling. "You didn't give me a *chance,* God damn it! Here it is, and *shut up!*" I threw the red manila envelope on the desk. He stared at me, shaken. He started to say something, stopped, started again, and blinked. Finally, words came.

"What is it with you? Your period, or what?"

"None of your goddam *business!*" I said.

A silence. Then his placating voice, even more irritating than his scolding voice. A kind of whine.

"Come on, Midge. I was *teasing.* Having fun. You know that. What's the fun of the business if you can't have some fun. Right?"

"I'm too old for teasing."

"All right. I'm sorry. Right. My apologies. O.K.? *Mea culpa.*" (Where did he get *that?*) "Have dinner with me?"

"No, thanks. I'm not hungry."

I was thinking: Thank you, darling Vartan. I *did* listen. I *do* remember: "Listen. Always remember. The way to handle a bully is to bully him back. Most of them are insecure cowards. Give 'em a good screech and they fall apart."

AC moved to me and actually patted my cheek.

"That's a nice little stack you blow there, Kiddo."

I decided to let him off the hook, smiled sweetly and said, "Yes. A birthday present from my Irish mother."

"Dinner?" he asked.

"No, but thanks all the same."

"You on a permanent hook-up? I should've asked before I let Clay hire you."

"I'm as loose as a goose, Mr. Clune. Free-lancing, just at present."

"Not for long, around here," he said. "*What* a pack of wolves! Including me."

"Howl somewhere else, if you don't mind. I've got two principles. One, never with the boss. Ruins the work. And two, never with a married man. Never. Tried it twice. Disaster. You mix it up with a married man, and you find yourself alone a lot and at the strangest times."

"Well, I'm married—but not very. The boss part—what can I do?"

"Do nothing, and we'll both be happier."

"Plus ça change . . ." he said.

I had no idea what the hell he was talking about, and neither did he.

He picked up the red envelope, hefted it once or twice, and said, "Memo to Christopher Feller." I picked up my pad, and began taking it down. "Thanks for the new Scene Three   It is no doubt an improvement on the old Scene Three   However I am sure you can do still better   I have all the faith in the world in you and I know you are going to come up with a Scene Three that will have us all cheering   The only thing is dash time is getting short and I would appreciate you giving this your attention right away   I would like to have a final Scene Three for the first day of rehearsal

   Best wishes. . . . Got that?"

"Yes. Would you like me to read it back?"

"God, no. I *hate* the sound of my memos. So smarmy."

SHINE ON, HARVEST MOON
Company Bulletin
Tuesday, September 4

FIRST REHEARSAL CALL: Today, on stage at The Imperial Theatre at 3:00 P.M., will be the first rehearsal call for all members of the cast. Today's detailed rehearsal schedule will be posted on the Call Board at the Theatre. We look forward to seeing everyone then.

GODSPEED: We extend a hearty and hopeful welcome to all members of the company. For the moment, nothing is more important than the mastery of the material. I know that most of you know most of your lines, but if not, please get to do so as soon as possible. Progress will begin only from that time.

L.G.

PRODUCTION MEETINGS: Following is a brief notation of the production meetings which will be taking place daily beginning September 12. As each meeting comes up, greater detail will be given in the Bulletin. All will take place at The Imperial Theatre at 2:00 P.M.

Wednesday, Sept. 12 — Organization/Schedules
Thursday, Sept. 13 — Sets and Lights
Friday, Sept. 14 — Music   .
Saturday, Sept. 15 — Costumes and Wigs
Sunday, Sept. 16 — Musical Staging
Monday, Sept. 17 — Logistics and Take Out
Tuesday, Sept. 18 — Props

THE COMPANY YOU KEEP: PATTI ROLPH (Mary Anne)
 I grew up in Indiana on the shores of Lake Michigan and I am a firm believer in the mysterious powers of the Midwestern soil. I began acting and singing in children's theatre in Ann Arbor when I was 12 and spent six summers as a teenager working both backstage and onstage at The Cape Playhouse, Dennis, Mass. Yale Drama School. California School of the Arts. GODSPELL (several roles). THE ROBBER BRIDEGROOM in Vermont. I now study acting with Uta Hagen, singing with Keith Davis, dancing with Alvin Ailey. I am bucking for sergeant. Keep your eye on me. Someday you'll be able to say, "I knew her when."

Or, "I used to buy her coffee." By the way, anybody
wants to buy me coffee, O.K. Light, no sugar.

HIGH HOLIDAYS: Mr. Clune wishes to inform the He-
brew members of the company (if any) that he has received a special dispensation from The Chief Rabbi
of Show Business to rehearse on both Rosh Hashanah
and Yom Kippur, since "rehearsing" is not—by Tal-
mudic Law—considered "work." Did you all know
that? Seriously, folks—if anyone plans to take either or both of those days off—please inform Clay
Botsford or Midge as soon as possible.

RUNNING ORDER: The latest running order is dated
September 1, and is mimeographed on blue stock. If
you do not have a copy of this, contact Midge Maghakian, who will provide it. In any case, please de-
stroy any other versions. The rewrite of Act I,
Scene 3, will be distributed at rehearsal on
Wednesday.

QUOTE TO REMEMBER:
    "On with the dance, let joy be unrefined."
Carrie Watson, star madam
of the World's Fair, 1893

There are now 39 rehearsal days remaining until the
Boston opening.

· IV ·

First day of rehearsal for the full company. The dancers have been at it for two weeks, the singers, for one—but this afternoon, at 3:00 p.m., the full company assembles on the stage of The Imperial Theatre for a go-through of the whole show.

They begin to arrive shortly after 2:00. What an eager bunch! Promptly at 3:00, Clay calls for order and there is the required Equity procedure. A representative is there to check contracts, the rules are read, a Deputy is elected (Gracie Mills, who plays one of the Everleigh sisters).

Each member of the staff, cast, and crew has been given a paste-on badge bearing his or her name and the name of the part he or she is playing. Or position on the show.

The girls are stunning, the men interesting. Hy Balaban is at the piano, doing some last-minute coaching.

Hy is the composer. He looks like Pablo Picasso with hair. Piercing eyes, an infectious laugh. A girl-watcher of the first water. He plays beautifully and although his voice is not much, he performs the songs better than anyone. I wonder what his face looks like without the cigar in it? His lyricist (on this show) is Fred Monroe (formerly Monroe Friedman), a lanky, languid, moody type. He seems to take little joy in life or work or the people around him. Sad. But his lyrics are witty and winning and often wonderfully romantic.

During the Equity hour, Clay comes up to me and asks, "Have you seen Mr. Clune?"

"No. Not today."

"He isn't here."

"I noticed that."

"Call the office. If he's not there—try The Plaza."

He was not at the office. I knew he would not be at home—how *could* he be on the first day of rehearsal? But I have learned to take orders and carry them out no matter how wild they seem.

I was stunned when he answered the phone in his suite at The Plaza.

"Hello!" Angry.

I could not speak.

"Hello!!" A wild cry.

"Mr. Clune?"

"Where the hell *are* you? Where *is* everybody? What the fuck's going on? God *damn* it!"

"I'm at the theatre, Mr. Clune. So is everyone."

"What theatre?"

"The Imperial, of course."

"Don't give me that. I've been to The Imperial this morning. Twice. There was nobody. It's all locked up. I banged—but there was nobody in the lobby."

"Oh," I said, half to myself. "The front."

"What? I can't hear you."

"The *stage* door, Mr. Clune. It's on Forty-*sixth* Street."

"Well, nobody told *me*, God *damn* it!"

He hung up.

I sought out Clay and told him. He could scarcely believe it. He did not laugh, or even smile. He merely shook his head.

"Don't tell anyone," he said. "It's one of those damnable repeatable things."

"No, of course not."

"And let's see if we can stall the start for a while. I'll get Hy to run a couple of Act Two numbers, and do the girls once with the new 'Loving Living' lyrics."

Twenty minutes later, AC came bursting in.

"O.K., everyone," Clay called. "Places, please. We're ready."

An enormous semicircle. Everyone there—dancers, singers, principals, supporting. Hy at the piano facing them. The production staff in a small semicircle across from the larger one.

"Quiet, please!" from Clay.

The response was instantaneous.

"Good afternoon," he continued. "This is a read-through, so stand by for your entrances and cues. Jenny will describe the dance numbers—and maybe sketch in a few, roughly."

"*Very* roughly," said Jenny.

The dancers laughed and applauded.

"When you've got a number to perform, please come to the piano and let's have it."

"And stand close," said Hy. "So I can belt you if you make a mistake."

Light laughter.

Clay again. "We're going for a tentative, preliminary timing, so read or play at performance pace and don't stop. We'll take a twenty-minute break between Acts One and Two. A reminder. No smoking on stage. No food or drink. Just talent. Thanks."

Larry came forward, but before he could begin, AC jumped up and faced the company.

"My name is Jimmy Carter," he said. "And I'm running for President. [*Laughter and applause.*] Thank you. Maybe I oughta sit down and quit while I'm winning, huh? No. I'm your producer and I want to welcome every one of you—including the tenors—and wish you well. Hell. Wish us *all* well. This is a great show and I'm proud to be connected with it and I hope all of you are likewise. [*Applause.*] We've got a great Star, a great score, a great book, a great director, choreographer, designer, and so forth, so what have we got to worry? You notice how I didn't say 'great producer'? That was modesty. That's on account of what happened this morning. I got here before any of you, and I couldn't get in. Fact. Know why? Because I went to the *front* of the theatre—twice. Fact. Nobody told me about the stage door. [*Laughter.*] So instead of 'great producer'—up to now you'd have to say 'schmuck producer.' But I hope to improve and I hope that goes for the rest of you, too. Thank you." [*Applause.*]

Larry's turn.

"A tough act to follow, ladies and gentlemen. But. The next thirty-eight days are going to be among the most important of your lives and mine. I sometimes hear players beefing about certain rehearsal calls, and cheering when they hear they're getting a day or a morning or an afternoon or an evening off. This mystifies me. The rehearsal period should be regarded as that magical time when we learn our crafts, perfect our techniques, use our imaginations, experiment, take chances, discover, and grow. I did a survey once on the average time an American player spends in rehearsal in the course of his career. Any guesses? I'll tell you. Two per cent! That's all. We should welcome this chance to work and practice and create. Let's enjoy it. After all, nobody beat you with a stick to go on the stage, did they? Feel free to do anything at any time. Be bold. If it's wrong, I'll tell you and we'll edit it out. But let go. Show me. Give me stuff to work with. Be audacious. It's easier to mold material than it is to drag it out. No one should be working in the theatre who's afraid of making a horse's ass of himself. Or herself. I agree with the producer —not about him being a schmuck. No one who's been in a negotiation with him can think *that* [*Laughter*], but about this being an extraordinary show—potentially. All the ingredients are here—right here on this stage—and with all respect to all, the greatest is the ineffable magic of our Star. [*Applause.*] How She got so good in so short a time is her secret, or God's. All I know is I'm glad we've got her. The show is going to be built around her—and we've all got to help. Look at those little shoulders—they're beautiful but delicate— and they've got to carry this whole production. . . . What else? Nothing for now. You'll be hearing plenty from me as the days go on. Maybe too much. A final note. Do not direct each other. Leave that to me—if you need help or an adjustment—come to me. I can hear and I can speak. I love you all. So far. Godspeed." [*Applause.*]

"Here we go!" said Clay. "Overture!"

The last syllable had scarcely left Clay's lips when Hy hit the long cluster of low chords with which the overture begins. It was as though he could not wait to get going.

I don't know about the others, but I was all at once a mass of gooseflesh.

Phil Rosenberg, the musical director, stood by the piano and with his baton conducted all afternoon. It is his way of learning the show, of making the show a part of himself.

The playing of the overture turned out to be far more than that. As Hy hit the rhythms of "Chocolate Cakewalk," two of the dancers —a boy and a girl—got up, and in the stage area beyond the chairs, began to perform the dance programmed for it. Jenny herself joined them, with Buddy, and a minute later most of the dancers were on their feet dancing. Everyone applauded when it was over, including the dancers themselves.

When Hy got to "Sing It Again"—the Jack Norworth number from Act One, he tried to make Calvin Sharp get up and do it, and when he refused because he wasn't ready—*She* got up and sang his song, and beautifully, too.

Near the end of the overture, the number we're all counting on comes in—the ballad—"Remember Me." A few of the singers began to sing it, and it was so seductive that before we knew it, everyone had joined in—including Larry and Jenny and Ivan—even I could not help but sing. Everyone but AC. I suppose he didn't know the words.

Cheers and applause when it ended—a great, good, communal feeling. Hy was taking bows à la Leonard Bernstein.

Soon we were into Scene One, and under way.

The whole show read and sounded interesting. I was aware of the vast difference between the written word and the spoken word. Some lines and jokes and ideas that seemed pale on paper were explosive when spoken by a comedian such as, say, Sammy Smith.

Other scenes, which had read impressively, went bland and lifeless when acted.

Larry was dictating notes one a minute into my ear. He impressed me. The smallest detail absorbed him.

During the twenty-minute break, he took me up to the production office and dictated a series of memos to Chris and Jenny and Ivan and Alicia and himself.

He paced around the small room, rubbing the back of his head and from time to time, pinching his eyes.

"Also," he said, "for the bulletin, later. Reminder. Calcium tabs. The color scheme. Projection. And add to Alicia's: Rehearsal muslins as soon as possible. Schedule prop meeting. . . . And you, Midge. Talk to Jenny about the girls' curse calendar—she'll know what it is—and based on that decide if we need an extra swing girl."

Later, I say to Jenny: "First, you've got to help me."

"Sure. If I can."

"Two definitions. One, what's a swing girl? And two, what's a curse calendar?"

"God!" she said. "Somebody'll be sending you out for the key to the curtain any minute."

"What?"

"A swing girl is a chorus standby. Tough job. Because she's got to know the routines in every position. I did it a lot in my day. I was good. . . . And the calendar, I was going to talk to you about that myself. You'll have to get the menstrual dope from every one of the dancing girls—also, a line on can they work while. Some can, some no. Then, if it turns out we've got overlaps—two, or God forbid *three* —we *will* need an extra swing girl." She looked at my surprise, laughed, and said, "Some business, huh?"

"I love it," I said.

Whereupon Jenny sang a full chorus of "I Enjoy Being a Girl," and high-kicked her way out of the office.

COSTUMES: The wardrobe for the production will be executed by Ray Diffen, 43 West 61st Street, LT 1-7217 (our Star's costumes for "Nightfall" and "Wondering"). The remainder of the costumes will be done by Brooks-Van Horn, 117 West 17th Street, 989-8000. Najan, 41 West 72nd Street, 555-5280, is doing the wigs.

THE COMPANY YOU KEEP: CHRISTOPHER FELLER(Author)
  Born in Alexandria, Virginia. Long line of State Department employees in the family. My life in that atmosphere seemed to be leading in that direction. But then—Catholic University and Walter Kerr and the theatre department, and I became the family black sheep by becoming a playwright. My first play a disaster. My second, BREAD AND CIRCUSES, a big hit, thank you. Hollywood. The black sheep got blacker still. Back to Broadway with my third—an *undeserved* catastrophe. Back to the sunshine. Seduced. I am now a Californian and love everything about it: the work, the life, the people. So what am I doing here on the battlefield again? Art Clune. A man I would do anything for. Probably the most astute producer in films today. After this, back to the safety and comfort of movies. No more Broadway —unless Art Clune asks me.
  I live in Big Sur, California.

MORE PUBLICITY: Larry Gabel and Clay Botsford conferred with Paul Cooley of the Press Department on various ideas of publicizing the Everleigh Girls as a unit. Any suggestions from the company will be welcome.

A SCRIPT MEETING: will be held in Larry Gabel's office tomorrow, at 10:00 A.M. Present will be Mr. Gabel, Hy Balaban, Chris Feller, Fred Monroe, Clay Botsford, and Stuart Bender.

CASTING: The long search is over. Roger Corman has been signed for the role of Claude Gordon.

VOTES: We will be in Boston on Nov. 6, Election Day.

Make arrangements for an absentee ballot now.

<u>GIRL DANCERS ONLY</u>: Please see Midge re calendar info as soon as possible.

<u>THE REAL NORA</u>:
  "I am a commedienne by accident. It all came about when I first sang 'Down Where the Wurzburger Flows,' which I had planned to sing straight—without the interpolations that I later added to it. One night I forgot my lines. I got through two verses safely, but when I plunged into the chorus I was lost —I couldn't for the life of me remember a line. In desperation I simply made motions with my hands and did the chorus in pantomine. To my surprise it was a hit—the audience laughed itself into spasms."
  Among other songs made popular by Nora Bayes and her husband, Jack Norworth, were "Strawberries," "Shine On, Harvest Moon," and "Has Anybody Here Seen Kelly?"

There are now 36 rehearsal days before the Boston opening.

· V ·

There is friction almost at once between Larry and Art. It is hard to figure out why. Certainly too early for important artistic differences —everything is still in a vague, undefined state. It can't be about money or authority—those lines are clear. I suppose it is personal. Art resents Larry's talent and experience and reputation and know-how and charm since he himself possesses none of these important attributes. Larry has contempt for Art's purchase of power, amateurism, boorishness, and theatre ignorance. They are different in other ways, too. Larry is fastidious, always beautifully groomed and dressed. Art is a slob. Expensive clothes sloppily worn; shoes off at conferences; a nail-biter, of all things; a nose-picker; a soup-slurper. He dyes his hair. Nothing wrong with that, I suppose, but he, to save money, does it himself, and the results are far from happy. He scratches his privates, no matter who is around.

Art has a large alligator steamer trunk—the first I have ever seen —in his suite at The Plaza. It is filled with boxes, large and small, from Gucci, Cartier, Tiffany, Hermès, Ted Lapidus, Pauline Trigère, and God knows where else. Scarves, jewelry, digital watches, neckties, wallets, silver pens, gold pencils, belts, cigarette cases, and so on.

He uses all this largesse in the way I suppose a football team's trainer uses a first-aid kit. The minute Art senses a problem, a moment of disaffection, an irritation, a wound—he is there on the spot with one of his inevitable little boxes. It is surprising to observe how effective the method is.

"Something for nothing," Larry comments. "One of the most powerful anesthetics in all the world. It works—even on me. Look at this." He shows me an ivory shoehorn from Hermès, a recent gift from Art.

The day I reported for work for the first time, he gave me a Trigère scarf. I wear it a lot, and it sometimes softens my harsh thoughts about him. I am ashamed of myself, but a fact is a fact.

Today, Larry and Art, in a discussion that soon becomes an argument. I take it down for practice.

LARRY

You didn't tell me, Art, that you're going to be—you know—producing a movie simultaneously. With this show.

ART

What's it your business?

LARRY

I need a producer.

ART

You got a producer. Me.

LARRY

I need one around when I need him. There are often, I mean, decisions have to be made on the spot. Sometimes they can't wait —not even ten minutes.

ART

You ever hear of that wonderful new invention they got? The electrical telephone?

LARRY

Not the same, Art. We can't show you like, say, a sketch or a dancer on the phone.

ART

You want me do your job, too? That it?

LARRY

Not at all. But responsibility without authority is useless.

ART

Jesus! What're *you?* A Dale Carnegie graduate?

LARRY

I've done lots of shows, Art, and—

ART

—and *I* haven't done *any*. That's what you're gonna say, right?

LARRY

No. I was going to say—

ART

Bullshit! Don't tell *me* what you were gonna say. Don't *ever* say that to me again—because—

LARRY

Again?! I haven't said it *once*.

ART

You were *gonna!*

LARRY

Oh, Art!

ART

Let's get ourselves like organized around here, O.K.? This is *my* property that I bought with *my* money—or money I raised—so it's my show. Everybody else, see?—including you—is a hired hand. *Everybody.* And if they work good and do their jobs right, they won't be sorry. If they fuck up, they're *out*. Or if they make trouble. So, so far you're concerned, just do what you do very well—you're supposed to be excellent—that's why I hired you and not any of those other hundreds of clowns who were kissin' my ass to get the job. I don't have to like *you*—I like your work. I didn't buy *you*, I bought your work. And I don't give a shit if *you* like *me* or not. We're not gettin' married. We're only doing a show. So we clear?

LARRY

As crystal. But I'm still worried about you being away so much.

ART

Look, boy. You don't know me. I'm organized, f'Chrissake. I'm an *executive*. I'm an administrative *genius*. How the hell do you think I got—with two years' high school—from the William Morris mail room to trainee to junior agent to agent to quittin' and takin' six hot clients with me, to half of Berger-Clune, to gettin' rid of that putz who cared more about his name first than pullin' his weight, to The Clune Agency, to my own independent producing organization with six hits out of eight pictures, and would have been eight out of eight if not for me makin' the mistake of givin' those two old farts final cut? I'm gonna be doing my picture, sure. And this show, goddam right. Easy. I've got it all taped. Each week four days here and four on the coast. In that way—

LARRY

Say that again.

ART

Say what again?

LARRY

What you just said.

ART

The whole thing?

LARRY

No, just the part about every week four days here and four days there.

ART

Who said?

LARRY

You did.

ART

The hell I did!
(To me)
Did I?

ME

I thought it was a slip of the tongue.

ART
(To Larry)
That's what it was—a slip of the tongue. Jesus Christ, a little nothing *secretary* understands and you don't.

ME
(Getting up)
I'm *not* a little nothing secretary, Mr. Clune. I'm an administrative genius.

(I go into the kitchenette, drink three glasses of water and consider quitting. When I return, they are still at it)

ART

—will always know where to find me—day or night—home three numbers, Hillcrest, studio four numbers, even on the set I have my private line. And my mobile in my car. And even my portable *briefcase* phone. You seen it? Stop bellyachin'.

LARRY

All, right Art. I see we're going to have to try it your way. But don't say I didn't warn you.

Inconvenient as this system proved to be in the very first week, it did have its comic aspects and furnished the creative team with a good many laughs.

The prerehearsal conferences were all held at Hy Balaban's elegant town house on East 73rd Street because Hy insisted on using his own Steinway grand.

For the first four days, while book revisions were being discussed and new songs demonstrated and models being shown by Ivan and sketches by Alicia, Art was on the phone in the library next to the sitting room, talking to the coast most of the time. At six o'clock, he joined us.

"O.K.," he said. "I think we're in *great* shape. *Great!* You've all done a *great* job and this is going to be a *great* show!"

"Midge," said Larry, "remind me to buy a present for Mr. Clune. A thesaurus."

A mistake, but Art let it pass. "I'll see you all Monday. In the meanwhile, keep up the terrific work. Oh, and Larry, can I talk to you a minute private?"

"Certainly," said Larry.

Art went out to the library followed by Larry, who turned to us and made a moue before disappearing. The door closed, and before long, Art's angry voice could be heard. Then Larry's—soft, pacifying. Art's less loud. Larry's. Art's, quiet.

They came out, Larry's arm across Art's shoulders. Apparently, Larry had succeeded in recovering from his careless gaffe.

"Ladies and gentlemen," he said. "I wish to apologize to Art for the dumb joke I made a while ago. It was uncalled for, even though it was made in the spirit of fun. I think we'd all—especially me—do well to watch our language and our jokes and our gratuitous comments. Everybody talks too much anyway."

Art. "Listen, I apologize, too. I mean, why get hot over a word? And he's right. Everybody talks too much. Except me."

A big laugh, bigger than warranted.

Art went around the room, shaking hands with the men, kissing Jenny and Alicia and me. He left and Larry resumed.

"Fred," he said. "In the girls' number in Scene One—"

"Yes?"

"Would you give some thought to a few more snappers in the lyrics? There's nothing I love better than laughs in the lyrics. Remember how superbly Larry Hart used to do that? And Hy's an expert at designing the music to make room for the laughs. Cole Porter did it marvelously, too."

Fred. "Why don't you get Porter or Hart, then?"

Larry exploded. "Holy sweet fucking Jesus! Am I going to have to put up with touchiness from you, too? Listen, you knucklehead— With the Big Cheese, I have to apologize—it's his ball and bat—but not with *you!* If you were a professional, you goddam daffodil, you'd be able to handle a suggestion without getting testy and sulky."

"A great act," said Hy. "Testy and Sulky. I used to see them at the Palace."

"I'm just as much a professional as *you* are," said Fred.

"A professional *what?*" said Hy.

"If you are," said Larry, "then behave like one."

"See y'," said Fred, and left.

"Wouldn't it be nice," said Larry, "if we only saw *him* four days a week?"

"He's O.K.," said Hy, noodling at the piano. "He's got problems, that's all."

"Who hasn't?" asked Jenny.

"His are bigger and better," said Hy. "Bear with him. A big talent —*big.*" He sang, accompanying himself:

> " 'I'm *prac*tical
> *Back* t' call-
> Ing a spade

A spade.
A mistake I made
In the past was
Calling a spade
An arrow from Cupid—
Stupid!'

"You don't get chunks like that often."

"No one's putting him down," said Larry.

"I know, but he's nervous," Hy explained. "A nervous man. Insecure. So when you start mentioning the gods he panics. He'd like to be those guys, but how can he be?"

"Who's asking him to?" asked Larry.

"I'll spell it out," said Hy. "You do a musical, it's bound to be a mixed grill, right? Have you ever seen one not? We're full of straights and gays and both—present company, of course, excepted."

"Speak for yourself," said Jenny, laughing.

"But Fred—he's a tormented kid. He's minty, but he doesn't *want* to be. He's not like, you know, the great British ballet dancer—what's his name? What's the difference?—when he got mugged in New York and two days later all his hair fell out—remember?—and they told him that since it wasn't physical—but mental—he needed psychotherapy and hypnotism. So he went to the great Dr. Kubie, but before they started, he said, 'Listen, Doctor, I certainly want my hair back—but I must tell you this—I'm as queer as a coot—and if you do anything to change *that*, I'll *kill* you!' Well, Fred's not like that—he'd like to switch; he's tried, can't—so it makes him—his torture—A: a great lyric writer, and B: a nervous wreck."

"And C," said Larry, "a pain in the ass. . . . I'm not interested in his sexual problems. There're clinics for that. I'm interested in getting the best out of him—and the rest of you—and myself. So if you ever see him again, tell him. And tell him not to be such a baby."

"I'll tell him," said Hy.

"So now what? Can we hear the new chorus?"

"Sure," said Hy. "I'll sing it. I sing fifty times better than he does anyway—but I have to let *him* demonstrate all the time. Never mind. Here we go."

<u>SHINE ON, HARVEST MOON</u>
Company Bulletin
Monday, September 10

<u>PRODUCTION STAFF</u>:

Clay Botsford: Production Supervisor
Stuart Bender: Stage Manager
Phil Rosenberg: Musical Director
Henry Wadsworth: Company Manager
Buddy Rice is assisting Miss Flagg
Patti Rolph will be the Dance Captain

Until further notice, Jenny Flagg plans to rehearse on an 11:00 A.M. to 7:00 P.M. schedule.

<u>LINGO</u>: Please, if you can avoid it, don't use the word "cross," nor the words "enter" or "exit." Thinking in these terms eventually leads to artificiality. In life, we move, walk, sit, stand, and so on, but we seldom cross.   L.G.

<u>PUNCTUALITY</u>: Due to our full schedule, it is absolutely essential that all members of the company be absolutely punctual for all calls, rehearsals, run-throughs, fittings, etc.

<u>PREPARATION</u>: Mr. Gabel would greatly appreciate immediate attention to line and lyric learning. This is in our mutual interest, since much more can be gained from the rehearsals if time is not used for the private and mechanical job of committing words to memory. It is our plan to make no changes in text or lyrics after Friday night, September 14. Please let's have any queries or notions before that time.

<u>THE COMPANY YOU KEEP</u>: HENRY WADSWORTH
(Company Manager)
I write under protest and at the persuasive insistence of Miss Maghakian.
I come from Christmas Cove, Maine, where I was born on December 5, 1895. When I survived that winter, it was clear that I was indestructable. I owe my longevity to the harsh climate of my birth which fortified me against all slings and arrows—including two World Wars and 119 theatrical productions.
I began as a part-time usher at The Lyceum in Prov-

idence, Rhode Island, while attending Brown University. My father was a physician and wished me to follow in his forceps, but when I developed a syndrome of fainting with some regularity during my pre-med training, I abandoned it as unsuitable. My father was dismayed but resigned. After service in WWI, I became Assistant Manager of The Lyceum (2 years), Manager (4 years), and afterward got my first show: SCRAMBLED WIVES. I have worked in every state of the union with the exception of North Carolina (odd!). I have known the best and the worst. I have been associated with Minnie Maddern Fiske, Winthrop Ames, Winchell Smith, John Golden, Lee Shubert, Florenz Ziegfeld, Max Gordon, and many others. I was on two shows with Nora Bayes (ever hear of her?), SNAPSHOTS OF 1921 and a revival of LITTLE MISS FIX-IT.

War is, by and large, more peaceful than the theatre.

What I observe mainly after all these years is how everything that happens has happened before, in one form or another. There are few surprises.

I have seen this show before (in a way) and I have seen all of you before, and if I live long enough, I will most assuredly see you all again.

SPECIALITIES: We would very much like to know about any special talents in the company. If you can play a musical instrument, speak a foreign language, whistle, ride a unicycle, stand on your head, or imitate four Hawaiians, please convey this intelligence as soon as possible to Clay Botsford. This is a Show Business show, and we can probably use everything if we know about it in time.

QUOTE TO REMEMBER:
     George M. Cohan to Spencer Tracy:
     "Whatever you do, kid, always serve it with a little dressing."

There are now 32 rehearsal days until our opening night in Boston.

· VI ·

Production meeting. Present: Larry, Art Clune, Hy, Fred, Phil, Chris, Russ, Buddy, Ivan and his young wife-assistant Nadia, Clay, Jenny, Val, Nick, Stu, Alicia, Aki, and Millie. Absent: Paul Cooley and Cindy Sapiro. Larry is talking.

"I know that some of you—maybe even *many* of you—feel these sessions are a waste of your time. Obviously, I don't agree. But we're going to have a lot of them, so I advise you all to get used to them and what's more, to use them.

"As you all know, I am a democrat—both small and big D—except when I do a show. Then I become a Dictator—both small and big D. By that I mean only this: I'm going to make the final decisions on each and every one of the thousand questions a day that come up.

"I'm trying to be—as you can see—a *benevolent* dictator. No, listen. No kidding. Let me see if I can make it plain. I want—no, I *need*—everything every one of you has to contribute. I want everyone's ideas and, yes, even criticisms. What I'm saying is that after we've all had our say, one person has to make the decision and that's that. I'm talking, needless to say, about artistic and creative matters. Anything to do with business, budget, money, bookings, advertising, PR, and the like is not my concern—nor should it be yours. I'm sure in such esoteric areas, we're all willing to defer to Our Leader, Art Clune."

Art applauds loudly—he is the only one—and shouts, "Hear! Hear!"

Larry again. "Would anyone here seriously propose that the artistic and creative decisions with respect to our show should be made by committee? By majority rule?"

ALICIA

It's been done.

LARRY

Where? When?

ALICIA

When I worked with Joan Littlewood—in the East End.

LARRY

You don't say.

ALICIA

The whole company had a say.

LARRY

Well, all I can say is—if you don't like this country, why don't you go back where you came from?

(Laughter)

ALICIA

Thanks awfully, but no.

LARRY

Now, look, everybody. I ask you to keep one principle in mind and that is that we're all on the same side, right? The important thing to remember is that we're all doing one show. We don't have the dreamy advantage of being a permanent company— like the National in England, or the Comédie Française or the Royal in Stockholm. We're a pick-up band. A scrub team. But if we all blend and co-operate and help one another—we can top even those established establishments. Because, department by department, our individual talents are probably greater.

ART

For what it's costing me, they better be!

(Light laughter)

LARRY

Believe me, I respect each of you enormously—and it wouldn't occur to me to interfere with your individual methodologies— but let me confess something. The first thing I do every morning these days—right before breakfast, I mean—is—I tell myself the story.

ART

I'd like to see that. Do you ever sell tickets?

LARRY

Settle down, Art. I'm talking seriously.

ART
(Beating his breast)
Mea culpa, my boy. Mea culpa.

LARRY

I tell the story. Sometimes I dictate it to a cassette—that's the *small* dictator I was telling you about—

(Laughter)

ART

Can I ask a question? May I?

LARRY

Certainly.

ART

How come if I make a joke I get put down—and you make a joke and it's O.K.?

LARRY

Because my jokes are better.

ART

You've got a point there.

LARRY

I tell myself the story. If I record it, I play it back and listen while I'm having breakfast. The point is: I was taught always to keep the *whole* story in mind. Not to get involved with one scene, say, or a single character—or a number—no matter how good it may be. It's the whole—the entity—that has to have unity and style.

IVAN

Very good said.

LARRY

You know how when a painter's working on a canvas, he may have his face only this far from the canvas at times—like

· 58 ·

this—but every so often, he steps back a few steps and takes in the whole canvas. And that's what we've got to do. . . . Now today I'm going to tell our story and every time we have a full production meeting, I'm going to ask one of you to do so. I expect that here and there our versions may vary—but in the main I hope we're all going to find the same wavelength, as it were. . . . Now. What complicates things a little is that there are really *two* stories—the true story and the one we're telling.

                         ART
Hold it.

                         LARRY
What?

                         ART
Can we take a break here?

                         LARRY
No.

                         ART
                    (To the group)
Take ten, folks. Coffee. Or maybe you need to do this—or that
—or both.
     (We all recognize the tight moment. Just as LARRY *is pro-
     claiming his authority,* ART *takes charge. Everyone takes
     off. Except me.* LARRY *sits down.* ART *moves over and sits
     near him)*
What *is* this, baby?

                         LARRY
What is *what?* Baby.

                         ART
This two-story shit? What're you trying to open up here?

                         LARRY
Take too long to explain.

                         ART
I've got time. Go ahead.

                         LARRY
Later.

                         · 59 ·

ART

Now.

LARRY

I've got a whole staff on my hands, for Christ's sake, Art.

ART

You've got *me* on your hands.

LARRY

I sure in hell have.

ART

Go ahead.

LARRY

The point is, Art that the script we've got is *bland.* I know all about the reasons we can't fix it—make it truer, more explicit. But I've got a theory that if everyone knows the *real* story—even *this* book'll come out stronger. Like Hemingway once said, "Don't ever worry about making a cut—if the stuff was any good it'll still be there." And that's *my* theory, too.

ART

Some theory.

LARRY

Can't hurt, can it?

ART

Sure it can.

LARRY

How?

ART

Starts up all that bullshit gossip and upsets my old lady and she doesn't give a damn, Neysa—but the kids and who knows? Someday *their* kids.

LARRY

But Holy God—Art—there's a published book—

ART

Sold four thousand fucking copies. And *three* thousand of 'em—*I* own.

LARRY

I see. So my job is not to *tell* the story. Just to suppress it.

ART

Not exactly.

LARRY

I tell you what, Art . . .

(Long pause)

ART

What?

(Longer pause)

LARRY

Let me out.

ART

What the hell are you talking about? Do you know?

LARRY

Look, Mr. Clune. If we do it now—a nice, clean break—it'll be easier on everyone. I'll hang in until you replace me—

ART

You've got a contract, mister.

LARRY

Oh, sure—

ART

The one thing I don't take—never—is threats. You quit and you don't collect a dime, you know that?

LARRY

Yes—but I get to keep my balls, baby—and they're worth more than a dime.

(AC turns into another character before our eyes. I have never quite believed the Jekyll-Hyde story. I do now. The monster Art becomes the angel Art.)

ART

Hey, baby.

(He moves to LARRY *and embraces him)*
What *is* all this, huh? What's going on? This is nuts here, y'know

it? We must be sufferin' from rehearsal willies or something. It's a point we're talkin'. So what? A little point. A little nothin'. Jesus —if you're gonna quit, it better be for some reason, right? Like you decide you hate the whole show or something. Or if The Queen of Light gives you a too hard a time—or sick, God forbid —or something. But not on account of some small nothing, right?

LARRY

Small to you, Art. Big to me.

ART

So fine. Call it forty-love. Your point.

LARRY
(Losing his temper and breaking away)
Good sweet Jesus Christ, Art. This isn't one of your stupid goddam tennis games—this is the theatre—this is my *life!*

ART

Hey! Hey! Hold the scream. A figure of speech. A joke. What're you racing your motor?

LARRY

Oh, God.

(He sits down. His head is in his hands. ART *goes over and touches him)*

ART

Sorry, Larry. I didn't mean to upset you. Swear to God. Come on. Let's be professional.

*(*LARRY'*s head comes up. He looks at* AC *and can barely suppress a smile)*

LARRY

Sure.

ART

Call 'em in. Tell 'em any goddam thing you want—I'll handle Neysa—and as far as the grandchildren—shit—they're not even *born* yet.

LARRY
(To me)
Call the bunch.

(I went out into the passage, found Clay and told him. A few minutes later:)

I mentioned candor a while ago. So let me be the first to use it. Mr. Clune and I had a disagreement—we've discussed it, resolved it. You'll know in a minute what it was. But my point is that that's the way to run a company. Instead of cliques and intrigues and scuttlebutt and double dealing. Let's all have everything out in the open at all times. Everybody with me? Hands.

(All)

Fine. . . . Now I'll tell you. I mentioned two stories. You all know that the basis of our project is a book called *Nightingale for Sale* by Gene Bowman and—

ART

Can I say a word here, Larry, please?

LARRY

Certainly. As soon as I finish.

ART

But it fits, right in here.

LARRY

Go ahead.

ART

This book Larry just said, this Bowman. We commissioned him, see, six years ago—me and my wife—to do this book. Paid him a big advance—gave him all the files on Nora—Neysa's great-aunt and Jack. Letters, diaries—notebooks—scrapbooks—pictures. Practically the whole book. Hell, *I* could have written it with all that. . . . So what does Bowman do? He goes back to Chicago—he hangs all around—he listens to all kinds of stuff—puts it all into the book. When we saw it we damn near fell out. It put my wife to bed for a week with migraines. This son of a bitch—this Bowman—he double-crossed us. Put in a lot of stuff we didn't want in there and wouldn't take it out. We tried to stop the whole thing—but there're crazy laws in this country and we couldn't. So he went ahead. Thank God the book was a bust. Sold six copies. A lot *I* bought up. Then I bought all the rights from him—he stung me, but what the hell? There's a saying: "When you are the anvil, bear—when you are the hammer—*strike!*" So I was an anvil—but anyhow, I got everything: movie, stage, TV, even further print or paperback. This guy is money-mad. The only bad point was credits. So that's why you see the bastard's name on our credits. There was no way out. That's all.

LARRY

Thank you, Mr. Clune. That was most illuminating. . . . What I was saying was that there are two stories—one, the life story; two, the stage story. . . . The life story is, of course, full of contradictions and mysteries. Like all life stories. The stage version is neater. Everything comes out even. But I have an idea—what I was trying to explain to Art, to Mr. Clune—that all of you ought to know the *real* story. Or stories. Apocryphal as they may be. And I want to make sure that later the *players* know it, too. Because I believe that if they do and you do—something of the truth will communicate itself to the audience. And when you come right down to it—that's the most important element in theatre—the audience. More important than the writing or direction or music or dancing or whatever. The audience. What goes on in the audience's head. What we can make happen there. . . . The story as Gene Bowman tells it—

ART

Lotsa lies in that book.

LARRY

All right, Art. At the proper time, you can tell us all what they were.

ART

I will.

LARRY

Good. But not now.

ART

When?

LARRY

Later. We're going to be doing a lot of this.

ART

O.K.

LARRY

Gene Bowman opens his book with three chapters on The Everleigh Club—one of the most celebrated bordellos in America in the early part of this century. We've condensed this into one big opening scene with two numbers: "Ladies of the Evening," by the chorus, and "Nightfall," sung by Nora.

IVAN

Beautyful nomber.

HY

Thank you.

LARRY

And already there's a basic change. Bowman says she was one of the favorite girls at The Everleigh Club—

ART

How does he know? Was he there? He wasn't there.

LARRY

In our version, Nora is *not* one of the girls, but plays the piano there. All right. We can live with that. Remember how brilliantly Fosse handled it in *Sweet Charity?* In the Fellini they were street whores. In the show, they were dance-hall girls—but hell, when they sang—
(He sings)
"Hey, good lookin'!
Spend a little time with me. . . ."
There was no question. So all right. Nora plays the piano in this whorehouse. She's known there as "Lovey Kelly."

ART

But we don't call it that—whorehouse. We never use the word, do we, Chris?

CHRIS

Never.

LARRY

Cathouse, bordello, brothel, whorehouse—what the hell's the difference?

ART

Bordello has *chic,* that's what.

LARRY

Oh my God!

ART

You can say oh my God all you want. It's a fact.

LARRY

O.K., but the point is—and this is part of *your* job, Alicia, and you, too, Ivan. There should not be too much differentiation between Nora and the other girls.

ALICIA

I didn't plan any. You've seen the sketches.

LARRY

I didn't say you did, Alicia—we're just reviewing.

IVAN

And me—you mean more with the lighting, yes? Not the design.

LARRY

Well, design, too—insofar as, say, the placement of the piano is concerned.

NADIA

You have not so much of the choice there—because the lady She plays not the piano—so must be fake—so must be in position for the faking, no?

LARRY

Of course.

CLAY

And by the way, we've worked out that trick piano. By putting it against the wall, left, we can shove the real piano into the prop one—so that when Nora fakes playing, the real music will be coming out of the piano She's faking on.

HY

Terrific.

CLAY

She'll still have to get a lot of coaching to make it look right.

LARRY

Don't worry about her— She can do anything.

ART

Anything She *wants* to do.

JENNY

Who's going to do that? You want me to?

HY

No, no. Me. I'm a pianist.

LARRY

But will you have time?

HY

I'll *make* time.

CLAY

Schedule-wise, it'll have to be worked into *her* moves.

HY

I'll try.

LARRY

Hey! Idea. Whenever Hy *can't* do it—we can use Midge.

HY

Great idea!

(My instinct was to yell, "No!" But I suppressed it)

LARRY

Now. The main line. A raffish spot in a wide open town—Chicago
—in an anything-goes period. A bordello—O.K., Art?—catering
to politicians, stage stars, tycoons, writers, and artists. They had
style, the Everleighs, and in their way—class. The girls were
hand-picked. Not so much hookers in the end as American gei-
shas.

ART

Hey! That's good. Put it in the script, Chris.

(CHRIS makes a note. LARRY goes on:)

LARRY

And young. The Everleighs had a slogan—"If they're big
enough, they're old enough!"
(Laugh)
Consequently, they had—

HY

Hold it a second. Did you say, "If they're big enough, they're old
enough"?

LARRY

The *Everleighs* said it.

HY

Well, God damn it. Where's *that* been, for God's sake? Not in the script.

LARRY

It's in Bowman's book. If you'd read it the way I *asked* you to, you'd have seen it.

HY

I read the goddam book. All right. Maybe not every single goddam word—but—

FRED

Hey! I got it. You mean a number—a patter, a comedy song—

HY

Damn right. For the two Everleigh Sisters. Holy Cow—this is what I've been *looking* for! A third song for the opening scene. And these two great old dames—be sure they can belt—and they'll sing:
(He is at the piano and strikes up a rollicking, period-style honky-tonk tune. Singing)
"If they're big enough,
They're old enough."

FRED

(Improvising to the tune)
"They can all be tall
Or fat or hot
Or cold enough.
(Slower)
"They don't have to be twenty-one,
They will da da by the time
That they are done.
If they're big enough,
They're old enough.
They can something something fill in.
Or be *bold* enough—"

HY

Finish!

(Singing)
"So as long as they've got the *stuff!*"

(Fred joins him:)

FRED AND HY
(Harmonizing)
"They are—old—*enough!!*"

HY
(Jumping up)
Two days! Give us two days. A showstopper!

LARRY
If this show stops any more, it's going to stall.

HY
You don't see it?

LARRY
Promising.

HY
You could *use* some comedy in that first scene. A cathouse can
be depressing. I know. I've been in plenty.

LARRY
Work on it. Can Gracie and Enid sing well enough for this, Clay?

CLAY
I'll let you know by tonight. I think so.

HY
Wait till we finish the number and then let *me* see. I'll tell you
in ten minutes.

LARRY
That's right, Clay. If it doesn't work out—we haven't ruffled any
feathers.

HY
It'll work out, I promise you.

FRED
But give him Arpège.

*(*FRED *laughs. No one else)*

LARRY

All right. So. Where were we? Oh, yes. The club. It's all one grand nonstop party. Superlative food and drink. Dancing. Entertainment. The only difference between this party and the snooty ones on Lake Shore Drive is that at this one—you can choose a girl—retire to privacy—and buy lovemaking, if not love. . . . All this has to be reflected in Scene One. Scene Two is, of course, Jack and Nora—alone at the piano in the middle of the night—we've got to get the audience to think they're going to kiss. They don't. Instead, they take off on a four-hand reprise of "Nightfall"—and it's got to feel like they're making love.

HY

I want to do that by segueing from the original key to one higher then higher and so on.

LARRY

Sounds fine. . . . Now the great set Ivan's done of the stage within the stage—we see both wings. Jack is out doing his turn. Nora in the wings, watching. Big finish. He takes his calls with that vaudeville music—

HY

I know, I know.

(He sings)
"Ya-ta-ta
ya ta *ta* ta *ta* ta
Ta
Ya ta ta ta *ta* ta
Ta ta ta ta ta
Ta ta ta ta taaaaa!
Tsing!!!"

(All laugh)

LARRY

Fine. Now he grabs Nora—pulls her on and does his marvelous "discovery" intro. Could be a touch shorter, Chris, by the way.

(CHRIS makes a note)

She's in the spot. Music. She sings a number we've heard her play at The Everleigh—but we've never heard the words—"Wondering." That's a cunning notion by the way, Hy. They'll have heard

· 70 ·

the tune before—sort of subliminally—so it'll sound familiar, better. Great idea.

HY

It's Chris's.

LARRY

Good. Thanks, Chris. Dressing-room scene. The argument. She won't go. They quarrel. He grabs her. She slaps him. He slaps her. A moment. *Now* the kiss. When the audience doesn't expect it. O.K. Train scene. Ensemble number: Overnight. Scene: Jack and Nora. Lights begin to dim. One by one. Sleep. Now—pin spot Nora—got that, Clay?

CLAY

It's done.

LARRY

She sings "Where Am I Going?" Maybe the best number in the show.

HY

Jesus, I hope not. If it is let's move it to Act Two.

(Laughter)

LARRY

All right. Hotel room. Upright piano. Nora in bed. Jack and Von Tilzer writing the ball-game song. Jack wakes Nora. They do it for her. She doesn't like it. Jack agrees. She says she likes the one about the moon better. Von Tilzer says, "That ballad? It stinks." Von Tilzer out. Jack gets her up for the audition. Funny scene —could be funnier.

ART

I'll bring in some gag men, don't worry. You'll be up to your ass in one-liners. Guaranteed.

(CHRIS is getting smaller by the minute)

LARRY

Audition scene. Bare stage. Jack plays for her. Top of the act. She sings the moon song. Showstopper or else. Now Ivan's big transformation do. From bare stage to fantastic production number. I'm still not clear about how Nora goes from street clothes to sensational.

ALICIA

Not to worry, ducky. It's all in hand.

LARRY

How? Can you tell us?

ALICIA

Can, but won't. Tricks of the trade, don't y'know?

LARRY

Opening-night party. What did you decide, Ivan? Rector's or Delmonico's?

IVAN

A creation. Call what you want.

LARRY

Chorus number. Dance. Polka. Jack and Nora table downstage right. The son-of-a-bitch turns up. Claude. Drunk.

ART

Not *too* drunk.

LARRY

A *little* drunk.

ART

Better if not drunk at all. More menace.

LARRY

You have a point. Let me think on it. . . . Anyway, whatever. He tells her he knows her from The Everleigh Club. Jack says mistake. Claude says, "No, I'm sure. I used to be in there every night when I was in Chicago." Jack says, "Wrong." Claude says, "Sorry," and off. Nora troubled. Jack, too. They go. Party goes on. Hotel room: undressing scene. Another hard one, Alicia.

ALICIA

Not for me. It'll be smashing.

LARRY

Jack calms her down. She says, finally—"So what?" "What if?" "Would it matter?" Now—his big speech on hypocrisy and morals and manners and double standards and tells her not to be so brave—she'll ruin everything and he'll get to the Everleighs and so on. They get into bed and hold on to one another. . . . New

York street. The son of a bitch accosts her. Have a drink. No. A cup of tea. They walk—this is the treadmill bit—turn and into Palm Court. Trio playing. Blackmail. She pays off. . . . A show number. . . . Montage of payoffs, ending with the one in the dressing room—Jack busts in. The jig is up. Fight scene—oh, God, I hate fight scenes—will you help me, Jenny?

JENNY

Certainly. They're not so bad, so hard, if you stage them like a dance number.

LARRY

But I need blood and all, according to the script.

JENNY

You'll get it.

LARRY

O.K. The guy pulls himself together—threatens to expose her. . . . "You do," says Jack, "and I swear to Christ I'll kill you. I'll kill you and I'll get away with it. You're a swine. The world would be better without you." I'm paraphrasing.

ART

God, I *hope* so!

LARRY

Guy goes out—no, is *thrown* out. Jack and Nora. Scene. Then he sings "I'm Here." Scene. She sings "You're Here." Safe—but when the curtain falls, it has on it a front page blow-up of a scandal sheet:

"FROM BROTHEL TO BROADWAY"
The Story of Nora Bayes

ART

Bordello.

LARRY

No, Art. This time brothel.

ART

Why?

LARRY

Jesus *Christ!* If you can't *see* it I can't *explain* it! Brothel, Broadway, Bordello, Broadway. Clear?

ART

No.

LARRY

Oh, God. Thank you, ladies and gentlemen. That will be all for today.

The meeting is over.

RUNNING ORDER: At tomorrow's run through, "Overnight Ride" will follow "Where Am I Going?"

SCRIPT: The script is still being retyped, and will be distributed to all concerned as soon as possible.
Let us all remember that the script of SHINE ON is confidential and should be read only by the cast. No one outside the show should have access to any of the material, i.e., jokes, lyrics, music, etc.

PHOTOGRAPHER: Paul Cooley of our Press Department has announced that photographer Peter Simon has been engaged to cover SHINE ON from start to finish. Mr. Simon will work quietly and unobtrusively under our control and direction. All photographs taken by Mr. Simon are subject to approval before release.

JENNY FLAGG: Miss Flagg was interviewed today by Corry of the *Times* regarding the Everleigh Girls and Nora Bayes's vaudeville days. His article will appear (we hope) on Friday, December 21.

CAST ADDITION: Stephanie Caylon is our charming swing girl.

THE COMPANY YOU KEEP: SAMMY SMITH (Charley)
I was born when I was very young—in a little log cabin that I helped my father to build. . . . The place was a small town called Shlabotka near Kovno in Lithuania. The exact date was exactly two years before my younger brother and three years after my older sister. (What the *HEY!*) I was brought to America by my parents at the age of five. I don't *know* how old *I* was. . . . (I never had a father, I had two mothers.) The first show I ever saw was Fred Stone in THE WIZARD OF OZ, Montgomery and Stone. From that day to this all I care about in life is being on the stage. Wrong. Being *good* on the stage. . . . I have been in burlesque, carny shows, musicals, legit, radio, TV, industrial shows, and all kinds of movies (except porno, I couldn't pass the physical!), and I

will tell you what I have found out. They are all the same. You have to connect with the audience and sell them a bill of goods. . . . Al Jolson was the best entertainer I ever saw. . . . The best actor—John Barrymore (stage), Spencer Tracy (movie). Actress —Laurette Taylor (stage), Greta Garbo (movie). I weigh 142 lbs. (stripped), am 5'5" (stripped), brown hair (stripped), blue eyes (stripped), and am considered quite a ladies' man (stripped). . . . I would like to die on the stage. In fact, I *have* several times. . . . I am glad to be in this great show. . . . And that is how I spent my summer.

Sammy Smith
Age 12

REMINDER: I would appreciate it greatly if *every* member of the company would prepare for publication in the Bulletin a short autobiographical note. 100-200 words. We want to know you. Hand in to Midge. Be candid, frank, revealing—or mysterious.

L.G.

HOTEL RESERVATIONS: Will everyone in the company please sign the hotel reservation list on the bulletin board by the close of rehearsal on Tuesday, September 18.

QUOTE FOR TODAY:
"Whatever the endeavor, make of it a lallapalooza."
Michael ("Hinky Dink") Kenna, circa 1909

TRAVEL: The entire company will leave for Boston on the morning of Sunday, October 14. The time will be announced.

ADDITIONS TO THE COMPANY: Maurice Summerfield will be our wardrobe master, and Bonnie Green has been engaged as our Star's maid.

Sharon Vaughn has joined our company as one of the Everleigh Girls, and Yvonne Reynolds becomes an additional member of our singing group.

There are now 28 rehearsal days until our opening night in Boston.

· VII ·

Larry talks to the whole company this afternoon. They sit around on the stage, in chairs, or on the floor. Some of them, mostly the dancers, are lying down. Two or three snooze, but Larry doesn't seem to mind.

Larry says: "Ladies and gentlemen, I want to talk to you today about *moments*. One of the reasons for this is that we're in the *business* of moments. We're charged with the responsibility of creating a *series* of moments. Funny moments, thrilling moments; if we're lucky and work hard, perhaps even two or three unforgettable moments.

"The fact is that we—all of us—remember moments. If I mention a show to you, say *A Chorus Line*, or *Ain't Misbehavin'*, you conjure up instantly in your mind a few moments from those shows. No one remembers a whole show. But you do recall moments in the same way that you recall the great or the sad or the marvelous or the important moments in your life.

"If a show has in it six or seven great moments, you can be sure it's a great show. The hard part is that sometimes it takes an hour to create one moment. Still, it's worth it.

"Sometimes we manufacture the moment externally. Very often the moments happen unexpectedly, spontaneously, magically. Those, I suppose, are the best ones. A look, a gesture, a move, a note, anything. What I'm asking all of you to do is to become conscious of this responsibility. Consider the scenes you're in, the numbers you perform, the character you play, and, each of you, try to discover the hidden spark that has at least the *potential* for the creation of a memorable moment.

"I'll be on the lookout, too, and when we find even the germ of one, let's get to work on it and try to frame it, to present it, to perfect it, so that it becomes, indeed, unforgettable.

"Thanks. . . . Scene Four, Act One, please. From the top."

· VIII ·

Production Meeting. Same as previous one with the exception of Jenny—who had to be at her dance rehearsal today.

LARRY

I think we're coming along. At about this time it's par for the course to start having misgivings and doubts and fears about the whole damn thing. I'm sure every one of you has had a moment or two when you've said to yourself, How'd I get roped into *this* turkey?

ART

Not me, boy. I *know* it's a great show.

LARRY

It isn't *any* kind of a show *yet,* Art. We're all hoping it's *going* to be.

ART

It's a great show. I'm holding it right here in my hand. So don't tell *me!*

LARRY

What you're holding in your hand, Art, is a script. Not a show. And a score. Not a show. What you're holding in your hand is a set of instructions for the acting out of a story—with numbers. The show, the one to come, is going to happen one of these days right here on this stage—if we follow the directions. It's like having the blueprints and specifications in your hand for building a house. The difference is that you can't move into the blueprints. Correction. When I said awhile back that the show happens here on this stage—not quite. It actually happens only in the mind of the audience. We supply the material that stimulates their imagination. That's why—at all times—everyone—we have to remember the audience—pretend every seat in the house is filled every time we're at work. Simple things. They have to be able to see. They have to be able to hear—and not only to hear—but to understand. We're going to respect the audience. One by one, they may not be the best and the brightest—but believe me—as a group—they are terrifyingly brilliant and sensitive and intelligent. "An idiot genius," Moss Hart used to say. There's no light so powerful—not even if Millie got every piece of equipment in town—as the light shed by three thousand eyes all focused on one stage or on one spot on one stage. That's why I've always thought actors and actresses the bravest people on earth—they stand there and deliver—even when they're a pain which they often are. . . . Now. What I'd like to do today is outline the rest of the show overall. Last time we got together I gave you a sketch of a sketch of Act One. You'll recall it ended with the front-page–headline drop. I'm not sure yet if we're going to go to black on that and bring in the house curtain or if we're going to leave it there for the whole intermission.

ART

Leave it there. It's costing a fortune.

CHRIS

The only thing is—won't it get boring? I mean what can you look at for fifteen minutes without it getting boring?

ART

Liz Taylor's tits.

(Laughter)

LARRY

Is there any way, Ivan, to do a *whole* front page that would be readable from every seat and—

IVAN

With a projection, maybe. Not paint.

LARRY

Well, how *about* that? Hey, this could be pretty good!

ART

Projection. Doesn't ''   mean another guy up there to run it?

CLAY

No—between the two follow-spot men—one can handle it.

RUSS

Or put it on automatic—from the balcony rail—then all Clay has to do is push a button.

CLAY

That's good, Russ. You're right. That could work.

ART

Very good, Russ. Remind me to give you a raise. Someday.

LARRY

If we decide to leave it and if we want it readable.

CHRIS

That'll take a little research—but it could be good maybe—for period feel and atmosphere. Like if it was the whole front page and there were seven or eight stories: political, social, sports, crime, personalities—you *know?*

LARRY

O.K. Let's all give it some thought and—as you say, Chris—research, and decide later.

IVAN

Meantime—I should put a hold on the drop, no?

ART

Yes! Absolutely.

LARRY

All right. Now. Act Two. We open with an innovation. A scene instead of a number. Let's pray it works. Otherwise we've got a number more or less ready, haven't we?

HY

More.

FRED

Less.

LARRY

I hope we can do without it—I like the surprise of opening with a scene. It makes the story stronger.

HY

Never in a million years, boy. An Act Two has *got* to start with a number.

LARRY

I don't like rule books for the theatre. Guy once said, "In the theatre, there ain't no never and there ain't no always." Anyway. We'll see. Either way, Act Two—Scene One is The Everleigh Club. *If* it's a scene—it's the Everleigh Sisters alone—later the girls. The standby scene is the number from the girls—"Poor Nora"—then the sisters' scene. Now in comes Jack. He needs their help. Has anyone been around snooping? No. Not yet. What if they do? The Everleighs say, "Leave it to us." "What about the girls? Can we count on them?" "Well. . . ." "What well?" "All but one—Ginny. She's always had it in for Nora. " " Let me talk to her." Ginny-Jack scene. He buys her off—but we somehow feel she can't be trusted. It's a tough scene.

CHRIS

Too tough for this poor kid we're letting out. Have you got a replacement yet?

LARRY

I don't think so. Have we, Clay?

CLAY

Not definitely.

CHRIS

The point I want to make is—I hope you get a sweet, innocent-looking, adorable type. I mean not a heavy.

ART

No, no. The audience has to hate her right away—

LARRY

Hold it, Art. Let him finish.

CHRIS

Seems to me offbeat casting would be better here. Less obvious. After all, in real life—the bastards are sometimes very attractive—

What're you lookin' at *me* for?

(Laughter)

LARRY

I like that, Chris. I like it a lot. Who've we got, Clay?

CLAY

With *this* concept—nobody. We were looking for a tough bimbo.

LARRY

O.K. Talk to Howie and give him this new idea and see if—

ART
(Reading from the script)
"Ginny comes in. She is tall and powerful, tough and hard. One of the older, more experienced girls. She looks at Jack with hostility."
(He puts down the script)
I rest my case.

CHRIS
(Irritated)
All right, Art. I know that. Jesus, I *wrote* that. So I've changed my mind. What's wrong with that?

ART

I believe usually the first idea is the best idea. I've seen more pictures fucked up because everybody started changing their mind and trying this and trying that. Just because you change something doesn't mean it's better. Maybe it's worse.

LARRY

Well, we disagree again. A show in this stage is an infant. And we're supposed to nourish it so it can develop and grow. I don't mean that if it's a boy we should try to make it into a girl. But of course we ought to be able to change our minds about detail.

FRED

They used to say, Shows aren't written, they're rewritten.

ART

Bullshit!

CHRIS

If it's bullshit, how come you're on my back all the time for rewrites?

ART

Because too much of your stuff is lousy, that's why. And your contract says. And if you think I'm on your back, my boy—I've got a solution for you.

CHRIS

Yes?

ART

Yes! Take your back somewhere else. One thing in mind, O.K.? You didn't *write* this show. You *adapted* it. You're a hired hand, so don't act like you're a Tennessee Williams.

LARRY

That's enough of that. Let's not start biting on each other this early in the game. If we do, there'll be nothing left for Boston and Philadelphia.

ART

Sorry, Chris, I got hot.

CHRIS

Nothing.

LARRY

Last show, a big name actor who shall be nameless says to me, "Do you realize the direction you just gave me is absolutely the opposite of what you gave me yesterday?" "Yes," I said, "I do. And I've got some advice for you. Every night when you're kneeling by your bedside in your little jammies saying your prayers—and you've thanked the Lord for giving you this marvelous part in this wonderful show and you've said '—and God bless Mommy and Daddy and make me a good boy'—add: 'And thank You, God, for giving me a director who changes his mind and not one of those stubborn sonsofbitches who gets one idea in his head and sticks to it no matter what.'"

(Laughter)

HY

We had a number last year—it was in five different scenes—sung by four different characters until we found the right person and the right spot.

· 84 ·

LARRY

Scene Two. Nora's room. Alone. She's dressing. Number: "Was It Wrong?" Now, with all due respect to the number—a beaut —the scene is really yours, Alicia.

ALICIA

Oh, dear. *What* a burden.

LARRY

It's a kind of period striptease in reverse. I want it daring and brazen and sexy as hell. . . . How far can we go, do you think for a start? If I had *my* way, I'd bring her out of the bathroom naked.

ALICIA

I say, steady! You can't mean absolutely starkers, can you?

LARRY

I'm telling you what I think would be *perfect.* Then we'll get as near to it as we can in a practical way.

RUSS

Even if you could, would She do it?

CLAY

If She thought it would get a hand, She would. Or a laugh.

ART

Or if I gave her a hundred a week more.

LARRY

Hold it, men. . . . Let's say She's wearing as little as possible for a start. Then, as She sings, "Was It Wrong?" she dresses.

HY

Great for the song, of course. That beautiful ballad competing with her bare ass. Place your bets, gentlemen.

LARRY

Hy, if we do it right—it'll *enhance* the song.

HY

Oh, sure.

LARRY

I'll give you a whole second chorus after She's completely dressed.

HY

You will?

LARRY

In a spot. In one.

HY

Deal.

LARRY

But we ought to have a new set of lyrics for the second chorus.

FRED

Oh, thanks a bunch!

HY

You know what, Freddie? Hold *this* lyric for the second chorus
—and write some filler for the undie scene.

ALICIA

I think I may have something, Larry. Look here.
*(She starts to sketch. LARRY and RUSS and ART move
around and stand behind her, watching. HY leans over to
see, too)*
It stems from your bath idea.

AKI

I got some great splashing if you want—on tape.

ALICIA

Good. And suppose She *does* come out, drying herself with an
enormous—well, at least outsized towel—

RUSS

Did they have them in those days?

LARRY

Of course. Shut up.

ALICIA

And She moves about the room . . .

RUSS

Dripping would be good.

ART

What?

RUSS

So everybody would know She's been in the bath.

ART

Why the hell else would She be drying herself, you pinhead?

RUSS

It'll look stagey if She doesn't drip.

ART

All right, so she'll drip, you drip!

ALICIA

And here is where we'll need massive assistance from Jenny—and especially you, Ivan.

IVAN

Sure. I see. You need all kinds masking.

ALICIA

Right. Now, once She has her underclothes on—we're safe.

LARRY

And what are these underclothes, exactly?

ALICIA

Corset, camisole, garter belt.

MILLIE

I could set up a special somewhere behind her and give you some great peep stuff even with clothes on.

LARRY

Great. So She comes out—

RUSS

Dripping.

LARRY

She moves around—we know She's naked. She gets her underclothes—from where?

ALICIA

The bed?

IVAN

Yes, good. I can have there a good chair.

LARRY

Corset on—and then we're all right. Damn. If we can convince her to just flash one for a split second—or her behind—a glance only—

ART

What's the point? These days they see everything. Frontal. The works.

LARRY

Yes, but not the star's. And not in a high-class twenty-two-dollar-ticket Broadway musical—and anyway—it's unexpected.

ART

Go ahead and do it. I'm not stopping you.

LARRY

Wait a second. Just so we all understand. I'm not after titillation for the sake of titillation.

ART

Watch your language.

LARRY

The point is to dramatize the aloneness of Nora at this point. And a girl, by herself in a room—dressing—doing all the small, personal things a girl does when alone—damn!—this can be *sensational!* And what's more, she can do it. Midge, find out what women did then—I mean kinds of perfume and atomizers, there must be some period kinds. And what did they do about armpits, and so on. . . .

ALICIA

You see? Here are the basic stages.

LARRY

Excellent, Alicia. Many thanks.

(All return to their places)

ALICIA

This can work.

LARRY

Why is it stuff like this is always more erotic in period dress?

ALICIA

I don't know—but it *is.*

LARRY

Silk stockings, right?

ALICIA

Oh, yes!

LARRY

Nothing sexier. And putting them on—I mean watching them
being put on. God Almighty! I remember—in the silent-movie
days—they'd do it sometimes. Clara Bow. Vilma Banky. It was
electrifying.

ART

Oh, I don't know. Pantyhose aren't bad.

LARRY

No contest.

ART

Let's try it. Alicia, you put on silk stockings—and Midge, you do
pantyhose and we'll all vote!

LARRY

Where were we?

ME

Scene Two. Over.

LARRY

Scene Three. Tough one. Rector's. Main dining room. Midnight
supper. The big waltz number. We don't see them right away,
but as the waltz goes on—we discover Jack and Nora waltzing.
Lovely, this. They're part of the crowd, part of life, lost in it. And
it's romantic and the tune is a winner. "Midnight Waltz."

HY

A sure standard.

FRED

If the waltz comes back.

LARRY

Digression. Alicia—I've been thinking. That towel thing of yours
is superlative—a real inspiration. Thank you.

ART

What do you mean, "Thank you"? That's what she gets paid for, isn't it? An arm and a leg. . . . I'm only kiddin', Alicia. I think your towel thing is superlative.

(I begin to notice something about AC—a habit. He kicks someone in the groin and immediately does what he can to soothe the pain. Like those nutty mothers who sock their kids in the head and then kiss it to make it well. Is he getting it both ways? Why does he do it? It keeps everyone so on edge. Is that the reason?

Larry has been looking at Art for some time. I wonder if there is going to be another blowup. No. Larry stands up, begins pacing around, and talks:)

LARRY

A few years ago, Art, I took five weeks off and went down to Sarasota, Florida. Just a whim. I wanted to see how a circus is put together.

ART

With money!

LARRY
(Ignoring him)
I've been a circus buff from the age of—I don't know—maybe five, when I saw my first one in Seattle. And for the next ten years or more I had one driving ambition—to be a clown.

ART

You *made* it!

LARRY

I've seen circuses everywhere in the world—the Russians are the best—and I've watched the American ones deteriorate—just slick commercialism now. Too bad.

ART

What *is* all this?

LARRY

In Sarasota, everything was enthralling. I learned plenty. About precision and training. And patience—God, it can take seven or eight years—*years*—to train an animal. And about discipline.

ART

(To the group)

Anybody here know what he's talking about? Hands, please.

LARRY

And the single greatest lesson I learned down there was one called The Pat on the Head. Just that. In caps: THE PAT ON THE HEAD. These extraordinary trainers working with the animals—people think they beat them or force them. Not at all. The animals are shown how to do something. They try. If they do it *right,* they get a pat on the head. Oh, sure—sometimes a chunk of fish or meat or dog biscuit—but I watched that process for five long weeks and I'm convinced that The Pat on the Head was more important. That was the lesson. Think about it, Art.

ART

Listen, I once patted a guy on the head so hard—an actor—it took seventeen stitches.

LARRY

So. We're on the Roof Garden. Number over. Jack and Nora to their table with two friends. Orchestra off. Trio continues. Sonofabitch—Claude—comes in with a party of six. Will there be room, Ivan?

IVAN

We make room.

LARRY

Jack sees them. Nora doesn't. Her back is to them. S.O.B. spots Jack and Nora. His party—heads together—they look over at Nora's table—then back together and big laughter. Jack stands. Sits. Trio off. Orchestra on. They play the one-step. How's that coming, Hy?

HY

Bloodcurdling. Trouble is, I never danced the one-step in my life. But don't worry.

LARRY

All right.

HY

No sense the *two* of us worrying.

FRED

We'll get it, we'll get it.

LARRY

One-step. Everybody on, dancing. Except Jack and Nora. Claude and partner. When we've got the number—the dance—really riding—S.O.B. and his partner sit there and stare at Jack and Nora. They're trying to cool it—all at once, Claude points. That's the moment! That's the signal—Jack makes a running lunge for him—he shoves the girl in front of him and dashes onto the dance floor—we lose him—meanwhile Jack piles into the girl—knocks her ass over tip—gets up and piles into the crowd—looking for Claude.

ART

Jesus! How're you going to do *that?*

LARRY

Do what?

ART

Knock the girl over. Eight times a week. Can we get insurance on a thing like that?

LARRY

As in all things, Art, we get experts, professionals. It's a tough trick I grant you, but important. It's action. And audiences these days are action-oriented, you know that. And they're going to get their share from us, believe me.

ART

Yeah, but *how?*

LARRY

Stand up, Nick.
(NICK *gets out of his chair and takes a step forward. He is a short, elderly, chunky, scarred, tough-looking trainer type. He wears glasses)*
Ladies and gentlemen—Nick Pappas, our stunt man. He's here to help us with falls, trips, fights, and so on. Anything physical—we'll refer to Nick.

ART
(*To* NICK)

O.K. *You* tell me how we're gonna do it.

· 92 ·

NICK

The knockin' the girl out of the chair bit you mean?

ART

That's it.

NICK

Well, first off—it's not gonna be no girl.

ART

What?!

LARRY

Hold it. Listen, everybody. This is classified information. Keep it dark. No leaks. It'll hurt us. After a while, I suppose—it'll come out, but by then it won't matter, now it will. So this is— for the present—a real "Burn Before Reading," right? Go ahead, Nick.

NICK

No girl. I got a good man. A tumbler. He'll look an O.K. girl all right.

HY

If he remembers to shave.

NICK

Don't worry about the guy. The way we'll routine it, see— there'll be no physical contact whatsoever. Way shape or form. I figure the jumper to dive right *past* my tumbler—right into the wings and offstage where I got a foam-rubber mat. My tumbler takes his own fall. Also, he's gonna be wearing this dress and nothing underneath—I mean no pants no nothing—

ART

But if he's a—

NICK

Wait. No pants no nothing—only a false twat.

ART
(To LARRY*)*

Is this guy putting me on?

LARRY

Why would he?

· 93 ·

NICK

No! See, the idea is that on the jump, she—I mean *he*—goes over in his chair and the skirt goes up and everybody's attention naturally goes to the one spot and whatever they see or don't see or think they see it takes off their mind from the action and we got it made. Y'unnerstan' this whole bit is a split second.

ART

So if it's such a great trick—why can't you do it with a *real* girl, and a *real* twat? After all, there's got to be girl tumblers.

NICK

No. No, sir. Not for this. This is gonna be a rough fall—also, there's always the chance of a accident. I would not handle this stunt unless with a man doubling woman.

LARRY

Can I keep going, please? Now comes the top of the act to this point. The fight. Nick's going to work on it with Jenny and me. Part One: we see Jack grab him. They disappear in the crowd. People are still dancing. Now the couples begin to stop—one by one—women scream—men try to break up the fight—the dance stops—but the music goes on—louder and faster. Part Two: they're squared off now and it's a real bloody battle. Blood. Torn clothes. Rough-and-tumble. Not like a boxing match—it's anything goes—wrestling, rolling, punching. Part Three is the surprise ending to it. Jack is the *loser.* Knocked cold. Nora breaks away, jumps on Claude and he flattens her, too. Part Four: police arrive. Two of them start working over the out Jack and Nora. Curtain.

IVAN

A fine scene.

ART

If it works.

LARRY

That's our job. To make it work.

CLAY

It can work.

LARRY

It's the toughest I can remember, physically, I mean. But what the hell. That's the game. Next. Hospital scene. Jack in bed. Nora visiting, her arm in a sling.

ALICIA

This is it, Larry. What I asked you about. The place I worry about the change. Can you get me a crossover or *something?* I'll need two minutes at least—well, all right, *one* minute with break-aways.

LARRY

And the cops who kneel down to look at them can be dressers. Crowd gathers around—masking—hell, we could probably make the whole change onstage in the dim. A slow dim.

ALICIA

I doubt it.

RUSS

Would you want to use the projection again? With another news-paper? I mean, if they're celebrities and there's a brawl, wouldn't it? . . .

LARRY

That's damn good, Russ.

ALICIA

Certainly helps *me.*

CLAY

And the players.

LARRY

You know what? We ought to carry this forward and back. Use at least *six* projections. Three in each act. No. Wait. Seven is better. Four in Act One. Three in Act Two.

IVAN

Better than if only one place. Style.

LARRY

Thanks, Russ. Real good. Right. So we're in the hospital scene. And we find out Claude has really let loose now. The lawyer in. Discussion of what to do. A suit for slander—otherwise the man-ager is worried about the consequences. Decided. Jack says,

"Well, if you can't lick 'em, sue 'em." Lawyer leaves. Jack and Nora. Number. But now we're stuck. Number. But what? Who?

HY

The two of them.

LARRY

About what?

HY

I love you I love you I love you.

LARRY

We *know* that, for Chrissake. A comedy song, maybe?

FRED

Unlikely.

LARRY

Well, not comedy exactly. More irony.

HY

No.

LARRY

Like *we've* seen him get his lumps and *she* sees it as a great victory.

FRED

"Darling, you were wonderful!"?

HY

Yeah!

LARRY

No. Too on the nose.

CHRIS

"Win or Lose"?

LARRY *(To* HY*)*

Anything?

HY

I don't know.

FRED

Could have a shape. It's about—the fight—win or lose no matter —and the upcoming lawsuit—win or lose—and about whatever

—win or lose, up or down, hit or flop—they're all right because they're together.

HY

What I said in the first place—I love you I love you I love you.

LARRY

Want to try it?

HY

Sure.

LARRY

On. Courtroom scene. Like Gilbert and Sullivan. *Trial by Jury.* That's the model. Now what saves this is that there's not one word of spoken dialogue.

CHRIS

Oh, thanks.

LARRY

No. What I mean is that after all these years and fifty thousand courtroom scenes—it's usually a yawn. "Do you swear to tell the truth the whole truth and nothing but the truth so help you God?" "I do." "State your name." Who cares? But hardly anybody's ever heard it *sung* before. That's the kick. And the lights fading out and in and every time we come back—we see the courtroom from *another* angle.

IVAN

Was very hard to do. Was *impossible.* I did it.

LARRY

You sure as hell did, Ivan. So. Claude's testimony and two more guys. They all three identify her as Lovey Kelly of the Everleigh Club. Things look bad. Now on come the Everleigh sisters themselves—with their girls. The big cantata. They all swear they've never seen Nora before. Don't know her. Do know Claude and the other two. Lousy lays, all three. Kinky types. Finally barred, say the Everleigh sisters. Big fuss. The Everleigh sisters with their big red book—names of all clients. Want to hear them? No! Objection!! A new witness. Ginny. *Uh*-uh! She heard them all plotting. Being coached. She was, too. But she has quit. Gone straight now. But can't lie. Went to her minister, who advised her to tell the truth. How can they take the word of a bunch of whores? Uproar. Fade-out. Fade-in. Really looks bad for Nora.

Now. Surprise witness. "State your name." "My name is Lovey Kelly. Worked for The Everleigh Sisters. Know Claude and the others. Kooks. Refused to have anything to do with them—so they got mad." "Prove you are Lovey Kelly." Birth certificate. Grammar-school records. Auto license. Mother and father are in court. Summons. Jury dances out. Jack and Nora. Jury dances in. We win. Big sum. Celebration. The twelve men dance with the twelve hookers. Judge with The Everleigh Sisters. Back to the theatre. Dressing room. Nora and Jack getting ready. Nora: "But how did they do it? Who was she? Who is she? Is she me?" Jack: "Honey, when you've got the answers, don't ask the questions. In Chicago—The Everleigh Sisters are a power. They could produce George Washington if they had to." Nora: "And they may *have* to before we're through. I don't know. I have a feeling I'll never get to Heaven." Jack: "But, Lovey—you're in Heaven now." And the revolve—*and* the fanfare—and the finale and they sing "Shine On, Harvest Moon."

HY

Or whatever.

ART

Great show. Greatest show of the year.

LARRY

All right. That's it for today. Many thanks. See you all tomorrow. Oh—by the way—tomorrow I want to hear Act One from *you*, Ivan. And Act Two, Alicia.

ALICIA

I'm expecting to be in bed with laryngitis.

ART

Laryngitis! I'll kill that Greek.

LARRY

Hy, Fred. Can you stay a few minutes?

HY

Sure.

FRED

You bet.

Everyone left, except Larry, me, Art, Hy and Fred. I hoped they were not going to begin that interpolated-songs argument again. It

· 98 ·

had come up every three or four days and was invariably acrimonious and bitter and ultimately nasty. My hopes were dashed as Larry began.

"Hy, let me ask you something candidly."

"Go ahead."

"Having been through the whole show in outline," said Larry. "Now that we're beginning to get a feel of the shape and color and flavor of it all—don't you see how desperately we need the authenticity of the two Norworth numbers?"

"Candidly, you said."

"Yes."

"Candidly, no."

"What about you, Fred?"

"Me. I don't know. I'm of two minds."

"Yes, but only one of them counts," said Hy. "The one that works with me."

"I have nightmares," said Larry, "about the pasting we're going to take from critics who identify those two songs with the Nora Bayes story."

"Fuck 'em!" said Hy, getting hot sooner than usual.

"We're hardly in a position to do that," said Larry.

"Talk sense!" Art yelled. "If you're going to talk at all! And somethin' else. I'm gettin' goddam sick and tired of this discussion. How come we left it till now?"

"Mistakes," said Larry. "We've all made our share. I was sure I'd be able to convince the boys once we got under way. You, Art, made a great mistake signing a contract with them that specified no interpolations. . . ."

(Note: I found out later, much later, what had happened. Art is a real contract reader. He has read, Clay assures me, every contract to do with this show including the ones with the scene builders, the musicians, the understudies. When he read the Dramatists Guild contract with Hy and Fred, he of course read the clause about interpolations—but did not know what the word meant and was ashamed to ask. So he thought, what the hell, it's a standard contract. All printed. Boiler plate. Not a rider, not a special condition. So he signed it. It was only later, when the arguments began and Hy invoked the clause, that Art realized the blunder he had made. But it was too late. He had to brazen it out.)

"I thought the way *you* did, that they'd be reasonable."

"Don't ever count on anyone in this business being reasonable, Art," said Larry.

"Reasonable!" shouted Hy. "What the fuck's 'reasonable' got to do with anything? This is *me* you're talking about. My *work*. My whole goddam career. What kind of an asshole credit is it if it says 'Music by Hy Balaban, Lyrics by Fred Monroe'—then ' "Shine On, Harvest Moon" and "Take Me Out to the Ball Game" by Jack Norworth and Nora Bayes'? Jesus! It sounds like we couldn't hack it or something."

"Not at all," said Larry. "It sounds like since the show is *about* Nora Bayes and Jack Norworth we're including the two numbers that have always been identified with them."

"I'm going to give you two *better* numbers," said Hy.

"That's not the *point,*" said Larry. "They won't be the same."

Art broke in. "What about the title of the show, even? *Shine On, Harvest Moon.*"

"This may come as a surprise to you, Mr. Clune," said Hy. "But it so happens that I *know* the title of the show."

"But going with you, we'll have no title song."

"So what?" said Fred. "It's an old-fashioned notion anyway. Most shows don't have title songs anymore."

"Some do," mumbled Art, and was silent.

"But not *Annie,*" said Hy.

"Or *A Chorus Line,*" said Fred.

Hy. "*South Pacific.*"

Fred. "*The King and I.*"

Hy. "*Funny Girl.*"

Fred. "*The Wiz.*"

Hy. "*Pippin.*"

Fred. "*Grease.*"

Hy. "*Porgy and Bess.*"

Fred. "*Pal Joey.*"

Hy. "*The Music Man.*"

Fred. "*West Side Story.*"

Hy. "*Gypsy.*"

Fred. "*Ballroom.*"

There was a tired pause, then Art chirped up, brightly.

"*My Fair Lady!*" he said.

I was about to laugh, but held it in as I saw the look Larry gave him.

No one said anything for a time but the atmosphere was tense.

"And talking about—about *Funny Girl,*" said Hy.

"What *about* it?" asked Larry.

"Fanny Brice. So did you hear Streisand sing 'My Man'?"

"Or 'Second Hand Rose'?" asked Fred.

"Or any *one* of her numbers?"

"In my opinion—she *should* have," said Larry.

Hy laughed. "Oh, brother. I guess you wouldn't settle for the hit *they* were, huh?"

"Gladly," said Larry. "But that's got nothing to do with it."

"It's got *everything* to do!" shouted Hy.

"Hold it down, Hy," said Larry. "I can hear you."

"The title," said Art.

"Oh, for Christ's sweet sake!" Hy yelled. "Will you shut up about the title? *Change* the fucking title! Who cares about a title?"

"When they did the *movie* of *Funny Girl,*" said Larry, "and Styne wasn't in control anymore, they sure in hell *did* use 'My Man'—and it was *electrifying.*"

"That's right," agreed Hy. "It was."

"So?"

"So when *you* do the movie of *this*—put in any goddam thing you want. Who gives a shit what's in a movie, anyhow?"

"Would you do *this* for me, Hy?" asked Larry.

"What?"

"Let her sing 'Shine On' for a couple of run-throughs? Maybe you'll begin to feel what I feel."

"No chance."

"As a favor?"

"I don't owe you any favors."

"As a professional courtesy."

"As a professional courtesy, I'd like you to get off my ass."

"Boy—I heard you were stubborn—but I didn't know *anyone* could be *this* stubborn."

"You heard, huh? You want to know what I heard about *you?*"

"No, thanks. I can imagine."

"I heard you don't know your ass from a hard rock about putting on a musical—and that you come up with a bit once in a while because you keep the kid close. Russ."

"Really?" Larry smiled, but he had gone pale.

"Who'd you hear *that* from?" asked Art. "Russ?"

"I move we adjourn," said Larry.

"Not yet," said Hy. "I've got one more thing I want to say. It's this. I don't want this goddam subject to come up *again.* I've fucking *had* it. I've written a great score and if you people don't like it—if you don't think it's enough—I'll tell you what you can do. You can give it *back* to me. I'll return your advance. Then you can go shopping and that's it. Also. Go fuck yourselves. Or each other. But stop trying to fuck *me!*"

He walked out, slowly.

Art looked at Fred. "That go for you, too?"

Fred was clearly miserable. "Jesus. I don't know. He's an excitable guy. He's my partner. What can I do? I've got to stick with him. Also —there's a big difference between him and me. He's loaded and I'm not."

"His *wife,* you mean," said Larry.

"What's the difference? It's all the same. He's got her in his pocket."

Larry spoke. "It sounds more like he's in *her* pocket."

"So he can *afford* to blast," said Fred. "I wish *I* could. See you later, huh?"

"Yes," said Larry. "Take it easy."

Art and Larry and I sat there for a while.

"Get me some coffee, Midge," said Larry. "Would you, please?"

"Me, too," said Art.

I went off to get the coffee from the chorus urn downstairs.

When I got back, Art was sitting on the edge of his chair, leaning toward Larry.

"—from where millions? Are you sure?"

"Thanks, Midge."

"Thanks."

"If you mean have I seen the millions in a box in their home," said Larry, "no. But hell, the way they live. The houses: in New York, in Martha's Vineyard, in Nassau. And an apartment in Paris. Oh, yes— and a condominium in Beverly Hills for when he goes out there a few times a year. Rachel doesn't like hotel food or restaurant food. She's a true gourmet."

"She looks it."

"What do you mean?"

"Too healthy," said Art. "I *hate* healthy-looking people. They're always so goddam smug."

"Money is power," said Larry. "I just made that up. Make a note, Midge. I don't want to forget any of my great thoughts."

"Don't be fooled by front," said Art. "People think I'm a hell of a lot richer than I am. Know why? Because that's what I *want* them to think. Also, I've noticed something. The *really* rich don't spread it around so much. Where did she *get* the dough?"

"Her first two husbands. Both tycoons. Both died."

"That's what they do, tycoons. They die."

"So she's twice a rich widow," said Larry.

"The husbands. On the old side?"

"I believe so, yes."

"Figures. She's probably one of those."

"Of what?"

"Plans it. Hooks 'em, then balls 'em to death."

Larry laughed. "Well, she's not going to ball our Hy to death. He's well known for his prowess."

"He is, huh?"

Art began to scratch his palm, nervously.

"So he fools around, huh?"

"I didn't say that, Art."

Art looked at me.

"Does he?"

"How on earth would *I* know?" I asked.

"You hear things. You're around. Especially around the company."

"Yes. I hear things and then I forget them. They're mostly nothing. Gossip. Junk. Who cares? I try not to feed my mind on garbage."

"Well, if you hear anything along *these* lines, let me know."

I was about to reply, when Larry caught my eye and winked. I said nothing.

"Yeah," said Art, more to himself than to us. "Yeah."

"What?" asked Larry.

"Nothing, nothing," said Art, making it sound like something, something. He looked at his watch. "I gotta go," he said, and left abruptly.

"Did you notice?" asked Larry.

"What?"

"He didn't say goodbye."

"He seldom does."

"Come on," said Larry. "I'll walk you home."

"Fine."

"Have I eaten today?" he asked.

"Not much."

"Maybe we'll stop on the way."

"Fine with me."

The Russian Tea Room. Blinis with red caviar.

"Well, missy. What do you make of all this? So far. Do you wish you were back in the peace and quiet of Doubleday?"

"Not so peace. Not so quiet. Anyway, no. I don't miss it. I like this job, if that's what you mean. Every day I learn something."

"And we don't all seem like a bunch of raving maniacs to you?"

"Not the ones with talent, no. If you're talented, you're *allowed* to be a little nutty."

"You've got a point."

"What I object to, though, is the proportion. We've got some small talents who are *very* nutty—and some great talents who aren't as nutty as they could be."

"Name names."

"Oh, no. It's a matter of opinion."

"Hy?"

"As far as I'm concerned, he can go as ape as he wants to. His music is simply breathtaking."

"I agree. Isn't it curious where God sometimes puts talent?"

"Let me *ask* you one. Ivan."

"He's the best we've got—and yet—sensible and levelheaded and controlled."

"And Alicia?"

"An enigma. Bright, practical, a pro. But she's so good—she must have some nuttiness. Keeps it hidden."

"Yes," I said.

"About the song. What do *you* think?"

"I don't know. See, I never even heard of Nora Bayes before this. I guess if I had—and knew that 'Shine On, Harvest Moon' was her song—I'd want to hear it in the show. As it is, it doesn't *matter* all that much to me."

"So the question is—*you* think—what percentage of the audience, or the critics, *will* care."

"Yes. Also. I think I've heard *you* say, several times, that the show has to stand on its own—and not lean on the nostalgic appeal of Nora Bayes."

"*I* said that?"

"Yes."

"Brilliant. Of course—it has to work even if the character's name is Minnie Slipansplitit."

"Well, then why so much fuss about the song?"

"I don't know. Instinct. Stubbornness. And I love the song."

Then he sang it, softly and beautifully. I listened, watching his lips and his eyes. He sang with feeling, the only kind of singing that counts:

"Shine on,
Shine on, Harvest Moon
Up in the sky.
I ain't had no lovin'
Since January, February
June or July.
Snow time
Ain't no time to
Stay outdoors and spoon,
So shine on,
Shine on, Harvest Moon
For me and my gal."

He finished. The customers at the tables to either side of us applauded.

"I'm a hit," said Larry.

"It *is* a nice song."

Outside, he said, "Walk me to The Plaza and I'll buy you a cab home."

"All right."

We walked, slowly.

"Oh, hell," said Larry.

"What was *that* particular hell about?"

"I wish I could do something else in life."

"I'm not sure I—"

"Sing or dance or act or write or anything. What I do is an *awful* job."

"Not the way you do it," I said. "It's fascinating. What's more, it works. I see you make it all come to life."

"That's because I know a few secrets—don't tell anyone—like the best direction is the least direction. You get good people and leave them alone or try to and it comes to life, as you say. And attention to detail. But the rest of it—God! The politicking and the infighting and double-dealing and logrolling and dealmaking—what a waste. And in the end, thankless."

"Movies?"

"Worse. And TV, *still* worse. No. No use. I'm trapped. But you don't mind if I complain a little? It feels so good."

"Complain away."

"See, if the moment comes when the director loses control of the show—it's all over. Not only for him, for everyone. Like a bus or a train or a ship. Got to have a driver or an engineer or a captain in charge. *Someone* has to be in charge, otherwise it's dangerous. . . . I don't have any *pride* about any of this. Or insecurity. That's not it. It's a question of *method,* that's all. Look, if Art wants to be in charge, that's all right with me. A relief, in fact. But he can't do it. He doesn't know *beans* about this business. Or Hy. Or anyone. The nearest would be Russ. He's got the talent, but not enough experience. Or Clay—the experience, but not the talent."

"How about Larry?"

"He's fine—but trouble with Art. Art wants him to run it all—insists that he run it all—and then won't let him."

"How about a simple heart-to-heart?"

"Tried it, but he— Hey! Here we are. Come in a minute."

We went through the lobby to the desk. He got his key. His box was stuffed with messages.

"Want to come up?" he asked. "I feel like talking."

"Perfect. I feel like listening."

"Milk. Or I could get you a drink."

"Milk's fine."

"Maybe even a Carr's wheatmeal cookie if you play your cards right."

"I'll do my best." In the elevator, I asked, "How come you live *here?* I thought you were a New Yorker."

"I live on Cape Cod. Barnstable. Between shows. I adore New York, but it frazzles me."

His rooms were tidy but disorganized.

"Sorry about the mess," he said. "What this place needs is a woman's touch."

"Yes. Or a man's."

He seemed not to hear what I had said.

"My wife is in London. Know why?"

"No."

"She always takes off the day I go into rehearsal and comes back in time for the opening—if there is an opening. If I get fired, I usually join her—London or wherever—and we stay stoned for a few weeks."

"Well, that can't happen *this* time."

"It can always happen, Midge. Directors are always getting fired. Stands to reason. Who are they going to fire? The producer isn't going to can himself, the author can't be, contractually. The stars? Too costly and dangerous. So it's usually the director takes the fall. . . . Funny. When I was offered this one, I turned it down. I said to them, 'If you don't mind I'd just as soon not be the first director on this project.' And now I am."

He got a carton of milk out of a small refrigerator and poured two glasses.

"I love this show," he said. "It's about things I care about. And I don't care about much. It's about morality—real and phony. Nora is a truly moral human being—but according to the rule book, she's a scarlet woman who eventually subverts the law. It's about talent—what makes the world go round. Not love, not money. Talent. And it's about gossip and the crimes of libel and slander."

"What's the difference? I'm not sure."

"Libel, printed. Slander, spoken."

"Oh. And in this case, it was both."

"Yes. Curious the differences in laws—France, England, here, Japan. In some countries, you could say publicly and print that, say, I'm a narcotics addict. And I could sue and prove I'm not, but I'd have to prove damages. How did it hurt me materially? In other countries, you could say it about an addict and if even you *proved* it —it would matter how *much* he was damaged. All mixed up with ideas of right and wrong. . . . But what the show is really about is love. Love. Our culture's sold the idea of love as candy. Something nice and tasty and easy to find and available to anybody who wants it. What a crock! Love is rare. I've loved. Been loved. Never been *in* love. Have you?"

"I take the Fifth."

"My wife. Fine woman. But a wife would be here. Sitting where you're sitting. Listening to me. I'm stuck on her, I suppose. Not she on me. We manage. Like most. It's not so bad. My first wife died. Four years and two months ago. We'd been married just over a year —and it was beginning to be real. We were—"

The phone rang.

"Yes? . . . About twenty minutes ago. . . . Oh, you did? . . . I may have—I haven't looked at them."

He leafed through the little stack of messages on his desk, shrugged, and made a face.

"Oh, yes. Here we are. 'Call Mr. Clune. . . .' Sorry, Art. I'd've got round to it in time. . . . Oh? Like what? . . . Sure, I'm right here."

He hung up.

"The Lord High Executioner. He's coming up."

"I'll go," I said.

"No, no. Stay where you are."

"I don't think I—"

There was no time to argue. A sharp knock at the door. Larry opened it and Art piled in—a bit high. Not smashed, just flushed. Shirtsleeves. No tie. Velvet slippers. A drink in hand.

"Happy times!" he said. "What's goin' on here? A little 'Upstairs, Downstairs' hanky-panky?"

"Good night," I said.

He blocked the door.

"No," he said. "I need you. In a professional capacity. Professional stenographer, I mean. Didn't you get my messages? Twice."

"I've been busy," I said.

"I can see that," he said.

"Settle down, Art," said Larry.

"You always say that to me. How is that? Do I ever?" He sat down and said, "Sit down. All."

I sat. Larry sat.

He looked from one of us to the other.

"Come on. A joke. I know this is Plutonic. What the hell? You think *I* didn't give it a shot? I wouldn't insult a handsome girl like this by not making a heavy little pass at her. I'm a gentleman." He took a swig of his drink. "Business. A development. How long before you can get orchestrations on 'Shine On' and 'Ball Game'?"

"We've got them, Art. *You* know that."

"We *have?*"

"Don't you remember? We said just in case."

"When could they go in? Both numbers."

"God, I don't know. Depends. Staging. Rehearsal."

"Get ready and I'll tell you when to go."

"It's squared with Hy?"

"Leave it to me."

"Don't get me in the middle, Art. I've got a long way to go with this guy and a lot of work, so—"

"Did I tell you leave it to me? What am I around here? Chopped liver? I'm your *producer* and if I tell you go—*go.* There will be no trouble with Mr. Beethoven, I assure you."

Larry looked troubled and apprehensive, but said, "All right."

"Tell me again how they work," ordered Art.

" 'Shine On' in Act One, Scene Four. Where he comes in and gives her the song as a present. He sings it first. Then She. Instead of 'One Night.' "

"And that's out?"

"So far."

"Good. A dreary goddam dirge anyway."

"Then we'll use 'Shine On' in a lot of underscoring and finally, of course, the finale."

"Thank God. We'll have a finish instead of a fart."

"And then keep it going for the calls, of course."

"And 'Ball Game'?"

"Also in Act One, Scene Six—where he's writing it with Von Tilzer —then in the onstage, full production number."

"But not in the finale?"

"I don't see how."

"Would be good."

"Well, we'll see. And you're sure we're safe on—"

"Knock it off."

"I'm curious. What're you going to do? Pay him off? He doesn't want dough, does he?"

Art put his finger to his lips, smiled, and got up.

"Just go ahead, you two," he said, "from where you were so rudely interrupted." He made a sign of benediction. "I now pronounce you man and woman. See y'."

He was gone. Larry got out his inhalator, used it, looked at me for a time, then asked, "What's he up to? Any idea at all?"

"No."

"More milk?"

"No, thanks."

"Mind if I?"

"God, no."

He poured himself another glass of milk, slowly, watching it as though it might contain the solution to the present puzzle. He sipped his milk, his brow more and more contracted in thought. He moved about, behaving much like a man alone. Had he forgotten I was there? I supposed he had begun to worry about how to stage those new numbers, now that they were in. Should I leave quietly? He was at the window now, looking over the park. Nice man. Would he make a move at me? Or had all that crude comment from Art spoiled it— at least for tonight? Wait. What if he does make his move anyway? What should I do? What do I want to do—or not do? I like him. I like him as much—maybe more—as anyone else connected with this project. I admire him and respect him and find him attractive and entertaining and I love being with him. Why, then, do I hope to God he'll keep his distance and not try anything? That one daffy element is missing. That single unmistakable magnetic force that causes all the trouble. Here I am, hoping that this lovely brilliant talented dear man will leave me alone and that the night elevator man in my building will knock at my door when his shift is over and climb into bed with me. I looked and saw Larry poring over a big dictionary on his desk.

"Ha!" he said.

"What?"

"Listen to this: 'pearl: a silvery or bluish-white, hard, smooth, lustrous substance, of a roundish, oval, or pear-shaped form, formed around a parasitic worm or other foreign body within the shell of certain mollusks. The presence of this body sets up an irritant action, resulting in the deposition of gradually increasing layers of nacreous material, over the particle.' So on so on so on— 'Pearls are used as precious gems.' " He looked up at me. The frown was gone. "Did you get all that? 'Parasitic worm'? 'Setting up an irritant action'? Isn't that what we have here? Trying to create a pearl, a gem? I guess the irritant action is something you have to have. Creation is painful. Why do we never get used to that idea? Why do we expect it all to go smoothly and simply? It never does. It won't. It can't. Have you ever had a baby?"

"No. Not that I know of."

"Melanie and I tried. Jesus God, the agony. She was sick and in pain the whole time. Then, the month before, two false alarms. And finally —the morning. Too soon. Her obstetrician is one of these modern, progressive sons of bitches, so of course I had to be there—dressed like him, green cap and smock—and hold her hand and mop the brow and share the experience. Finally—stillborn. God! I have nightmares about it even now. . . . And that's all this. We're trying to create something that'll have a life of its own someday. So it's painful."

"I see that," I said.

He looked at me, lovingly, and said, "You are a dear girl, Midge Maghakian, and I am so glad you are with us. With me."

I was embarrassed, tried to respond in kind but all that came out was a whispered, "Thank you."

"Let's go to bed," he said.

I was framing what I hoped would be an inoffensive reply when he laughed.

"Oh, my God!" he said. "I didn't mean—well, please forgive me. What I meant to say—actually—was, 'Let's go to *sleep.*' It's late. You look tired. I'm about to keel over. Here's the taxi money."

"Never mind. I'll put it on expense."

He walked me through the hall to the elevator, leaned over, hugged me, said, "Good night. Pleasant dreams," and left.

At home, I locked the door and turned on the TV. The Late Show. Clark Gable and Deborah Kerr in *The Hucksters.* A hare-brained old friend but worth watching for those Gable dimples. I washed my underclothes and hung them up to dry. Mom used to say, "Don't try to do two things at once, you'll ruin them both." Baloney. Here I was doing *three* things at once—perfectly: my laundry, the TV, and thinking of the show and its troubles. And Larry. And Art. Four things. *Five.* TV off. Into bed. I wished someone were beside me. The last thing Larry had said was, "Pleasant dreams." Good advice. I tried, but failed miserably. How I tried was by thinking of a lot of pleasant thoughts as I was drifting off. Jean-Pierre. Paris. A new dress. Swimming naked in the surf at Del Monte. Bouillabaisse and chilled Montrachet on the terrace of La Loup in Saint-Tropez. But when sleep came, the dream or dreams were of Art beating people with a policeman's club. Watching an abortion being performed. Myself in a mirror weighing at least three hundred pounds. Fistfights. Many. Hy and Larry and Val. I woke in a sweat. Another shower. Fresh nightgown. What's the time? 4:05. TV on again. Alan Ladd. *The Blue Dahlia* in black and white. I watch it groggily. I sleep. The set is still on when I wake. The "Today Show." I get breakfast and wonder if I should quit. This world I am living in may be too much for me.

· IX ·

Larry to the company:

"Let's talk about acting today. We know that players in a musical aren't supposed to be great actors and actresses. We expect them to sing, to dance, and to play the scenes nicely. We don't look for, nor do we often get, great acting, even in the great musicals. But that's not to say we shouldn't aim for the highest form of this remarkable craft.

"There's nothing mysterious about acting. Nothing esoteric. There's no mystique about it, even though some celebrated gurus would like to make us think so. Everyone acts. Everyone acts every day. It's part of civilized existence to act. God forbid that everyone went around saying precisely what they thought, or reacting exactly as they felt, or doing what they felt like doing at any given moment. We all have faces and we all wear masks.

"Come to think of it, even animals act. Have you ever seen a cat stalking an imaginary mouse? Have you ever seen a cat pretending to be a tiger? Pouncing. On what? On nothing. Pouncing for the sake of pouncing. Acting the ferocious monster with the tiny atavistic atom that's left in the final mutation. No longer a tiger, but wants to act like a tiger. And what about puppies? Pretending to fight. They're not really fighting. They're *acting* at fighting. That's why they enjoy doing it. I doubt they'd enjoy fighting.

"Maybe the reason the public appreciates great acting is that they recognize it, envy it, admire it. They realize that they're watching actors do something they do all day long, except not as well. 'My God, I wish I could lie as brilliantly and get away with it!' 'I wish I could snow a girl the way *he's* snowing *her.*' 'Does he mean what he's saying, or is he pretending?'

"What I have to say next applies mainly to you, Calvin. The male-female game, as most of us know it, is essentially acting. The whole macho cult in present-day life is based on acting, on a pose, on assuming a character a man thinks is going to be appealing to the woman. By the same token, women act. They put on their makeup just as you do in your dressing rooms. They put on their costumes in order to play their parts in the ritual. And there's a kind of scenario for most people. 'What are you doing after the show?' 'Do you live with your folks?' 'Let's have a cup of coffee.' 'How about going up to my place for a drink?' These are lines in the boy-girl colloquy that's been going on for thousands of years in every language.

"Acting is nothing like brain surgery. Brain surgery is something only a very few people could do. Acting is something *everyone* can do, that everyone does. Some do it better than others; some do it professionally. Now, in order to do it professionally, techniques are required, disciplines that the actors in life don't necessarily need to follow. Up and down Madison Avenue, the boys who seem to be running our world these days live a whole life of acting, pretending. What else does it mean when they say, 'Listen, I think we can con them into such and so'? 'Why don't we do a hype on this product?'

"Policemen. Think of New York cops. I get the feeling they love to act. They have a fine costume, terrific props—pistols, handcuffs, walkie-talkies. They get lots of attention as they walk the streets. *You* look at them. *I* do. No one looks at a cop without some apprehension, so that makes the cop feel a little bit above it all. And cops act, believe it or not, like cops. When they're seemingly angry, I doubt they're truly angry. But I think they feel, correctly, that if they appear to be angry, the crowd will disperse or the suspect will be intimidated— so they put on a bit. When they're approaching someone they think may be dangerous or crazy, they act calm, but they're probably nervous.

"And that's what I want you to do. Act. Play. Pretend. Let go. Do it!"

SHINE ON, HARVEST MOON
Company Bulletin
Thursday, October 11

NEW NUMBER: Our show has acquired a new number which will be performed by Joey Faye in Scene 8, Act I. It is called "Merry-Go-Round."

WIGS: The girl dancers will be fitted for wigs tomorrow at 5:00 P.M. Appointments will follow shortly for singers and principals.

NAMES OF THE EVERLEIGH GIRLS: The Everleigh Girls listed previously as A, B, C, D, E, and F have been given names in the script and they will be played as follows:

Vera	Peggy Wells
Belle	Diana Van Rijn
Lily	Lee Nelson
Maggie	Rosie Zellen
Cathy	Gloria Fuller
Ginny	Sharon Vaughn

PRODUCTION CONFERENCES: are proceeding with the Production Carpenter, Louis J. Thomas, and the Production Electrician, Edward Kavanagh.

BACKGROUND READING: It has been suggested that the cast read *Come into My Parlor* by Charles Washburn. Copies may be obtained by calling Midge Maghakian.

REQUEST: Please give all information (name, address, and phone number) on your hotel in Boston to Midge today. A new directory has to be made up before we leave for Boston. Also, *IMPORTANT,* if any of you change your hotels in Boston, please let Midge know immediately. We must be able to reach you.

HEALTH AND STRENGTH: Our principal mutual concern at this moment is the health of the company. We are in very good shape artistically, and the only thing that could do us serious damage would be illness or accident. So this is a special passionate plea to one and all to button up your overcoats, take your vitamins, don't eat crazy, watch yourselves in the bathtub, cross on green lights only, and do not fool with electrical switches. Extra care as to rest, fresh air, exercise, and sensible foods will be greatly appreciated. We are now completely interdependent and have others to think of.

THE COMPANY YOU KEEP: EDDIE CONVERY(Boyle)
    I went—or was pushed—on the stage at the age of five. The great Elitch's Gardens Stock Company in Denver, Colorado, where I was born 42 years ago. The name of the play was SEEN BUT NOT HEARD. . . . My mother saw me as a meal ticket and that's what I was for the next thirteen years—all over the country with periodic trips (seven) to Hollywood, where nothing ever happened beyond a day or two here and there, or a bit, or a test. . . . Lessons, lessons. Dancing, singing, acting. . . . Twenty years ago I came to New York and right off got a job in THE WORLD OF SUZIE WONG (straight), next: REDHEAD (musical) with the great Gwen Verdon. Since then, I've done plenty, but I prefer to list the hits only: GEORGE M!, WEST SIDE STORY (revival), PIPPIN (2 years), HAIR (understudy), and GREASE. . . . I thank you.

REHEARSAL SCHEDULE: We endeavor to keep the rehearsal schedule as it is printed. However, it is sometimes unavoidable that we fall behind. Therefore, please do not leave one rehearsal place for another before you have checked with a stage manager. (Eddie Convery and Patti Rolph: Your "Big Town" rehearsal will be in the lobby at 5:00 P.M. today.)

In Boston we will be using some local dressers, probably two or three. They will be available to assist with changes, but remember that they do not know the show in the way that you do and will have to be carefully coached by you in what is required.

QUOTE TO REMEMBER:
    "Remember (particularly during the irritable stage) that you must not tell an actor too much at once. Not more than two or three important things can be borne at one rehearsal; and don't mention trifles, such as slips in business or in words, in a heart-broken desperate way, as if the world were crumbling in ruins. Don't mention anything that doesn't really matter.

Be prepared for the same mistake being repeated time after time, and your directions
being forgotten until you have given them
three or four days running."
                    George Bernard Shaw—
                        THE ART OF REHEARSAL, 1928

There are now 8 days remaining until our opening in
Boston.

· X ·

The fact that I am the Production Secretary makes all of them consider me something of a machine, a piece of equipment; like a tape recorder or an IBM Copier. They say and do just about anything in my presence. Well, actually, I *have* no presence. I am invisible (during working hours). At first, I found this disconcerting—and—what's the word? Dehumanizing. Yes, that's it. Then I began to see the advantage of it, the excitement, and, ultimately, the enjoyment. That Proust quotation: "Thanks to art, we are able to see a world not only with our own eyes, but to see as many worlds as there are original artists."

In my position—since I work at different times with every single member of this mad family, as well as groups of them in various combinations—my opportunity for an overview is complete. What fascinates me is the double-dealing and triple expression and quadruple chicanery that are the order of the day.

This includes Christopher Feller, a real operator. So far as I can see, there is nothing *not* devious about him. What he says to one, he does not say to the others. What's more, he does not say what he thinks —he says what he thinks they *want* him to say. I suppose that is why he is one of the most popular members of the whole company. He is an All-American boy. Male-model type. Athletic. Runs in the park. Swims at the NYAC. Suit and tie at all times. Efficient. Uninspired. Chris is a loner, and seems to be welcome in any and every group.

Right after rehearsal on Thursday, he asked me if I would go over the changes and inserts with him. His own script, he said, was a mess. I was not surprised. I am having quite a time keeping my own in shape.

"Where would you rather?" I asked. "Here on the stage? Production Office?"

"I don't care," he said. "Let's stay here."

We did, but after an hour or so—the pilot light (the only thing on) became oppressive, and we moved up to the Production Office, which is actually one of the small dressing rooms on the third floor. Half an hour in that airless atmosphere was enough. We stopped.

"The glamorous theatre," said Chris, mockingly. "Does the audience know, do you suppose, that behind all the beauty they see—is this horrid, stinking, massive urinal?"

"Awful," I said. "Are they *all* like this?"

"No. Three or four have been moved into the present century by human owners—but by and large—this is what we have."

"We could go up to my place," I said. "I'm not far."

"Or mine," he suggested. "Across the street."

"Oh?"

"Yes. The Edison. Not grand, but better than this."

"Fine."

"How about some food first?" he asked. "Unless you have a dinner date, I'd like to take you to dinner."

"Me?" I said. "I'm not allowed to have dinner dates. Not until after opening night."

He looked at the ceiling and heaved a sigh. "Do you think that day is ever likely to come?" he asked. "Right now, it seems like next to never."

"It'll come, all right. Too soon. All of a sudden. You'll see."

As we left the theatre, he said, "I've got a better idea."

"Yes?"

"My place now, and let's finish up fast—I mean, as fast as we can —then go have a proper dinner—no rush—drinks and everything."

"Suits me."

His room was neat and orderly—a reflection of himself. I used his bathroom, perfectly arranged, titillatingly "manny."

By the time I came out, he had set up a bridge table and two chairs, side by side.

We went to work. He made additional changes as we went along

—he is one of those writers who wants to get it over with—said, "Good enough" quite a lot. He seems completely uninvolved, simply doing a job of piecework; manuscript by the foot. When he cut a line I thought good, I mentioned it.

"Yes," he said. "I like it, too, but Art wants it out. I'm not here to argue. I give the customer what he wants. What's the difference? A show like this. However you slice it—it's still knockwurst."

We finished the last page and stood up. He said, "Thank you, Midge." He leaned over and kissed my cheek. I hate a man kissing my cheek. It suggests either that *he's* a woman or that *I'm* a faggot. He said, "I won't be a minute," went into the bathroom, but left the door open. He took off his shirt and washed up—the way Pa used to do when he came home from work—and came out. He put his soiled shirt into a laundry bag in his closet, got out a fresh shirt, and put it on. While he was doing all this, I framed a sentence, rehearsed it silently, was about to say it, changed my mind. The lost remark was: "You must think I'm made of *ice cream*, mister." Looking back, I'm glad I didn't say it. Who knows what it might have led to?

As he put on his jacket, he asked, "Where do you stand on the steak question?"

"Affirmative."

"Then how about Spindletop, down the street? I've been there, and I can recommend it."

"But can you afford it? We're not a smash *yet*, you know."

"Let's go. I can always hock my mother in a pinch."

We ordered a double sirloin, and nothing first to spoil it, so it took a while. We drank. I had a Stolichnaya Bloody Mary, he drank Wild Turkey bourbon and water.

The drink loosened us up.

"Midge," he said, and looked at me in a way that could have been interpreted as soulful.

"Yes?" (Was I batting my eyelids?)

"What's your other name?"

"What other name?" I asked, thrown.

"Your Christian name—if you're Christian. Or your Jewish name —if you're Jewish. Your *last* name. The one that comes after your *first* name."

"Maghakian."

"Again?"

"Maghakian."

"Armenian?"

"Irish and."

"From here?"

"California. Saint Helena."

"I know. In the Napa Valley."

"How come you know that? You may be the first."

"I know California. I'm a seduced, succumbed Easterner. But I like the north better than where *I* have to live—so I bang around up there a lot."

He saw me finish my drink, and asked, "One more?"

"No," I said. *"Two* more."

"Waiter!" he called. The waiter came at once. "Two more."

"Another round?" asked the waiter.

"No. Two more for the lady, and two more for me."

The waiter took our empties, and as he walked away, mumbled something. I thought I heard it, but could not be certain.

"Did you hear what he said?" I asked.

"Yes," replied Chris.

"What?"

"He said, 'Some lady!' "

"That's what I *thought* he said."

"Shall we leave?" he asked.

"Damn right. As soon as we finish our steaks."

He was drumming on the table with a sesame bread stick and seemed far away—somewhere inside himself.

The waiter appeared and put down two drinks before each of us. He was clearly disapproving.

"Thank you," said Chris.

"Thank you," I said.

The waiter left, silently.

"How do you like the show?" asked Chris.

I laughed and took a swig of my drink.

"Now, why the hell's that a comical question?" he added, miffed.

"Sorry—but it made me think of a story Hy told the other day— at the orchestration meeting. About George Gershwin's father. He said that at the end of an opening night—I think he said it was *Girl Crazy*—George Jean Nathan, the critic, came up the aisle, and at the back of the house he ran into Gershwin's father. So he asked, 'Well, Mr. Gershwin, how'd you like the show?' And Mr. Gershwin said, 'Me? I *got* to like it!' "

"And that's what you feel—that you 'got to'?"

"Of course."

"Why?"

"Because I'm part of it—not much of a—but still, part. So I can have feelings and opinions and ideas of this and that or a detail here and there, but overall, I feel I have to be *with* it—*for* it— Am I talking too much?"

"Yes."

"Look. I've finished my second."

"Look. So have I." The waiter removed our emptied glasses.

"And when I finish my third," I said, "I'm going to tell you something more. . . . Is celery good for you?"

"Very well . . . Yes."

"Are you married?" I asked.

"Not at the moment."

"Oh."

"I'm—you might say—between bouts. I've had two rousers. And I've come to the conclusion that all women—including you—are crazy. And that all men—including me—are pricks."

"I'm inclined to go along with the second part of that," I said.

"Figures. . . . Oh! Food."

The steak had arrived and took over the focus of our interest. It was superb. The best I'd ever tasted. Baked potato, beautiful—with sour cream and fresh chives. A salad of red-ripe beefsteak tomatoes, with a spectacular dressing. We gloried in the food. Every now and then, I said, "Thanks," or "Thank you," or "Oh, I do thank you."

The waiter picked up Chris's empty glass and reached for mine. I grabbed it and said indignantly, "Just a moment, please. I haven't finished it!"

"Yes, you have," said the waiter, and took it out of my hand.

I *had* finished it.

"What do you have on draft?" Chris asked.

"Michelob, Beck's," replied the waiter.

"Two Beck's."

As the waiter left, I asked, "Were they beauties?"

"Were who?"

"All those two wives of yours."

"They were. They weren't very different—one from the other. In fact, there are times I think they were the same one. Except that the first one liked me—I mean, she really liked me—and my stuff. And we laughed a lot and played and traveled and spent too much money —and I tell you—she really liked me. But she didn't love me. Never. So she hung out with me until she fell in love—four and a half years. Turned out love turned up in the form of a caddy at The Beverly Hills Country Club. I hope that doesn't sound snobbish. Some of my best friends are caddies." The beer was served. He tasted it. "Perfect," he said. I took a sip of mine, as he continued. "The second one *loved* me —I mean, she really loved me—too much, almost. It was sometimes smothering—she loved me to pieces—but she didn't like me. The way I dressed or talked or ate—and worst of all—she hated my writing. 'Tacky'—I think that was usually her word for it. Or 'grindgy'—whatever the hell *that* means. So after a while, I got sick of it and flew around the world, and that wasn't much, and when I got back, I found that a friend of mine had moved into the house— fine cameraman—and I didn't think it was big enough for the three of us, so I moved in with a girl who neither loves me nor likes me, and we live happily ever after. . . . Go ahead."

"Go ahead where?"

"You said you'd tell me 'something more' when you finished your third, and you finished your third some time ago, and you haven't told me something more yet."

"Yes," I said. "It's this. With the possible exception of you—I know the script of our show better than anyone. Do you know how many times I've typed it from beginning to end?"

"No idea."

"Seventeen."

"I believe you."

"And every time I do—I'm a little less happy. At first, I thought— well, no wonder. It stands to reason. You can't keep loving it—but then I began to see that, no, it was something else. Sure, every change was sensible, and sometimes I could see the reason for it— like when the whole scene between the Everleigh sisters and Nora turned into a number—O.K., fine—a showstopper, probably—but the overall everything keeps getting damaged. In my humble."

"Don't be so goddam humble," he said, fiercely. "You've hit it bull's-eye. Do you know anything about plastic surgery, I mean, have you ever had any done?"

"No. Do I need it?"

"I've seen a lot of it around the business. Eyes, noses, chins, legs, ears, breasts—all improved. But a curious thing happens—they fix the nose and spoil the face. That's what's happening to my book. We're straightening its teeth and building up its bosom—but it's losing its charm because it's been robbed of its reality. . . ."

"Right."

"Another beer?"

"No, thank you."

"And the hell of it is there's nothing I can do about it. Not one damned thing. Even if I wanted to, which I don't. I'm in this for the bucks."

"Even so. Why not try?"

"Because, lady, the writer of the book of a musical is the low man on the totem pole. He's the one who sparks it all—but once it's under way, he has to move over for everyone. Gangway!—for the songwriters, the director, the choreographer, the stars, the designers. All at once, *they're* all more important. It's the way of this particular world —and I'm too old to be a revolutionary or try to change it all. No. Change that. Not too old. Just too tired. And not even *that.* Just too don't-give-a-damn. Does it matter, really?"

"Sure it does."

"Why does it?"

"Because it's your action, that's why," I said. "And if it isn't, what is? What we *do.* That's our existence, isn't it? That's what it seems like to *me.*"

He leaned over and kissed my cheek again. Son-of-a-bitch. I could have slugged him.

We finished our steaks, considered dessert, decided against, and ordered coffee.

"I'm fed for a cheek," I said.

"What?"

"Week, not cheek. Fed for a *week.* Excuse me." I got up—not as steadily as I would have liked, but steadily enough.

"Where're you going?" he asked.

"To the Men's Room," I replied. "Where do you think? And don't keep kissing my week! Got that? *Cheek!*"

And off I went. By the time I returned, he had paid the check. On the table, a fresh pot of coffee, two clean cups, and two frosted drinks in small wineglasses. I sat down and asked, "What have we here?"

"Stingers."

"Did you ask me?"

"No."

"And what did I say?"

"Yes."

"Thank you."

We picked up our glasses.

"Cheers," he said.

"Up yours," I said.

"You still sore?"

"I don't like my cheek kissed. I'm allergic," I said. I took a sip of the stinger. "Say, this is *great!*"

"Shall we each have two more?"

"No, thank you. I suggest that we each two go home."

"I'll take you," he said.

"What does *that* mean?"

"I'll take you *home.*"

"No, no. Taxi's fine."

"I'll take you home."

"But *you're* right here. Next door. At the Thomas Alva Edison. Inventor of the electrical lights and stuff like that."

"And you?"

"I never invented *anything.*"

"I mean, where do you live?" he asked.

"Pretty sneaky, aren't you? Trying to worm my address out of me."

"I'm taking you home."

"Oh, yes. But to *whose* home?"

"To your home."

"You mean the one at Fifty-four West Fifty-Five Apartment Nine-D, for Detroit, five eight six seven three one one?"

"You got it on the first guess."

One of us—I don't remember which one—decided that it would be the better part of wisdom to walk. Whoever it was—the decision pleased me. I was worried as to what I might do if we got into a taxi together. Inventory: Three Bloody Marys (!), one beer, one stinger, all in the course of an hour and fifty minutes. I thanked Fortune for all that food, otherwise, I might be horizontal.

We walked. He took my arm, and I was grateful.

In front of 54 West 55, we stopped. He offered his hand. I leaned over and kissed *his* cheek.

SHINE ON, HARVEST MOON
Company Bulletin
Monday, October 15

BOSTON LIFE: I suggest a walk on Beacon Hill, including Louisburg Square; a visit to Goodspeed's
Secondhand Bookshop, the Boston Museum of Fine
Arts, one of the best in the world; the unique and
fascinating Gardner Museum; if you want a treat,
the Faneuil Hall Market and have lunch at Durgin-
Park, a marketman's restaurant, which has been
there for more than 100 years; or go out to Fenway
Park and walk. For the more adventurous, Cambridge, Harvard Yard, the great glass flower collection at the Agassiz Museum.

L.G.

VISITORS: No visitors are allowed backstage at any
time without an O.K. from the stage management.

CASTING: Correction of scene breakdown: Mrs.
Fowler will be played by Alice Cort.

PRODUCTION MEETINGS: Shubert Theatre at 2:00 P.M.
 Today: Sets, Lights, Sound (Ivan Kurlansky,
    Millie Kramer, Stu Bender, Aki Fukado,
    and production staff)

THE COMPANY YOU KEEP: NICK PAPPAS (Stunts)
 I am not so showbiz like the rest of you so not much
of this.
 I am Greek born into a circus family. Everybody.
When I was four I was already getting tossed back and
forth in a trapeze turn. Twelve I was a top-notch
tumbler. Then America. Ringling Brothers Barnum
and Bailey nine years. Then Hollywood, where I made
a pile in stunts. Now I run my own Gym and Training
Workshop: 404 West 56th Street, N.Y., N.Y. 10019
(212) 586-7717. I offer 15% discount to all in this
company. I will get you in shape. Some of you need
it. Real bad.

SMOKING: There have been serious backstage fires
in Boston. The theatre is constantly patrolled by
inspectors. No smoking backstage by anyone,
please.

RESEARCH:
The Everleigh Sisters were amused at the report of the vice commission:
"The (X523), at (X524), (X524a) Dearborn Street. This is probably the most famous and luxurious house of its kind in the country. The list received from the general superintendent of police August 16, 1910, did not give the address of this house, nor of eleven other similar places on the street."
Those code numbers meant The Everleigh Club at 2131-33 South Dearborn Street. They appeared so well protected the Chief of Police did not care to mention them!

QUOTE FOR TODAY:
"Girls will be girls, but they should be restrained."

Lucy Page Gaston,
Anti-Cigarette Crusader

There are now 2 days remaining until our first preview.
There are now 42 days remaining until our Philadelphia opening.

BOSTON

· XI ·

Boston. The Ritz-Carlton. Larry's suite. 1204–5. Conference: Larry, Hy, and Fred.

"I like the score more and more," says Larry.

"Are you gonna talk in rhyme all day?" asks Hy, at the piano. He plays and sings:

> "'I like the score
> More and more;
> More and more
> I like the score.'"

Larry ignores the levity. He has a serious purpose for this meeting. I can tell by the concentrated way he sits there, aiming his whole spirit at the others in the room. I have seen it a number of times, usually when he wants or needs to convey something from inside his head to the inside of another's head. Not only thoughts or ideas or notions—but often emotions or feeling.

As usual, Hy does most of the talking for the songwriting team, as well as the reacting and arguing and defending. Fred sits somewhere apart, looking bemused, doodling on a yellow pad, and looking a bit scared. The team is like a husband-wife, with Hy the domineering, bullying man, and Fred the put-upon, passive spouse.

Larry goes on. "What I mean is that it sings well and dances well. I appreciate its variety. I really love it. I hope it isn't just that I'm getting used to it. That happens sometimes, doesn't it? You hear a tune over and over and it automatically takes hold."

"This is a big score," says Hy evenly. "Important. We've got two-three potential standards and a half a dozen could-be-hits—and every goddam number in the show is useful. Wait and see."

"I agree."

Hy bursts into song again.

> " 'Wait and see
> How I agree;
> Tea for two
> And two for tea.' "

A sign of nerves. Hy may be gross, but he is no fool. He knows there is something in the air. Some problem. So does Fred. Larry does not call meetings to give people rubdowns.

"A *lovely* score," says Larry

A long silence follows, broken finally by Hy.

"But? . . ."

"But nothing," says Larry, stalling.

"O.K. It's perfect, so how can it be improved?"

"Are you asking *me?*" says Larry.

"Yes, if you want me to."

"Period period period. Flying machines are beginning to get off the ground. Electrical automobiles. The Pierce-Arrow. The Peerless. The Locomobile."

"What *is* all this?" asks Hy.

"Jim Jeffries and Jack Johnson. Teddy Roosevelt. Ellis Island. Happy Hooligan. The Follies. Frank Merriwell. Jokes: I'm sending my wife to the Thousand Islands for her vacation—one week on each island. And: You can drive a horse to drink but a pencil must be lead. Weber and Fields. The Cherry Sisters."

"So what?"

Larry continued, softly, despondently. "What can we do to get that sound in our songs? That feeling. That time."

"Speak up!" said Hy. "I can't hear you."

"Period sound, Hy. Feeling."

"It's all there now."

"No, it's not."

"Why not?"

"I don't know. I'm asking *you*. You're the expert."

"If I'm the expert, why don't you take my word?"

Larry is on his feet, pacing. "Let me ask you this, Hy. You, too, Fred. Could it have something to do with the orchestrations?"

"Yes," says Fred.

"No!" says Hy. And to Fred, "Butt out, Fred."

"He asked me."

"Butt out of the orchestrations, I tell you. They're not your department."

"Still," says Larry. "We're all on the same show, no?"

Hy is angry. "I've got banjos in there and a honky-tonk piano. I've got wood-blocks and soprano saxes and cornets. What the hell are you *talking* about?"

"With all that," says Larry, "we're still getting a seventies sound."

"Of course," says Hy. "For a seventies audience. With seventies ears. You want a *real* period show—dig up a nineteen-oh-eight audience and do the show for *them.*"

"Look, Hy. I'm trying to approach this problem reasonably—so don't go off the handle and—"

"God damn it," says Hy, "if I—"

He stops.

"Yes?" asks Larry.

"What?"

"You were going to say something."

"I've said it."

"Let me point something out," said Larry. "The book has been rewritten fifteen–sixteen times."

"It needed it."

Larry lets that pass, continues. "And it's *still* in a state of flux. I consider a book—in fact, a whole show—to be a living, breathing thing. Developing, growing. The thing about a show—where it differs from a movie, say—is that it's not frozen, ever. It can't stand still. There are never two performances exactly alike. So it's always in action—which means that either it's getting better or else it's getting worse. And that's why—"

"I've done more shows than—"

"Don't interrupt!"

"Don't tell me what to—"

"Don't interrupt when I'm talking, Hy. God *damn* it!"

"You talk too *much,*" says Hy.

"I have to with you, because you don't listen. And when you do, you don't hear. You don't know how."

"If I—"

"What I'm pointing out is this. The text changes. We've made hundreds of set adjustments. Alicia's never out of the wardrobe room. The only part of the show that's preserved in amber is the score."

"Horseshit."

"What changes have you made? Or Fred?"

"We dropped four songs."

"That's not a change."

"What?! And put in two new. *That's* not?"

"No," said Larry. "I'm talking about the lapidary work that everyone—"

"Hold it. Gimme a dictionary, Midge. He's starting in with that Yale Drama School noise."

"Lapidary," says Fred. "It means polishing. That's all."

"It does?" Hy asks Larry.

"More or less."

"Then why don't you say so? Those egghead words of yours. Show me one in a hit song."

"Why do we all go on working and polishing and stuff and—you know what polishing means, don't you?"

"Of course," says Hy. "It means lapidary."

We all laugh, relieving the tension a little.

"Think on it, Hy. Think how you can get more period feel in your stuff."

"You know what's your trouble?" asks Hy. "Why you're always gonna have troubles on musicals? And be miserable? And get ulcers? And grow old? I'll tell you. You hate songs. You don't admit it, but you do. You hate songs. You think they get in the way of your great storytelling—but where you're wrong is songs *make* musicals. Books are clotheslines, that's all. But you love books and you hate songs and that's what makes you an out-and-out all-time Olympic champion card-carrying *putz!*"

The discussion has degenerated into acrimony and nothing constructive is going to be accomplished today.

Larry says, "Oh, how wrong you are. How you ever could have gotten such a wrongheaded notion is beyond me. I *love* songs. I can sing you six hundred songs—with verses—and second choruses. I adore songs. What I do hate is song*writers.*"

"You do, huh?"

"I do—yes—and with good and sufficient reason. They've got—you've got—one of the easiest pitches in show business. You know what Dick Rodgers once told me? He told me he'd never written a song in his life that took him more than twenty minutes. He said if it took more than twenty minutes, he knew it was no good."

"So what? I've never taken more than fifteen. Have I, Fred?"

"Sometimes ten," says Fred. "Lyrics take longer. Sometimes ten days."

Larry again. "Burns my ass," he says. "If we need a line on a scene or a curtain or an idea for a number—we sweat blood and lie awake nights and throw up mornings. But a songwriter? What's *his* problem? *Anything* is a song. Any sentence. Any statement. Any expletive. *Anything.*"

"You're talking a lot of cock, you know it?" says Hy.

"Not at all. Anything is a song. Hello. Goodbye. I love you. I hate you. I'm sorry. What's the trouble? Have a good day. I'm going home. I'm leaving home. . . . I'll tell you what. I'll make you a bet you can't say *anything* in the next five minutes that isn't a song."

"Fuck you," says Hy.

"That's a song," says Larry.

"Cut it out," says Hy.

"Another song. Right, Fred?"

"Sure."

"See you later," says Hy, starting out.

" 'See You Later' could be a hell of a song."

Hy, at the door, turns back to Larry and points. "I'm warning you."

Larry sings: " 'I'm warning you! It's you I'm after—' "

Fred sings: " 'Adorning you/With love and laughter!' "

Hy is all at once at the piano, improvising the next phrase, in their key. Fred, on his way, sings:

> " 'Take heed, I need
> What only you've got

My prick, I'll stick
Right into your slot.' "

Hy: (Singing a break)

   " 'I've hit the jackpot!' "

He collapses into laughter on the keyboard which moans and
reverberates. He stands.
"Period. You want period? You'll get it. I'll see that you get your
period. The orchestrations? I'll talk to Ralph. Come on, Fred."
They leave. Larry pours himself a glass of water, drinks it, and looks
at me.
"Would you believe we're all grown men?"
"Sure, why not?"
"Let's do some bulletin, you mind?"
"Not at all."
He sits down, uses his inhalator, and begins to dictate. "Health note
   To the entire company   In a few days we shall all be working
under strong lights for many hours at a stretch   I learned some
time ago that powerful artificial light of the kind we are compelled
to use enters the body through the cornea and destroys calcium
Calcium supports nerve ends   This may explain the temperaments and tantrums often associated with long sessions on stage or
movie sets   A New York insurance company having installed
extra-powerful fluorescent lights in its massive offices housing eight
or nine hundred young women per floor began to experience odd
happenings faintings hysteria fistfights and hair-pulling menstrual
irregularities and arthritis   Investigation eventually determined
that the young women were lacking in calcium   When it was
supplied up and down the aisles on a regular daily basis all the
difficulties vanished   So it might be with us if we do not take care
   I am asking the management to supply the company with
Squibb's Dicalcium with Viosterol phosphate compound   Please
take three a day without fail Dr. Henry Ross our company physician
approves but you may of course consult your own doctors for cor-
roboration   I have used this method for many years on shows films
and television productions with great success   If you have any
questions regarding this matter please take them up with me paren

or with Dr. Ross paren   That's all on that. Now let me lay the color scheme on them and see what happens. Screams and yells, no doubt. And controversy. And 'This guy's nuts!' But watch. In the end, they'll love it."

"Love what?"

"The color idea. Didn't I ever tell you?"

"No."

"My mistake. It's just— Well, take it down. You'll get it as I give it. O.K.?"

"Yes."

"For the bulletin. Soon. You can hold the calcium item for a few days."

"Right."

"To the Company   One of the difficulties faced by a Broadway director is solving the problem of establishing a uniform style in each company he organizes   You are a talented group of people the most talented I have ever had the good fortune to assemble   And yet   You come from different backgrounds have been trained in various ways have had divergent experiences and worked in dissimilar methodologies   In five or six weeks it is part of my job to blend you into a company make you seem like The Old Vic or the Comédie-Française or The Moscow Art   If I fail we all fail   Thus any and all ways in which we can attempt to become one are desirable   Note how athletic teams have a uniform how schools and stables have colors how clubs have insignias and blazer patches   All right then   Here is one I now propose for us all   A small one to be sure but a favorite of mine and one I have used in the past with success   Let me tell you first how it came about   Some years ago I was traveling in the South Seas   I stopped with my companion for a few days in an Indonesian village   I noticed nothing unusual on the first day but after two or three days it began to dawn on me that on each day every man woman and child in the village was wearing something in the same color   I mean that on Tuesday say everyone had on a green scarf or hat or skirt or ribbon or belt or something underlined   The next day the color would be pink or orange or violet   Apparently each day had its color and one felt the unifying effect of the custom   Here then is what I propose   Let us all join in wearing something anything of a given color on each day we are together   Here is the scheme Monday red   Tuesday

blue   Wednesday orange Thursday purple   Friday green
Saturday yellow and Sunday pink   Para   Now I realize that
it is going to be a lot easier for the girls than for the boys but let's see
some ingenuity and imagination   Further I know that on some
days we will not be together but on these days off it is even more
important to stick to the plan   Please understand that this is not
an order merely a suggestion but one that if carried out will do
something constructive for us   Thank you"

"Sounds interesting," I said.

"Some'll hate it," he said. "You'll see. Fascinating to observe which
ones pick up on it and which resist it."

"Does it mean everyone?" I asked.

"How do you mean?"

"Well, does it mean me?"

"Certainly."

"Good, but I'll have to buy something orange," I said. "I think I
have the rest one way or another."

"I can do mine with T-shirts and neckties. Look, Midge—be an
angel and get me seven T-shirts, one in each of those colors and seven
neckties—same. Will you?"

"Of course."

"Thanks."

"And what about Hy, Fred—Art, Ivan, and so on?"

"*Everyone.* The more the better."

"Well, excuse me—but that's not clear in what you just gave me."

"It's not?"

"No."

"Well, fix it up, then. Make it clear that it means everyone connected with the production in any way. On- and offstage."

"All right. Anything else?"

"Not for now."

I went back to my room to type up some bulletins and catch up with
a mound of paperwork.

I thought a lot about Larry and about how misunderstood he is in
many quarters of this organization. Art, for instance, has no ideas as
to what he does or how he does it. He thinks a director is a sort of
traffic cop who tells everyone where and when to come and go. The

subtle parts of Larry's work are lost on him. Some of the others? Well, Chris is too cold to think of anything much. Hy and Fred only of themselves. Ivan knows and Alicia cares, but they are *themselves* misunderstood.

SHINE ON, HARVEST MOON
Company Bulletin
Wednesday, October 17

RUNNING ORDER FOR THE THIRD PREVIEW: The present running order includes "Merry-Go-Round." It also includes the old version of the dressing-room scene preceding "Falling Star."
"Sweetie" is, for the present, eliminated from the running order.

REMINDERS: Please make it a point to review your material at least once a day away from the theatre.
Mr. Monroe reminds all singers that in musicals, the pronunciation of *fruit* is "fruit-tah" and *credit* is "credit-tah."
We still hear errors in the pronunciation of Everleigh. It is never "Ever-lay"—always "Ever-*lee,*" except for Nora's maid, who says "Never-lee."

FRIDAY, OCTOBER 19: There will be a run-through with music at the theatre at 2:00 P.M.

SUNDAY, OCTOBER 21: Will be the scheduled day off for all members of the company.

COMMENDATION: Alas, there is hardly enough time for praise, even when it is richly deserved. For the time being, it seems necessary to correct mistakes.
However, I want you all to know that I appreciate your efforts and that actions above and beyond the call of duty do not go unnoticed.
The more close-knit a unit we become, the more effective will be the performance on the stage.
Moreover, I am grateful to the company for its adherence to the necessary disciplines.

L.G.

QUOTE TO REMEMBER:
"I'd rather have run the scene eight times than have wasted that time in chattering away about abstractions. An actor gets the right thing by doing it over and over. Arguing about motivation and so forth is a lot of rot. Ameri-

can directors encourage that sort of thing too much. Instead of doing a scene over again that's giving trouble, they want to discuss—discuss—discuss."

Laurence Olivier

PREVIEW AUDIENCES: Preview audiences are traditionally unpredictable. They may respond too much or not enough. They seldom hit the norm of a regular audience. We are to consider these performances try-out performances and not concern ourselves too much with responses or lack of responses. The reason for preview performances is not so much to test the play, but to give the players and the crew an opportunity to work under performance conditions. We have a great deal of detail work still to be done, but in the main, we are in good shape. Play confidently. Godspeed.

THE COMPANY YOU KEEP: HARRY SILVERMAN (Detective Stone)
   One of the social activities of the ILGWU (International Ladies' Garment Workers Union) is the Drama Society. Right after joining the Union, I joined the Drama Society and soon became a leading player. We did a lot of Odets: WAITING FOR LEFTY, AWAKE AND SING, ROCKET TO THE MOON. Also WINTERSET and WHAT PRICE GLORY and DEATH OF A SALESMAN. . . . Then I began to direct. . . . Then both. . . . Mr. Lee Strasberg attended my production of THE HAIRY APE by Eugene O'Neill in which I also played the lead. He invited me to try out for The Actors' Studio. I did and was accepted and am still a proud member of the Studio, which has opened up a new world for me. . . . I am also still a member of the ILGWU, although I practice another craft. You never can tell.

There is now 1 day remaining until our Boston opening.
There are now 40 days until our Philadelphia opening.

· XII ·

Boston. The first time with an audience tonight. What an experience!

For a clear account, it is necessary to go back three days. Where did I get the idea that dress rehearsals are always chaotic? From the movies, I suppose. Those backstage musicals I have doted on all my life. Well—turns out the real world is different. The three days of dress rehearsal and previews were smooth and quiet and utterly professional. All seemed to know precisely what they were doing. I sat beside Larry and was impressed with his grasp of the overall situation, and the firmness with which he dealt with every crisis, usually nipping it in the bud. He is a man who knows his stuff and, what's more, who surrounds himself with top-notch people.

On the first day, he had Russ take the company to the ballroom of the Bradford next door and simply run through the whole show twice without interruption.

"Get it down firm and pat," he said to the company, "so that in a day or two—when you get hit with the sets and lights and costumes and all the rest of it—you won't be thrown. If we do it right, the production should *enhance* what we've got—not rip it apart. One more thing—for these run-throughs with Russ—take it at a fast clip —faster than usual, faster than normal. The reason is that the production is likely to slow you down—and on Friday night the audience will slow you down still more. Try not to let it. Lead the way. Keep it moving. Hold it together. That's our watchword for the next few days: Hold It Together."

Russ went off with the company and at the theatre Larry rehearsed the stagehands. The sets had been put into place earlier in the week under the supervision of Ivan and Nadia. Then Millie and her staff did the beautiful, atmospheric lighting. Now Larry started from the top and went through the whole show—every cue, every change. On the more difficult ones, he went back for a second or a third or a fourth time, until each member of the crew knew exactly what he had to do.

Art hovered about nervously, upsetting everyone with idiotic criticism and hopeless suggestions.

"I never saw a sky *that* color!"

"I can see all the bare lights from here, for Chrissake!"

"Why's that set so big?"

"Why's that set so small?"

"Jesus, is it gonna take *that* long for the change?"

And so on. Fortunately, everyone was too concentratedly occupied to reply or it might have led to friction or even physical assault. As it was, he yelled or whimpered mostly to the surrounding air while the artists and craftsmen went about their work.

By 4:30 P.M., we had set Act I. Larry broke until six, then tackled Act II, which took until 1:15 A.M. To my surprise, no one was tired. The excitement and activity and the achievement seemed to generate energy. In addition to everything else, I kept timing, timing, timing—until I had a small blister on my thumb from pressing the stem of the stopwatch.

The next day—Act I with the company. No orchestration, just piano.

"Keep going," said Larry before it began. "We're out here noting all errors. Just plow ahead no matter what. Pretend it's a performance. O.K. Overture, Phil."

Larry has often said that actors are a gallant, courageous breed, and that dress-rehearsal day proved to me that he is right. From the very opening, the company magically turned into a championship team, a cohesive entity. Every single member of the company was pulling in the same direction. The concerted, communal effort was so intense that it damn near made me cry—no, not damn near, to tell the truth—I *did* cry.

Then. At last. The first preview.

"It's one of those cut-rate clubs," Larry explained to the company before the performance. "So don't expect too much help. And if they turn out to be screamers—don't let them poison you. An audience can do that, you know. Just play the show. It's good and so are you."

Now I am stumped. How to report what happened? All went well. No technical errors of any kind. No fluffs. But somehow I knew, and so did everyone else, that the show as a whole did not get over.

Company onstage afterward.

"All right," said Larry, "settle down. Look, we're all thinking the same thing. Let me put it this way. We've done it. Call it a practice shot, call it an icebreaker!"

"Call it a *ball*breaker!" Art chimed in. "It was lousy. The whole thing lousy. Just fucking deadass. The way you all played it it was like *you* thought it stunk—so how can you expect *them* not to. Jesus, what a catastrophe!"

"Finished?" asked Larry.

"For now, yes. And if things don't improve around here the whole goddam *bunch* of you will be finished!"

He stormed out into the auditorium and buried himself in its comforting darkness.

Larry continued. "The show didn't get over tonight. Agreed. It didn't get over because it stayed up here on the stage. It wasn't projected and that, by the way, has nothing to do with volume. It has to do with what's going on in your heads and hearts. Concentration. They've got to know how and what you're thinking and feeling. I'm sorry about tonight. I know how hard all of you tried. I'm disappointed. But not upset. Tonight—and it's understandable—tonight you all had too many extraneous things on your minds."

Star said, "I thought *I* was sensational."

The company laughed, then applauded.

"I thought so, too," said Larry. "Now tomorrow night let's make *them* think so."

But the second preview was worse, and further complicated by a jammed turntable and by a faulty body mike on Star that set up an ungodly yowling, was killed, thus forcing her to perform without amplification while everyone else around her was blasting.

Art left before the first act was over, distraught and shaken.

Hy and Fred and Jenny started out at the back of the house, but kept leaving and returning all evening, each time a little more sloshed. By the middle of the second act they got the collective giggles and had to go out into the lobby.

"I like it," said Ivan in the intermission. "What is wrong, it can be fixed. Usually what is wrong *cannot* be fixed."

The record boys were silent, mysterious, noncommittal.

Cindy Sapiro kept asking everyone, including the ushers, "How do you like it?"

And then. And then opening night—like an advance Christmas present for everyone, onstage and off.

The color of the night changed, death turned into life. Down was up. Lazarus rose. *V* for victory.

Backstage, I said to Larry. "I've never seen so much hugging and kissing."

"Wait," said Larry with that wry little smile of his. "Wait. Now it all begins."

· XIII ·

The Barracuda dictated notes on the dress rehearsal until about 12:30, never using one word when he could find seven to say the same thing. He then asked me to type them up. I did so. He looked them over, said, "Perfect," and handed them back to me. (I suppose by "perfect," he meant his opinions, not my faultless transcript.) "Twelve copies," he added, and pointed to the IBM 2400 Copier in the sitting room of his suite. (God Almighty! A full-size copier in the sitting room. And how he uses it! Like a part of his anatomy. Sense of power? Every letter, memo, note, whatever—reproduced in threes or three hundreds. Does it give him a sense of being more than one? More than himself? Influential? Blanketing the world with his thoughts, ideas, opinions, pronouncements?) I got to work at once. He went into his bedroom. In a minute, I heard the sound of "The Tonight Show." A door sound, and soon after, the shower splashing. In my state of advanced bleariness, it seemed to me that the three going sounds: TV, copier, and shower were somehow perfectly coordinated rhythmically. Now, the singing on "The Tonight Show," the splashing (in the right key), and the copier—all on the beat. I shook my head, hand, five or six times in an effort to stay awake, and found I was shaking my *head* to the beat. Well, *I* was beat. He came back into the room and stopped just as the copier spat out its last copy. Life was turning into one big number, staged by the choreographer of the week. AC was wearing a tent-size terry-cloth robe. He was rubbing his wet hair vigorously with a huge Turkish towel—still keeping perfect time. I saw that he was standing in a puddle, and it occurred to me that he had had a nasty accident; but no, he was simply dripping. I collated the notes into sets. From the bedroom, the McDonald commercial came on. AC sang along with it, almost drowning it out. As it ended, I handed him the copies.

"Unless you want *me* to," I said.

"You to *what?*"

"Distribute them."

"What're *you,* the producer?" he asked.

"No."

"So?"

"Is that all for tonight?" I asked.

"How'd you like the show?"

"The dress, you mean."

"What'd'y'mean, 'dress'?"

"Dress rehearsal."

"Well?"

I stalled, then said, "Well, what?"

"How'd you like it, God *damn* it?"

"I thought it was a great dress. Dress rehearsal. But remember, I'm new at all this, so—"

He used his head to beckon me closer.

"C'mere." I moved to him. He looked at me in that disturbing way of his: both his eyes on both of mine. "Lemme ask you something, cookie. . . ." He laughed suddenly, startling me. "Funny!" he said, grudgingly, pointing to the sound emanating from the bedroom. "He comes up with good stuff sometimes, Carson."

"He certainly does."

"Only not *his.* Writers. You know how many writers he's got feedin' him those cracks all night? Maybe fifteen, sixteen. And people think, what a wit! What a wit, *shit!* Sixteen, seventeen writers. So he comes up with these great ad libs. Ad libs, my ass. He couldn't ad lib a belch after a full-course Hungarian dinner."

"Was that one of yours?" I asked. (I was *exhausted* and had turned waspish.)

"What one what?"

" 'Belch—Hungarian dinner.' I think I read it somewhere."

"So?"

"Nothing. It just seems peculiar. You bad-mouthing someone for using other people's funnies, and doing it yourself."

"What'd you take up there at Vassar, a course in Fresh?"

"Yes. Except they didn't call it that. They called it Assertiveness Training."

"You're gonna assertiveness yourself right out on your Vassar ass, y'know it?"

"What were you saying?" I asked, switching gears.

"Saying when?"

"Before. We were talking about the dress, the rehearsal, and you said you wanted to ask me something and then you laughed and then you got sore at Johnny Carson and then you got sore at me. What did you want to ask me?"

"I wanted to ask you if you were playin' with me or tryin' to, or playin' with yourself, or what. You don't snow *me*, Vassar ass. I've been around the block more than several times. I ask you how'd you like the show, you give me it was a great dress. Dress rehearsal."

"It was a great show," I said. (It was getting late.)

"God damn right! Those Broadway bums. They think they own the combination to the safe. Christ—they're *yesterday*. *This* is a show. What time's the call?"

"Ten."

"Ten. Be there."

"Sure."

"And listen." He handed me the copies of his notes. "Pass these around. I'm too goddamn busy. I got my hands full with the costumes tomorrow. That cunt really fucked up. Did you hear Star Baby burst into song when She saw that green one? She claims She told that limey bitch a thousand times green was her jinx color. I may have to get rid of the cunt altogether."

"You mean Star Baby?"

"Take off!"

"Good night."

"See you ten."

"Right. And by the way," I said, "I thought the costumes were the most beautiful part of the evening."

"You're fired!" he said.

"See you ten," I replied.

When I got down to my room, I broke the world's record for

Showering, Laundering, and Getting to Bed. All through my ablutions and preparations, the phone kept ringing. I knew who it was, of course, and thought, to hell with him. I've had enough for one night. And anyway, I'm fired. Maybe he's calling to rehire me? Or maybe to say *really* fired? In any case, I decided to let it ring.

My head just made it to the pillow. Out.

I sat with Larry at the opening last night. Fifth row on the aisle. His method of giving notes changed drastically. He explained that on a first night, it was best to let nothing interfere with the atmosphere. Moreover there were some big critics: newspaper, magazine, TV, and radio who might be disconcerted by a whispering director, and might think that the number of notes related to the quality of what they were seeing.

"They don't understand," he explained, "that at this point, it is the detail that matters and attention to that is endless."

So all he did throughout the performance was touch my arm from time to time, whereupon I would note the line or the action taking place at that moment.

Meanwhile, backstage, Aki was making cassette recordings of the entire performance, including audience reaction.

Early this morning, we played the cassettes against my notes and I was astounded at Larry's ability to recall what was wrong at each point.

No rehearsal call until 2:00 this afternoon, and that one is Jenny's for one hour. Larry takes over at 3:00.

"But let's go over at two," he says. "You mind?"

"Of course not."

He smiles, and adds, "I just want to see if we can run true to form. If we do, you'll see them rehearsing at two the number that stopped the show last night."

"Why that?"

"I don't know. Comfort, I suppose. And you can hardly bear to face the bad stuff. You're not sure what to do sometimes. But the good stuff—you like to stay with it and play with it and pat it and pat it and enjoy it like a new toy—that works!"

Sure enough, when we reached the theatre at two, there was "Midnight Waltz" in full blast on the stage. It had gone over sensationally last night.

Larry laughed, and said, "Well, at least we're normal."

The notices. I thought they were fine, but there is a lot of sulking.

"Depends how we read them," says Larry. "I'd say they were about what we deserve at this point. Even when they're good—they're never as good as you think they ought to be—and when they're bad, they're always worse than you think you deserve."

"They're great for *her,* aren't they?"

"Sure. Right now She's a pet, a fashion. If you pan her, it means you're square, not with it. Actually, She is far from her potential."

"But they said—"

"Sure, sure. But listen, there are damn few critics—hell, damn few *people* who can tell the difference between a good part and a good performer. They're reviewing her part—without knowing it. Do they think She's making it up as She goes along?"

The play's production is highly praised: sets, costumes, lighting. Reserved enthusiasm for the score. Hy sulks.

"Tin-ear creeps!" he says. "When we're one, two, three on the charts they'll begin to hear it, maybe."

Different players singled out by different commentators.

"Eliot Norton," says Art, "he's the only one up here means a goddam thing. That other idiot—what's his name? He wants to play it safe. I never saw so many ifs and buts and maybes in a review. What's his name?"

(Later, Larry says to me, "Do you know why he can't remember Kevin Kelly's name?"

"No, why?"

"Because Kelly didn't remember *his* name!")

"All the radio and TV are quite good, but Paul says they don't matter."

"Nothing matters right now except the audience," says Larry. "Wooing and winning the audience and eventually getting the show and the audience *married!*"

"They *liked* it!" says Art. "I watched them. I know."

"Of course they liked it, Art. They want to like it. They've paid for it in advance. They can't shut it off or switch to another channel."

"They like it," Art insists stubbornly.

"All right!" says Larry. "But it's not enough. They've got to *love* it—not *like—love.* Passionately, sexually—"

"What?" asks Art, confused.

"You don't marry someone you *like,* for God's sake. You have to *love!*"

"All right," says Art. "So make them love it."

"I will," says Larry. "I *will.*"

"How?"

A pause.

"I don't know," says Larry.

But I can see that he is thinking and feeling hard.

· XIV ·

Boston. Ritz. 901.

An adventure in the middle of the night.

I had gone to bed at 2:20 A.M., all in. Then, from afar, bells. Church bells. (A wedding?) Cowbells. (Uncle Hagop's?) Bicycle bells. (Me late for school.) Doorbells. No. Phone bell. Ringing. Ringing.

Light on. My phone ringing. Answer it, get it over with or the bastard will ring all night. It's just like him. . . . I decided on a greeting of controlled anger.

"Yes?!"

"Midge, dear?"

"What do you *want?*" It was out before I registered that it was not The Barracuda, but Alicia.

"Alicia?" I asked, although I knew.

"Yes, of course."

"I'm sorry. I thought—"

"I know, I know. I can't *tell* you how I loathe troubling you . . ." (I *adore* that lovely British speech of hers.) ". . . but I've no one to talk to, and I'm in *such* a scrum."

"A what?"

"Battle. Verge of. Oh, dear. I called you earlier—time and again. You were out."

(So. *Not* him.)

"Working," I said.

"Could you spare me a moment?"

"You mean *now?*"

"Yes."

"I've gone to bed."

"What of it? So have I." We both laughed. Why? "I'm right down the passage. Round the corner, actually. Next to the lift. Nine-ought-nine and ten."

Those elegant sounds did it. I looked at my clock: three-ten.

"All right."

"Frightfully grateful."

I put on my best peignoir, some lipstick, brushed my hair and tied it back. Slippers. Key. I padded down the hall to 909–10 and knocked softly.

"Yes, please," I heard from within.

I entered, closed the door behind me, went through the sitting room and found her sitting up in bed: a canopied, four-poster, with a carved headboard and a high footboard. Porthault flowered sheets and pillowcases. Pink transparent nightgown.

"Lock it out there, there's a dear," she said.

I went out, locked the door, and returned to her bedroom. *Her* bedroom. How is it that some women can take possession of a hotel suite and in a matter of hours make it their own? This one had, in the four days we had been there, taken on her personality and taste and artistry. Two lamps, with pink-frosted bulbs, lighted the bedroom into an indefinable size and shape. A long worktable out in the sitting room. A drawing board, somewhere. Flowers, flowers. The dressing table a dream. A Vuitton wardrobe trunk. A small booktrunk. A fragrance, familiar. Of course, it was hers. Did it have a name or was it something of her own? Later, I was to discover a tiny incense burner on a side table beside a small chaise longue. Beside the bed, a tray table, and on it, a Meissen plate of assorted small sandwiches and a silver ice bucket (engraved ADM), holding a frosted bottle of Crystal champagne. She motioned to it. I opened it (damn well, by the way), and poured us each a glass: fluted Baccarat, engraved ADM. We raised our glasses, toasted each other, and sipped. I am not overly fond of champagne, but this seemed to be something else again. She threw a pillow against the footboard and patted the edge of the bed. I sat down, adjusted the pillow behind me, and leaned back. She leaned toward me, offering the plate of sandwiches. I took one. Smoked salmon and cucumber. We sat there, sipping and munching. I did not think it at all strange that we were silent. We seemed to be in communication. The room was filled with comfort and solace. It was akin to music. Words would have spoiled it. We were sharing a soothing dream. We looked at each other from time to time, exchanging a variety of thoughts and moods. Once, she smiled an astonishingly young smile, and try as I would, I could not smile back. I was, all at once, frightened—no, apprehensive.

At other times, I could feel her looking at me, and wished to hell I had had my hair done, as planned, but canceled by that mad, early-morning call from the set builder. No matter. In this enchanting light, I would get by. She was looking off. At the wall? At the window? I seized the opportunity to regard her closely, something I had never done before.

She was not beautiful, but everything about her was: hair, eyes, brows, lips, figure. She seemed to have arranged every detail of her being. But beautiful, no. Handsome. That was it. A handsome woman. Age? Indeterminate. Forced to guess, I should say mid-forties. Strong in the jaw, and a prizewinning combination of neck and throat.

She turned and caught me staring at what I could see of her breasts. "Breasts" does not describe what she had. Tits? Ridiculous. Boobs? Of course not. Bosom? Not at all. Suddenly, it struck me. *Poitrine!* The first I had ever seen to fit the word.

"All right?" she asked, smiling.

"Yes, I'm fine," I assured, pretending to miss her meaning.

She laughed, and the laugh said, I know that you know that I know that you know.

"I thought you might want a snack," she said.

"I did. No dinner."

"Why on earth not?"

"Big bulletin today."

"Does it say, 'Alicia Marble stinks!'?"

"What?"

"That is precisely what *he* said today."

"Are you sure?"

"Perfectly. Since he said it to—"

Her voice broke. Unable to complete the sentence, she pointed to herself. She wept softly for a time. I poured more champagne. She found some Kleenex (flowered) and used it.

"Oh, bugger!" she sobbed. "I *loathe* doing that."

"Helps, sometimes."

"Not a bit of it. . . . Fatigue, I expect."

"We all are."

"Put your feet up," she said, "and let's finish this. And then let's have another. Not Crystal, though. Dom."

"What're you running here?" I asked. "A wineshop?"

"Nothing but the best," she said. "Except *me*, according to he. Well, sod 'im, I say."

"Yes."

"Right there," she said, "in that pocket fridge."

I did not feel like arguing. Moreover, I was enjoying myself. I found the new bottle, opened it, and we sipped its contents slowly as we talked.

"If you hadn't come to me tonight," she said, "I can't imagine what might have happened. That is to say, I *can* imagine."

"What?"

"Up the wall and out the window, for a start."

"You mean for a finish, don't you?"

"I do," she said, solemnly.

"But why?"

"Because no one, my girl, has an unlimited supply of confidence. And mine has just run out."

"Why? Because *he* said? What does *he* know about it? He knows about counting money and driving hard bargains and hanging up on people and seducing understudies who want to keep their gritty little jobs, but not about costumes. And that's not *all* not."

"Come here," she said.

"What?"

"Come here and let's kiss, please."

I shifted myself up and sat beside her. We looked at each other, then kissed, lightly, but long—and I thought while it was going on that it was the neatest, dearest, altogether *nicest* kiss I had ever experienced. It was soft and smooth and loving. And gentle. And the surrounding atmosphere was redolent with the fragrance of friendship. I was sorry when it ended, overjoyed when she said, "Again, please." The second was different—more confident, stronger, still tender.

"You dear creature," she said. "You've given me back a *bit* of my confidence."

"It was there all the time."

"Don't go," she said.

"I have to," I said. "I think I'm a little plastered."

"Impossible. *Never* plastered on champagne. Tiddly, perhaps. Plastered, never."

We laughed. It seemed excruciatingly funny at the time.

"Good God!" I said. "I haven't shared a bed with a girl since Chippawassett."

"And who, may I ask, was she?"

"A camp," I said.

"She *sounds* a *perfect* camp! Chippy *who?*"

When we stopped rolling about with laughter, we found ourselves lying, quite still, in each other's arms.

I felt comfortable, more comfortable than I had been for some time. The softness of it all was the key, I suppose. And there was such a satisfying feeling of having been able to help someone out of despair. She had been so tense when I came in, harassed and rattled and hectored, and now here she was—breathing deeply and regularly—completely relaxed, fast asleep. As she exhaled, the memory of the champagne returned—were those bubbles in the air? As a rule, alcoholic fumes or whiskey breath are a prime turn-off for me, but this was something entirely different. Pleasant. I was being wafted off into limbo. I decided to coordinate my breathing with hers. (An old trick Maxie had taught me.) I could feel myself going going and quite happily, most contentedly, almost euphorically—gone.

Movement. A coverlet of some sort was being thrown over me. By whom? Alicia was still at my side. Sleep again. A siren awakens us. My robe is off. Did I take it off? We look at each other, smile, kiss fleetingly and simultaneously, turn into sleeping positions again—back to back. I am happy.

When I next awaken—half-awaken—I am lying on my back, wearing nothing—a vague recollection of nightgown over head earlier—when? My spine is tingling, my middle is a sea of delight. I drift back to sleep. I am lying in an open field—a boy approaches—he looks at me—he *is* me—he kneels—carefully unbuttons my blouse—

becomes an infant, as he does so. I give him my breast. He feeds, hungrily, rhythmically.

As I come to—slowly—my nerve ends from tip to toe are alive.

I look down and see Alicia's hand holding on to my left breast as if it were a life belt. My right breast is in her mouth—her tongue is caressing my nipple in ways I have never known. She does not simulate feeding, as men have done. Or nibble. Or bite. She is fondling it, wooing it with love and understanding.

She takes her hand from my left breast and puts her fingers into my mouth, indicating that I am meant to moisten them. I do so. She returns the fingers to my left breast, and with the wetness, coaxes its nipple to erection.

I am not thinking at all. I am lost in a bath of sensuousness and feel alive. A sound escapes me. I touch her head. She moves it to my jealous left breast and begins to satisfy its longing.

I feel her hands now, her fingers, as they move ever so gently about my body—hips, navel, thighs. Her head lies on my belly now, and both her arms are stretched high to reach my breasts.

Presently, she moves—lower and lower still. Now one hand is touching my belly, the other is underneath me. Her head is on my thigh. She kisses it, finds the one electrifying spot on my inner thigh, tongues it—gently, tantalizingly. My juices are flowing, overflowing. My place needs her. She avoids it. Her tongue greets both inner thighs and peaks and valleys of my pudenda. I feel her heaving breath on my place, but no more.

Suddenly, her face is above mine—flushed, excited, wild, ecstatic. She has spread my legs wide and has mounted me. Her cunt has become one with mine. She presses it close and closer still. Her hips begin a steady, determined, powerful thrusting. She is opening my vagina with her own.

Her tongue is in my ear. I cry out and move to meet her motion. The other ear. Neck, throat, the space between shoulder and neck. I am delirious. Her skill and control and power are prodigious. She has found and exposed the most sensitive part of my anatomy, and is rubbing it with hers. She is hurting me, but I do not care. She holds me lightly, strongly—opens her mouth and covers mine—her tongue descends deeply, and now a paroxysm overcomes her and continues to shake her. She takes her mouth from mine and cries out. She holds me powerfully and I become part of her convulsion. Down there we have become seemingly inseparable. I feel her inside me.

We lie, thus, for a long time. I wonder if it is over, hope it is not, yet am fearful of what may happen next.

She speaks, finally, but says only my name: "Midge, Midge, Midge, Midge, Midge." Then, "Thank you, oh, thank you."

I say nothing.

"I want to taste you," she says. "May I taste you?"

"Yes."

She slithered down my moist-with-excitement body, placed her hands under my thighs, spread and lifted them to expose the inside of me. Then, as she had said, she tasted me. It was no more than that —a tentative, but hungry tasting. This went on for a time—until the movements of her lips and tongue became more playful: dancing, teasing, taunting, tickling—all of which served only to intensify my own hunger for gratification. I felt as though I were about to explode.

"Please!" I heard myself say, as I lifted myself toward her.

I felt myself being rearranged—how, I could not be sure, since my limbs and body seemed to be a floating jelly.

"Now!" I heard her say.

And then. And then. There are no words. There are feelings, actions, and sensations that defy description. I only know that never before had I felt so legitimately a part of living nature. Her tongue was a vital creature, a friendly snake, as it licked and lapped; her mouth an expressive animal, as it sucked me, devoured me. More and more and more—an endless variety of strokes and rhythms. I approached the edge of climax, hovered there for a lifetime, tried to hold back—no, no! Not yet. Not now. Not now. *Now!* It all happened. *I* happened. What had been unspeakably bearable became absolutely unbearable. And yet, she persisted.

"No!" I cried.

She went on.

"Please!" I begged. "No more. Not now."

To no avail. I am not sure of what next occurred, but I lost consciousness for a time—for how long I do not know. Seconds, perhaps. Minutes, more likely. As I returned to earth, to that enchanting bed, I found her head still lying on my thigh. Her exhalations sent a stream of cool breath to my still-quivering vulva. I began to reason out what had happened to me. Was I, after all, a lesbian? Did it matter? Or up-to-date and bisexual? I doubted it. A set of circumstances such as these or another Alicia seemed improbable, if not impossible. I felt well, satiated, strong, relaxed. Now sleep. I closed my eyes and tried to blank out, when I felt the tip of her tongue gently wooing my stiffened clitoris. I was about to protest and move away, but could not do so. The fact was that the memory of ecstasy was so fresh and young that the hunger had scarcely abated. Or was it, I considered, not an again, but simply and naturally a continuation? This time, her mouth and my place met, not as strangers, but as friends—and both reveled in the glory of it. Signals were passed and accepted. My hands were on her head. I wet my fingers and sought out her nipples. Time and again, her tongue left my bud and found its way into my vagina. How could it go so deep? It had seemed—back there in ordinary life—a tongue like any other, but the act of sex had apparently extended its design, for it was touching the inner walls of me. Then, back to where it was wanted even more—away—home. I was out of control now—crying out, thrashing about—willing her to desist—but she seemed determined to send me through the sky once more. I feared I would faint again—hung on—came undone with a sudden scream, and fainted.

What was that on the back of my neck? A cold mass. A sponge? A sponge. She was standing at the side of the bed, beautifully naked, ministering to me.

"I never faint," I said.

"In a good cause," she said. "Here."

"What is it?"

"Brandy."

"I don't think so."

"A sip."

I took a sip. Another and another. I lay back.

"God," I heard myself say.

"What's wrong with God?" she asked me, as she slipped into bed beside me. "Come here, let me take care of you."

She put her arm around me and fixed my head into a space between her breasts. She kissed my brow and asked, "Do you know how delicious you are? How ambrosial?"

"No, I don't."

"Here, then. I'll show you."

She grasped the hair at the top of my head, pulled my face up, and began to kiss me, transferring the residue. The unknown taste and scent dizzied me. It all seemed beautiful and right. We were one. We slept.

It must have been the smell of the fresh coffee that awakened me. It took me a minute to realize where I was, who I was, and who she was.

She came into the bedroom, smiling, and carrying a small silver tray with a cup of coffee on it. From the look of her, she had been up for some time. Not made up, but alluringly scrubbed, perfectly coiffed, wearing a long, flowing, pale-green dressing gown.

"Cream?" she asked. "Sugar?"

"Black."

"There you are."

"Woke me up. The coffee smell."

"Good. I was beginning to feel bereft, rather. Oh, good morning, by the way."

She leaned over and we kissed.

"Good morning."

"I've run a bath for you."

"Thank you."

"Unless you'd rather shower."

"Bath's fine. I usually shower—but as long as you've run it . . ."

"No matter. It can be unrun. Is that a word?"

"It is *now.*"

"And breakfast is ready when you are."

She left me. I went into the bathroom—fragrant and bright. Flowers. On the basin, a kit containing a toothbrush and toothpaste, a sponge and a washcloth, Vademecum mouthwash, Floris soap, dental floss, and God knows what else. I did what I had to do, then got into the iridescent bubble bath. Did I say it was a bubble bath? Well, it was. And perfect in every way. I luxuriated far too long, I suppose.

Alicia knocked and came in. Under the circumstances, the knock seemed funny. I laughed.

"What is it?" she asked.

"The knock."

"Oh, yes. Of course. I thought perhaps you'd drowned. Accidentally."

"No. It's just that it's so heavenly."

"How heavenly?"

"Indescribable."

"Well, in that case . . ." she said, and dropped her dressing gown and joined me in the tub before I knew what was happening. We sat face to face in the mountain of bubbles. She picked up an enormous sponge and washed my feet, legs, more, somehow moved behind me and worked on my back. We lolled about together until she let the water out of the tub, picked up a vibrating hand-spray and sprayed the soap from each of us. Now she was out of the tub, I was still in it, and she used the extraordinary flow as a sort of massage, concentrating on my mound, which was soon remembering last night. She helped me out of the tub, and we dried each other.

We put on robes and went out into the sitting room. A wood fire was burning in the grate. The table near a window overlooking The Public Gardens was set with what was obviously her own china. I wondered if indeed the canopied four-poster might not be her own. On a three-foot hotplate beside the table, Corning ware containers with glass tops held eggs and sausages and stewed tomatoes and lyonnaise potatoes and codfish cakes. On the table, baskets of buns and rolls, scones and bagels. Also, a pitcher of orange juice and one of tomato juice.

Two copies of *The Boston Globe* lay on a low end table beside the breakfast table.

I was hungry, ravenously so, and helped myself generously.

"Try the codfish cakes," she said. "They call them 'codfish balls' here, but don't let that put you off."

"All right."

"There's a rule I learned long ago, from a wise man. 'Eat the fruit of the land you are in,' he said. I've done so ever since."

We spent an hour or more at the breakfast table, eating, drinking, talking about the show, reading the papers.

On the subject of the show, I found her brilliant.

"Where they're wrong—badly wrong—is in assuming that the audience *knows* the Nora Bayes story. And so they don't properly tell it. The fact is—only a tiny fraction does. I'd never heard of her myself until the assignment. Of course, I *am* British—and yet I do get about, you know—and I am amazed at the number of people who think our girl is a fictitious character."

"*I'd* never heard of her, either."

"But you're an infant, love."

"Some infant!"

We exchanged a remembering look. She went on.

"If they were simply to begin at the beginning, and call her Daisy Jones—and think of the Jack Norworth character as Tom Smith—they might see the necessity to help us understand the evening."

She was absolutely right, of course. The question had been discussed, but not resolved.

"Have you said any of this to them?" I asked.

"Heavens no! I'm quite an old hand at the game, you see—and I've long since learned that the better part of wisdom is to speak when spoken to. In our system at home, one does not begin a conversation with one's king or queen. One responds. And in any case, my stock is rather low with our King at this moment. As you know."

"He's wrong."

"There are no wrongs and rights in these matters, dear young heart. . . . How did you like the codfish balls?"

"Delicious."

"Very well. Suppose he were having breakfast with us—"

"God forbid."

"—and loathed the codfish. Would that make him 'wrong'?"

"No."

"Subjective matters, these are."

"Oh, come on, Alicia!" My testiness surprised her. She looked at me, startled. I continued. "Jesus Christ! Do you think when he puts down your stuff, he means it?"

"Of course."

"Of course *not*. What amazes me, what I can't get, is how all of you —high up in what you do, clever or smart or brilliant or genius— you're all so intelligent in your own line and then dumber than dumb on other things. Take this. Don't you see that when he comes on and attacks you and puts you down—that's not what it's about. It's power. He has to use his power. Nothing in the world matters to him except that. Not even money. Only so far as money is power. You know what I heard him say a couple of days ago—to his wife, no less? He said, 'Honey, if this one goes, we'll have'—excuse me, but this is what he said—'we'll have the ol' "fuck you" money at last.'"

"That's all very well, dear, but I think he's going to sack me. Today, I should think."

"Sack—that means 'fire'?"

"Yes."

"Look. He fired *me* today—last night, rather. Doesn't mean a thing. He can't reorganize now. There isn't time."

"I'm not sure I agree," she said. "Still, if you could sway him—even so much as an inch—you do know what it would mean to me?"

"I've already done it."

"You have?" she asked.

"Certainly. Not for any reason except that I think your stuff is superlative."

She burst into tears. I began to see why women often irritate men.

"Thank you," she said, finally.

"Thank *you*," I said. Our eyes were clinging, pair to pair. "For everything. For too much."

"Never."

"A revelation," I said.

She came to me and embraced me. I got ready for the kiss, but it did not come. Her lips were close to my ear, as she whispered, "I enjoyed you more than I can say." She released me.

"What time theatre for you?" I asked.

"Nine-thirty. The fitters are flying down."

"Ten, me. I'll see you there."

"Please."

"And look, if we both do get fired today—sacked—we can fly over to Martha's Vineyard for the weekend," I said.

"Super. I'm told it's like the south of France—only more so."

"Bikes and lobsters and everything."

"Hum. I rather wish now he *does* sack us."

We were at the door. I looked at her, lovingly, and belched. We smiled and, inexplicably, shook hands.

I went back to my room. As I opened the door, I saw on the floor a slew of little white envelopes, containing telephone messages. I picked them up, went into the bathroom, sat on the toilet, and began opening them. All from The Barracuda. Every half hour, precisely, until 4:00 a.m.

"Call." "Urgent." "Please call." "Return call whatever time."

It was now 8:20. I called him.

"Yes?" he said.

"Me."

"Where the fuck've *you* been?"

"Out."

"I know that, you yo-yo, but where?"

"Do I have to tell you?"

"Goddamn right."

"But I don't work for you anymore."

"Since when not?"

"Since you fired me."

"What?!"

"That's right. And I quote. Quote: You're fired. Unquote. So I've been making arrangements. I'm going down by bus—the ten-twenty-two Greyhound—"

"Listen—"

"—and I had to let my sublet know I was going to need my apartment back. Meanwhile, I'll be at The Navarro, Eighty, Central Park South; Five-eight-one, six-six-nine-six, in case you need to know anything vital. . . ."

(Vartan had taught me how to lie. "Put in plenty of details," he said. "The more, the better; and the smaller, the more convincing. If you're very late for an appointment, don't say, 'I was in a taxi accident.' Say: 'I was in this Checker cab with an Israeli cabbie, and I noticed his license said void unless driver is wearing glasses, and I noticed he wasn't, and I wondered if maybe I should say something, but he was talking—flirting, I guess would be closer to the truth—and he kept glomming me through the rear-view mirror, and I saw this Itkin truck making a left turn, and I screamed, which was probably a mistake, because the Israeli got rattled and turned right into the path of the Itkin. It's a wonder we weren't all killed. Anyway, I'm terribly sorry to have kept you waiting.' See? Now who's not going to believe that?")

"Midge," he was saying. "Midge, *listen!*"

"Later. I'm packing."

And I hung up. *His* old trick. I counted one day, for the hell of it. He hung up on eleven people: agents, PR men, Hy, Larry, Alicia, his wife, and *The New Yorker.*

The phone rang. I answered it.

"Hello?"

"Don't you *dare* hang up on me, you goddam—who the hell do you think you are?"

"I don't think," I said. "I know."

I hung up again, and began to dislike myself.

Ring. Reply.

"Now what?"

"Listen, Midge," he said, in a voice so changed, so dulcet, that for a moment, I thought it might be someone else. "You know your trouble?"

"I know several. One of them is *you.*"

He did not hear me—an admirable trick. He hears only what he wishes to hear.

"Your trouble," he said, avuncularly, "is you've got no sense of humor. That was a joke. About fired. Can't you take a joke?"

"I thought you meant it," I said, trying to sound like a fourth-grader. Fifth, at the most.

"Come on. When you've been around show business awhile—you'll see. What the hell? Fun and games. The name of the game. If it ain't fun, what good is it? How could I fire you? Why? I need you right now."

"Well, I don't know."

The *old* voice again. "God damn it! Act professional! You'll never work again if you—" The soft voice. "Hey, Midge. Come on down and have breakfast. You like Nova Scotia?"

"I'll see you at the theatre," I said.

"Ten."

"Yes."

"Don't be late."

I took a shower, I don't know why, and got dressed. I put on my Halston pantsuit and eye shadow and everything. What I could not figure out was how come—in view of what had taken place—I felt more feminine than ever before in all my life. I had the feeling that marvelous things were about to happen to me.

I got to the theatre at 9:40. The activity was chaotic.

Hy Balaban was sitting in the front row—his feet up on the brass railing of the orchestra pit. I went over and sat behind him, one seat over.

"Hi!" I said.

He waved the back of his hand, indicating the whole stage, and said, "What hath God wrought?"

I felt like kissing the back of his neck. If I put my tongue in his ear, would he feel the way I felt last night when it was done to me? What if I said to him: "Hy, would you consider going somewhere—anywhere, with me right now, so we could fuck beautifully?" Instead, I said: "How's Mrs. Balaban today?"

"Well, let's see. She threw up once before breakfast and once after, and she's only had four Valiums so far, and I believe she's planning to murder our producer today. Inform the media."

"Does she know murder is against the law in Boston?"

"Don't you believe it. A client of mine brought a show up here last season—into this very Shubert Theatre, as a matter of fact—and the critics murdered it, and they're all still walking around free."

"Well, they won't murder this one," I said. "It's a great show."

"*Going* to be, you mean."

"Yes."

"If if if if and if."

"That's what we're out of town for."

"For what?"

"To get rid of the ifs."

He turned toward me with a jump and grabbed my upper arm. Strong hand. Glorious fingers. I turned into a mass of gooseflesh.

His eyes were laughing—black eyes—had I ever seen black eyes before?

"Did you hear about Boss Man and the press agent yesterday?"

"No."

"Oh, this is sensational!" He got up, kneeling on his seat, and leaning toward me. He looked around for possible eavesdroppers, came closer still. He smelled like Tupelo honey. Then he told me the story. "I walked over here with him from The Ritz yesterday—about this time—and they were just finishing the marquee and the house boards—and it all looked fine—glamorous, Broadway—and then we noticed it—me, first, I think, then him. Everything fine. Everyone's billing in place, so no beefs. Color repro splendid, except . . . except they'd gotten the TITLE *wrong!*"

"What do you mean, the title wrong? How could that *be?*"

"Wait. It read: 'Shine In, Harvest Moon.' "

"*In?!*" I said, too loud.

"Sssh! So I thought—and he did, too, I suppose, that it was only that *one* marquee. We looked at each other and moved around to the middle one—facing the street—'Shine In,' and so on. Other side, same. Then the house boards, and damned if they hadn't gotten *those* wrong, too."

"I can't believe it!"

"So. By this time, our man had turned puce. And he said to me, 'Where is he?' 'Who?' 'That idiot.' 'Which idiot?' I asked him. 'Seems to me you've got dozens around.' 'That goddam stupid asshole supposed to be a fuckin' press agent—' "

"Watch your language," I said. "There are ladies present. A lady."

"Sorry, madam. I am merely repeating word for word."

"Go on."

"Where was I?" he asked.

". . . 'goddam stupid asshole supposed to be a fuckin' press agent—' "

"Thank you, madam."

" 'I'll kill the son-of-a-bitch,' he said. So we went inside and immediately, of course, seven people tried to grab him with seven hundred problems, but he was like a deaf man—like a a crazy deaf man—and he just kept asking, 'Where's Paul? I need Paul. Have you seen Paul?' Finally, Paul came in with two of his assistants and one of the girls in her Everleigh Club costume—a knockout, by the way —and Jill Krementz, the photographer. Paul saw us and yelled, 'Whaddaya say, Chief?' And saluted in that jerky way of his. And the Boss just beckoned to him with his index finger—like this. And Paul came toward us, and all I was thinking was—Is it hard to get bloodstains off a gray suit? When Paul reached us, he claps the Man on the back and says, 'What's shakin', Chief?' And Chief says—so quietly, I could hardly hear him, he says, 'Have you seen the marquees?' 'The Marquise of Queensbury?' Paul asks. 'No, not lately. Why?' And breaks himself up. Our boy just waits, and then says, 'No. The marquees out in front of this theatre.' And Paul says, 'Sure.' 'And the house boards, too?' 'Sure, why wouldn't I?' Then there was a pause, and even that dolt, Paul, gathers something is wrong. So he says, 'Something wrong?' 'Well,' says the boss, 'depends what you call wrong. *You* might call it "wrong." I would call it the stupidest fucking idiot blunder that only a useless dumb shitass halfwit incompetent phony like you could make.' Paul had gone pale. 'What is it?' he asks. 'Nothing much. Just the goddam title of this goddam show is wrong. That's right. *Wrong.* So maybe you're right after all. Maybe wrong *is* the way to describe it.' Paul can hardly speak, but he does manage one word, 'Wrong?' 'The title of the show,' says the Boss. 'Have you got a pencil? Get a pencil!' 'I *know* the title.' And the Boss suddenly screams. I mean, screams. Like a woman. He screams, 'Get a pencil!' Paul gets out a pencil and stands there like a reporter. And the Boss says, quiet again: 'Write it down. The title of this show is— *Shine On, Harvest Moon.* Got it?' 'Come on, Chief,' says Paul, good and miffed now. 'Don't hassle me, will you? I'm busy. I know the fucking title of the fucking show.' 'Well, if you do—how come all over the front of everything out there it says, "Shine *In*"—not "Shine *On*" —"Shine *In*"—' *'In?'* asks Paul. 'Yes! *Shine In, Harvest Moon.* All over the whole everything.' Paul turns and walks off the stage, down those rehearsal steps, and up the aisle. The Boss after him, me following. Through the doors—lobby—out front. Paul looks at our house board, then at the other one—then one by one, the three marquees. The Boss just stands there out front, waiting. Paul comes over. He lights a cigarette, sort of nonchalantly. 'Well?' asks Boss. 'Well,' says Paul. *'That's what we're out of town for!'* And he turns and goes back into the theatre. . . . Now I know I shouldn't've laughed—but I swear I couldn't help it. So the Boss transferred his fury to me. 'You're as big an asshole as *he* is!' he yelled. And he went home. I mean, back to The Ritz. In a way—I'm sorry for the little cockalorum. He's out of his depth around here. Over his head. He doesn't even know the lingo—so half the time, he doesn't know what his own staff is talking about. It must be frustrating as hell. His only weapon is, 'You're fired!' But then what? Who's he going to get? It'll be the same again. And he needs all of us. And he knows it. That's why he's giving presents to everyone all the time. Even to *me,* for God's sake."

"But what *I* don't understand—" I began, but was interrupted by a burst of laughter from the back of the house.

I looked up and saw The Barracuda and Alicia and another man at the top of the aisle in animated conversation. They seemed to be sharing a great joke of some kind.

Then The Barracuda looked toward the stage and yelled, "Midge? Midge around? Find her, somebody. *Right away!"*

Six people started scurrying around. I started up the aisle, slowly. I looked at my watch: 9:56. So there was to be no nonsense about being late or any of that noise.

"Coming!" I called out.

"Hurry up!" he hollered.

So I slowed down. As I got closer, I could see that other man more clearly. My first thought was, Wow! Why did I notice his clothes before I noticed him? A shepherd's check tweed, not brown, but brownish, and a dark-blue shirt, yellow-figured knitted tie to pick up the yellow in the fabric of his suit. Tan suede vest, and the most beautiful shoes. His foot was up on the arm of the aisle seat in the last row, so the plaid socks added to the effect. His face—tanned—matched his suit. A strong face, a rugged body. An athlete, no doubt. Alicia and Art were head to head, talking. The new man was watching me as I came toward them. Our eyes met. Ah hah. He was one of those. The kind who makes a woman feel like a woman. Whoever you are, buddy, I thought, I'm ready for you. Just make your move, and if you don't, I will. All those old song titles were whirling through my head: "Some Enchanted Evening" (Morning); "You're the Top"; "That Old Black Magic"; "My Heart Stood Still." What's more, I felt confident. He smiled invitingly, as I passed him.

"Have you handed out those notes yet?" asked Art.

"Good morning, dear," from Alicia.

"Good morning."

"The notes?" he asked again.

"I just got here," I said.

"Good. Let me have 'em. All of 'em."

I took the copies out of my case, and handed them over.

He began to tear them up. We watched him, all three of us. The act of destruction appeared to be giving him blessed relief. He threw the torn bits of paper to the floor and said, "Changed my mind. That's the one thing about me. I change my mind. I'm not ashamed to. Afraid to. These bums stick to one stubborn thing—they're the ones go on their ear. Not me. I roll with the punches. I move with the times. Yesterday, I didn't like the costumes. Today, I do. Because I got the idea of the inception." (Did he mean conception? He avoided the word since that day in rehearsal when he had said to Calvin, "You don't fit into the whole contraception." It was no more than a slip of the tongue, but everyone howled. And he added—"As Sam Goldwyn used to say." But he didn't fool me.) "Listen—tomorrow, I may hate them again. That's all right—every day is different. Even in the sky, the stars change position. Always on the move. All the time in action.

Remember Walt Whitman, what he said? 'Do I contradict myself? Very well, then, I contradict myself. I contain multitudes.' "

The stranger was surprised by this from-left-field reference; Alicia and I were not. Art comes up with them from time to time. Also esoteric words and phrases: "It's turgid," he said about a song one day. "Déjà vu," pronounced perfectly, was one he used often. And during the auditions, when a somewhat bowlegged young actor-musician came on to read for the part of Tiny, the cathouse handyman, he said: "You know what Dr. Johnson would say?

'How now, what manner
Of man is this—
Who carries his balls
In parentheses?' "

These curious little intimations of erudition were mysterious indeed, until last weekend, when I met his son, Saul. How this monster could have spawned the brilliant, accomplished, charming Saul is beyond me. Saul, the scholar, preparing for teaching, was, at twenty-eight, about to take his third Ph.D.—adding philosophy to American history and world drama. An admirable young man in every way, with only one incomprehensible quality: he genuinely loves his horrible father. As for Art, he considers his son the greatest living human and dotes on him—often traveling six thousand miles to spend two hours with him.

"Come on," said Art. "Let's go across to the pancake house and have a second breakfast. You bastards probably haven't even had a first one, right?"

Alicia and I looked at each other. Art went on. "I don't mean you, John. But you're normal, not show business."

We started out.

"Oh," said Alicia. "I'm so sorry. Distracted, really. Midge, this is my husband, John Marble. John, this is our left lung, Midge Maghakian. We all breathe through her."

I stopped dead in my tracks, wondering if I would ever get the top of my head back.

John took my hand—what was he communicating? Something, surely.

"Maghakian," he said, and went on, in perfect Armenian, *"Va veela don sahg orcatt."* Which means: A new friend adds a new year to life.

Crossing the street, Alicia walked with Art. She was trying to explain why the period shoes had to be made, why they could not be bought.

John Marble had taken my arm as we crossed against the light.

"I don't speak Armenian, really," he said. "I wish I did. I wish I spoke every language on earth—or that we all spoke one language. Of course, in some ways, we do." His accent: American. Southern.

He got us across skillfully—and even more skillfully, managed to check out both my breasts on the way.

At the pancake house, I had a cup of coffee, but could not eat a thing.

· XV ·

Larry to the company this morning.

"During the performance last night, a few new things happened —good things. A simply stunning rhythm in the 'Brawl,' remarkable teamwork with the pit in 'Nightfall' and 'Big Town,' and that rollicky let-go feeling in the courtroom scene. And I found myself thinking about a crazy part of my career that happened many years ago, before most of you were born, I expect. Things were really rugged and the sister of a girlfriend of mine, who ran a traveling marionette theatre, offered me a job. It was going to pay fifty dollars a week, which was great. So I became part of this little troupe. I was a complete tyro—didn't know the difference between a puppet and a marionette, didn't know that a puppet was worked from beneath and a marionette from above. This particular production I was engaged for was a private-school tour—a production of the opera, *Hansel and Gretel* by the original Humperdinck. We used a recorded score, so it was only a question of learning to fit the movements of the marionettes to the record. There were passages where dialogue was spoken and, since that was not on the recording, we each spoke the dialogue for our own marionettes.

"There was my friend's sister, and her girl assistant, two more fellows, and myself. I think that was all. Five of us, and someone who ran the sound. Rehearsals were difficult, particularly for me. I was, by far, the worst, because I was the least experienced. And I found that marionettes were terribly complex. Each one had a string for each arm, for each knee, for each ankle, several for the head, the wrists, the fingers, and as you worked with the suspended marionette the tiniest movement of your finger or your hand would make the marionette seem either splendid and alive, or mechanical and ridiculous. The whole doll had to be supported by both arms at all times —extremely fatiguing—and there were also complicated logistic questions of bumping into one another, getting in one another's way. Moreover, when your marionette was finished with a scene it had to be hung back on the rack in exactly the right way, so as not to tangle with any of the others. During the early rehearsals, we constantly got our marionettes tangled, but I was assured that would all be straightened out.

"We rehearsed for about two weeks; then we gave about twenty performances.

"Now I'm getting to the point of this remembrance which has to do with *Shine On, Harvest Moon* and what's beginning to happen with it right now. Listen. One night near to the opening performance of *Hansel and Gretel* we were working late. Something had gone wrong technically. It got to be eleven o'clock, then 11:30, and finally midnight—no Equity deputies around to bother us, so we were still there, still rehearsing. I got terribly sleepy and was already bone-tired, but the music was playing and we were doing one scene for the fifth or sixth or fiftieth or sixtieth time, and all at once, now listen to this, I had the sensation that I wasn't working this goddamn marionette at all, but that *it* was working *me!* The marionette had taken on a life of his own. I wasn't doing anything to him; he was actually controlling my fingers and hands. I let go and relaxed to the situation completely, when suddenly I heard Dorothy—that was the girl's name, Dorothy—I heard her yell, 'Wonderful! Oh, that's just wonderful!' I didn't know what I was doing that was wonderful, I wasn't doing *anything*. I just kept looking down at this bloody doll and it was doing things it had never done before! There it was attached to my fingers and I was watching it doing its thing.

"I found this experience so extraordinary, so eerie and unnerving that I didn't say anything to anybody about it. But I thought about it for a long time. Now, what was even more interesting was that in every performance that followed, every time we got to that particular section, I found that if I just let go, the marionette would take over. As we went on playing *Hansel and Gretel* I was able to do that more and more—simply let go and let the marionette take over.

"In acting, you're not supposed to be thinking about being the character, or *trying* to be the character, you have to *become* the character. And it's that breakthrough moment you wait for in the course of your work.

"The reason I've gone to such length about all this this morning is that I feel not enough of this breakthrough has yet happened. I'm still seeing too much of the marionetteers and not enough of the marionettes. So, we're going to run the first four scenes of Act One right now, and please let me see as little of you yourselves as you can manage.

"All right, let's take ten and begin. Thank you."

SHINE ON, HARVEST MOON
Company Bulletin
Friday, October 19

We will be arriving in Philadelphia Thanksgiving
week. It is essential that our hotel list be comp-
leted by half-hour this evening. Thanks.

H. Wadsworth

MEN: Mrs. Marble requests that all male members of
the company refrain from getting haircuts until
further notice.

HEALTH: It has been determined that people working
under unusually strong artificial light, such as
theatre lights, motion-picture lights, or television lights, as well as fluorescent office lights,
lose calcium to a greater degree than normal. Long
experience has taught us that to counteract this,
it is a good idea to take calcium tablets. These are
easily obtainable without prescription at any
drugstore. The recommended form is Squibb's Dicalcium Phosphate with Viosterol, which comes in tiny
capsules or in mintlike wafers. Also, you can get,
at health food stores, the pure rather than synthetic form of the above, which is sold as bone-meal
tablets. The loss of calcium apparently weakens
nerve ends, causing nervousness and irritability.

THE COMPANY YOU KEEP: LARRY GABEL(Director)
   As Lawrence Gabel, I was an unsuccessful actor
from 1955 to 1962, when I directed my first play at
The Berkshire Playhouse in Stockbridge, Mass.
   I come from Milton, Mass. Educated at Milton Academy; Harvard, drama major.
   American Academy of Dramatic Arts, two years. Extremely valuable training, but too late. I should
have gone there directly from Milton Academy.
   The college years were a waste, which is why I advise all theatre-interested young people to get
going as soon as possible and learn by doing.
   I have directed many plays and musicals and TV
shows—but the one I am proudest of and love the best
is SHINE ON, HARVEST MOON.

<u>BOSTON GASTRONOMY</u>: We call your attention to the existence of the finest ice-cream parlor in the world, which has been doing business at a single stand for about 80 years: Bailey's, on West Street (follow Tremont Street past the "Touraine" and turn right on West Street).

<u>QUOTE TO REMEMBER</u>:
     "Actors should not talk to anyone for two or three beats before they go on. It is better not to. It's better to concentrate. You are apt to miss your cue, for one thing, if you are talking to anybody up until the last second before you go on. I never do and never have."

Miss Lynn Fontanne

There are now 38 days remaining until our Philadelphia opening.
There are now 64 days remaining until our New York opening.

· XVI ·

Art's suite.

"Get me Patti and monitor the call, right?"

I reach Patti at the Statler. Art goes across the room and picks up the extension. I get out my steno pad.

                        ART
    Patti, baby?

                        PATTI
    Well well well!

                        ART
    I'm glad to hear it.

                        PATTI
    Hear what?

                        ART
    That you're so well.

                        PATTI
    Wit-*ty!*

                        ART
    Listen. Could you use three grand?

                        PATTI
    Sure, but not as much as I could use a number.

ART

Don't make it too hard on me, baby.

PATTI

As the girl said to the sailor.

ART

Look, kiddie. I'm for *you*, but my deal is I'm supposed to stay out of the creative and they stay out of the business.

PATTI

I notice you don't, though, Bigmouth.

ART

Hey, *hey!* . . . How come you're comin' on so sassy?

PATTI

Because I know already you want something. You're the asker so far.

ART

I tell you what I *could* do.

PATTI

What?

ART

I could improve your billing and—

PATTI

Oh, *fuck* billing! Who cares? That's for either big stars or little gypsies—not for old warhorses like me. This is God help me my ninth Broadway show—so I know billing on the posters is bullshit. Billing up on the stage—that's what counts.

ART

And what about three grand? That doesn't count?

PATTI
(Quietly)

Not as much as *five* grand.

ART
(Yelling)

Hey, you crafty little bitch! What're you hondling already? You don't even know what it is and already you're hondling.

PATTI

I can imagine.

ART

What? Go ahead. Imagine.

PATTI

You want to set somebody up. Probably Larry.

ART

Wrong! Y'see, smart-twat? *Wrong!*

PATTI

What, then?

ART

Not Larry. Somebody else.

PATTI

Oh, I was wrong, huh?

ART

What d'y'say?

PATTI

I'll think about it.

ART

To do it right, I'll want you to move over here. To the Ritz.

PATTI

A suite.

ART

No, no. That's a giveaway.

PATTI

All right, then. Forget it.

ART

It's not the money, you little pisspot. But how does it look—*you*
in a suite?

PATTI

Looks lovely.

ART

So all right. Maybe.

PATTI

And what'll you need?

ART

One good cassette, that's all.

PATTI

And who's gonna make that? How?

ART

I'll make it. Through the wall.

PATTI

Uh-huh.

ART

So we set?

PATTI

I'll think it over. For five.

ART

Three.

PATTI

Five.

ART

Four?

PATTI

Five.

ART

Listen, stupid—you're not the *only* one can do the job.

PATTI

Oh-oh!

ART

What?

PATTI

You just tripped on your dick, mister. That one word. I was just
going to O.K. the four. But that one word—that's got to cost you
a grand.

ART

What word?

Stupid. You called me stupid.

Come on, baby. A joke.

An expensive joke. Now it's five take it or leave it—and a suite.

Wait a second. I need a layout. The next room and all. Maybe I can't *get* you a suite.

Sure, you can. You're a power. You're a barracuda. You're always telling me that. A real space cadet.

I'll let you know.

Do that.

He hung up and said, "Bitch." To me: "Did y' get all that?"
"Yes." (I felt sick.)
"Right. So you know what we need. Talk to Whathisname—"
"Mr. Seidel." (Should I quit? Of course.)
"That's it. Talk to Seidel—slip him a C-note, I mean, if you *have* to. Tell him I need a two-roomer on this side. And the adjoining single. It's gonna look funny—God damn it—I don't care *what* this little hooker says. Wait. How's this? Tell—Whathisname?—"
"Mr. Seidel?" (Or should I just disappear?)
"Yeah. Tell Whathisname this young lady—lady!—is gonna be doin' some coaching in there. Hey, that's good. That's what we can tell *anybody*—anybody who sniffs around. Tell 'em to put a piano in there—in the single—an upright. Right?"
"All right."
"Right away on this, right?"
I tried to keep myself from echoing, "Right," but failed.
I went down to Mr. Seidel's office and made the request on behalf of Mr. Clune. (What was I doing? I was moving about like a hypnotized zombie.)
"I'm terribly sorry," he said. "We're simply absolutely jam-packed

at the moment, and I would be reluctant to promise anything for next week or the week after that. What with the three shows in town —*and* the NFL convention—"

I handed him an envelope.

"What's this?" he asked.

"Mr. Clune wants you to buy yourself a cigar."

"I don't smoke cigars," he said, opening the envelope and peering in. He put the envelope into his inner breast pocket and said, "Let me see what I can do."

(Should I tip Hy off? Yes. No.)

An hour later, AC and I were looking over Suite 912–14.

"Son-of-a-bitch," he said. "It's better than *mine!*"

We went next door to look over 915, the single directly next to 914, the bedroom of the suite. AC rapped on the connecting wall, then said, "Listen for me, then rap back, O.K.?"

"Yes."

He went out. I waited, feeling lightheaded. I heard his rap, rapped back. A louder knock, then the same from me.

In the hallway, he said, "All right. Call her and tell her to check in tonight—or tomorrow morning the latest."

"Very well."

At the elevator, he said, "Let's go up. I've got a few memos and also some stuff for the bulletin."

"I'll be up in half an hour," I said.

"Why? Why not now?"

"I want to take a bath."

"What? Right now? In the middle of the morning?"

"Yes. I absolutely have to."

I cannot explain how it came about that I was part of the setup last night. A small part, yet I feel sullied and guilty and remorseful. I have the feeling it is something I'll regret for the rest of my life. I have been trying to explain it to myself, to rationalize, to understand. So far, no. I simply feel guilty and soiled. I cannot justify myself to myself. Oh, hell!

Aki, the soundman, came over between matinee and night and set up the equipment for what he called "a wall tap." It consisted of an extrasensitive microphone set in a pie-sized suction cup that was fastened to the connecting wall. The whole event had the shape of a dream, or was it a movie I was watching? Did such things really happen? Was *this* happening? *Should* I quit? I was in a quandary. And yet, to be perfectly truthful—there was a curious excitement to the affair. Could it be that I *was* mesmerized by the adventure?

Even though yesterday was a matinee day there was a morning-rehearsal call. Equity allows two hours on a matinee day, and Larry took it. Endless grousing throughout the company—but changes and putting in one whole new number for the girls in Scene One: "Loving for a Living."

I saw Patti do her come-on with Hy, but she is so skillful, so subtle an operator, that he had not the faintest notion of what was going on. She found a spot near to where he was sitting at the piano, going over the lyrics with two of the girls who were not up on them.

All the dancers were warming up, so it didn't seem strange or unusual for her to be doing what she was doing. What she was doing was driving Hy crazy.

I noticed—I'm sure he didn't—that she was wearing something other than her usual rehearsal clothes: violet leotard and sweater. Today, she had on white short shorts and a loose-fitting pink blouse. No bra. Near the piano, she began her bends and stretches. On the forward bends, her emanating breasts came into full view. Now she was on the floor, spreading her legs and closing them. Open, close, open, close. Hy hit a few clinkers—rare for him—but no one heard. Patti was moving her legs back over her body in the half-lotus position. As she came down, slowly, just a few delicate wisps of her pubes could be discerned—proving that she was truly a blonde, or else a mighty thorough girl, indeed. She sat up now and turned her back to Hy, who was still trying to keep his attention on his work. I saw his hand go to his lap and his body shift. He was, doubtless, having some difficulty with his equipment. Patti continued to undulate, but in a position that revealed little or nothing. Hy was playing louder and louder. A mating call? In time, Patti responded—stopped her teasing—and performed the frontal routine again.

"That's it!" shouted Hy, slamming his open palms on the upper and lower register of the piano. "For Christ's sake—if you don't know it by now—you'll *never* know it. A simple goddamn lyric." The two girls looked startled. What was he so uptight about so all of a sudden? He'd started out twenty minutes ago so nicely, even flirtatiously. They looked at each other and shrugged. Hy looked over at Patti, who was on her feet doing a jumping-jack, her breasts so alive that the movement seemed to be a performance by a trio. Hy turned back to the two hapless girls, stuck his finger into their faces, and yelled, "And if you *don't* know the words, don't *fake, don't* sing 'hudga-budga, hudga-budga.' Just lay out. Mouth something. But don't *sing!* Don't sing unless you know the words—the *right* words. That's all. Go practice."

The girls were off. Patti stopped. Flushed and damp, she moved to the piano, picked up her pink towel, and began to dry her face. Hy sat down at the piano again, and began to noodle—showing off, actually. He plays beautifully, and went into a richly embellished chorus of "Was It Wrong?" from Act Two. Patti, seemingly oblivious, actually calculating, began to mop her armpits, which were not cleanly shaven and so revealed a touch of golden down. She moved the towel up under her blouse and dried the skin between her breasts.

Hy stopped playing and lit a cigarette. His hands were trembling. "Hey, there, Miss Patti," he said. "You know what I like about you the most? Why I dig you the most?" She said nothing, and continued to slide the towel up and down her long arms. "I'll *tell* you why. Because you're a *great perspirer.* Y'know that? You sweat just *great!*" No reply. What a technique she has, I thought. Hy went on, his voice unsteady. "I'm serious. That's what an audience loves more than anything. They love to see the dancers sweat. It makes them feel they're getting their money's worth. What the hell, it stands to reason —they're sitting there, and sixteen beautiful kids are sweating their asses off for them, y'know what I mean?" Patti looked at him now for the first time, said nothing, but appeared to be regarding him with interest—as though he were a sofa she was considering recovering. "What do you do between shows?" he asked, gently. She shrugged. He seemed to have a physical need to hear the sound of her voice. Good God, so did *I.* How did she manage to turn the screw so deliberately? She was putting emotional distance between them, as he moved to her, patted her cheek, then impulsively hugged her, briefly. "I tell you," he said, "if our whole line could sweat like you, we'd have a smash."

"We'd have a *flood,*" she said.

He laughed. No. He laughed it up. There's a difference. He was— to use a phrase of Art's—"building character" with her.

Buddy called places for the dancers, and she was gone. Hy went out into the alley.

A presence behind me, too suddenly, and a voice in my ear. "Home free, right?"

I went flying out of my chair, not only startled, but alarmed.

Art, of course. Where had he come from? Where had he been? I have noticed this about evil people—they are frequently ubiquitous. Obviously, he had seen what I had seen.

"Jesus," he said. "What a worker *she* is! I could see his hard-on from the last row. Where I was sittin'. *Five* grand? This bimbo's worth *six*. I would say she's got a hook in him about seven inches down the gullet. Wouldn't you?"

Taking a cue from Patti, I said nothing. Silence, I was learning, is often better than golden—it could be, it *was* in this case, cast iron. Funny, that. *Cast* iron.

"Sit down," he said. "I have to do a few letters. Here O.K.? Or you rather the production office?"

I walked away, giving him his answer. He followed me across the stage, up one flight, down the hall.

"Be right with you," he said. "I got to take a leak."

Dainty Art.

He came into the production office, buttoning his fly. An expensive, tailored suit, no doubt. No zipper.

"I'm a little nervous," he said. "I admit it. A lot could go wrong. I don't mean mechanically. That I've checked out. I mean, he could think it over and conk out. I mean, later, when he cools off. Right now, he's hot—and like they say, 'A stiff prick's got no brains.' Pardon my French. Jesus—don't tell me you're blushing. I haven't seen a blush since New Utrecht High School. Look, I'm sorry—but I have to tell you. Around this bunch, you better get used to it. O.K. This first one is to Arnold Weissberger. 'Dear Arnold . . .' See, the thing about Hy is—oh, no. That's not to Arnold. I'm just sayin'. The thing about Hy is—he ain't smart but he's suspicious. He trusts nobody. Not me. Not even Fred—and Fred's his partner. Nobody. So if he even gets the teeniest hint she's playing with him for something—anything—he's just as likely to stand 'er up. Another thing: a lot of these guys around here like him—they talk a great game—but when it comes pants-off time they fold. They scare out. That could be him. I mean—he doesn't know this little broad. He might figure, hey,

What if she's a blab—some of 'em are. It gets around the company. It gets to his wife. Is it worth it? Y'*know?* . . . Where was I?"

" 'Dear Arnold,' " I said.

"Yeah. 'Dear Arnold   As you have no doubt heard by now we are a smash up here and that is why I believe we should try to wind up everything on rights before—' "

He paused.

"Maybe I ought to coach her—no love games, no kind of serious shit—just keep it frankly a nice hot ball, that's all. I heard he gets real sentimental sometimes and makes a whole thing out of it. Old-fashioned. Not like these kids, they just do it like as if it was dancing, and I don't mean only the dancers—I'm talkin' about the singers, too, and the principals and *everybody*. I hope he knows. And can play it like that. I wonder if she knows about stocking up on booze? Does she know what he drinks? Do you?" I shook my head. "Look, I'll do the letters later. Hotel. See y'." He was gone.

Between shows, I went to dinner with Clay and Chris. Locke-Ober's. A crowd waiting for tables. In a booth for six—Hy and Patti. He is in an expansive mood—probably because the matinee really did go marvelously—and he is going good, too. A bottle of Stolichnaya on the table. The manager drops by and sits with them for a while. I almost feel like calling Art to tell him not to worry. There's not a chance anything can go wrong. One odd note, only. Patti, usually a life-of-the-party type, is rather subdued. Or is this part of her routine? I wish I knew.

Art's suite.

This morning—or rather, noon—Hy comes in. He looks well—rosy, in fact—and is gotten up in his customary well-groomed, snappy-dresser way. He is a clothes ham and someone said the other day that when he and his wife go to Paris—which they do every year —*he* spends as much on clothes as *she* does.

"Tea?" asks Art.

"Coffee," says Hy.

"Anything with it?"

"Yeah. A hit song."

"I wish I could get you to kick coffee, Hy. It's bad for the heart."

"Wrong. You know what's bad for the heart? I'll tell you what's bad for the heart. Being number *two* on the Hit Parade—that's bad for the heart."

"Got that?" Art asks me. "Coffee."

"Yes."

I go into the other room and order from room service. By the time I return, they are at it. Art is saying:

"—and it's drivin' me to *insanity!*"

"Well, let's face it, Art. You haven't got far to go."

I sit down at the desk.

Art goes on: "I don't claim to know so much technically—I mean I don't know one music key from another."

"*I* do."

"But believe me—I'm like the audience—and I feel things—like them—and they're all ready for that Nora Bayes number—and it doesn't happen—boy! That's gonna cost us—you'll see. *Cost* us. It's like we've got them in the sack and we go on and on—and comes the moment, and nobody blows their load."

Hy says, "Listen, you cheap vulgarian—if you're going to talk like that—send her out."

"I've heard *you* talk worse."

"Not in front of this nice respectable Armenian girl, you haven't."

"Half Armenian."

"Really? Which half?"

"So come on, admit it. Deep down, God damn it—you *know* I'm right. You're no. fool. *You* feel it, too, standing back there."

"It's the orchestration," says Hy. "We're fixing it."

"Orchestration, my ass—"

"Didn't I tell you—don't talk like that with the girl here. It's embarrassing. Or tell her to go. Go 'way, Midge."

"You want the truth?" asks Art. "I'll give you the truth. We're gonna have a serious half an hour here in a minute—and I want a witness. That's been a policy of mine for many years' standing. I always have a witness."

The room-service waiter arrives. I sign the check. He leaves. I serve Hy his coffee. Silence.

"Go ahead," says Hy, sensing trouble.

"To put it plain, I don't think the substitute number works. Neither does anybody."

"I'll change it. We'll do a *new* number."

"How about 'Shine On, Harvest Moon'?"

"Never."

"O.K. How about this number?" He reaches over, picks up the little Sony and presses the play button.

(Room noises. Glasses. Ice cubes. A man laughs)

HY'S VOICE:

Come on, truth. Was that accidental this morning at rehearsal? That bending and stretching? Or were you trying to drive me nuts? Or drive my *nuts* nuts?

*(*PATTI'S *laugh)*

I cannot bear to look at Hy, but from the corner of my eye, I catch a glimpse of him. He is sipping coffee, but he has turned into a mechanical man. He reminds me of one of those people who work the shop windows on 5th and 57th Street sometimes; living mannequins who mystify the passersby with their trick of not moving a muscle or blinking or anything—but once every fifteen minutes or so giving a single wink.

PATTI'S VOICE:

Let me have a look at them—then I'll tell you.

HY'S VOICE:

I'll be Goddamned! First time my nuts've had to *audition.*

PATTI'S VOICE:

I've auditioned plenty for you, mister.

HY'S VOICE:

Hey. Like we used to say—I'll show you mine if you show me yours.

PATTI'S VOICE:

Why not? That's what we're here for, isn't it?

(A sound)

HY'S VOICE:

Jesus Christ, baby! What're you trying to do—stop my clock?

The coffee cup in Hy's hand begins to shake. He spills coffee all over the front of his white shirt. He puts down the rattling cup.

Art presses the fast-forward button of the machine. It screeches as though in pain. Now the play button.

> HY'S VOICE:
> —and be right with you. Where is it? In here—oh, yeah. I see. Thanks.

A pause. Hy is looking at Art. His face is crazily controlled to a point where I cannot read his expression. Is it anger or fear or hate or terror or all of them?

Another scream from the Sony as it races forward.

> PATTI'S VOICE:
> —to get you something to help.

> HY'S VOICE:
> What've you got?

> PATTI'S VOICE:
> Vaseline, cold cream.

> HY'S VOICE:
> No, no. Look in my briefcase there—you'll find a tube of K.Y.

> (PATTI's *laugh*)

> PATTI'S VOICE:
> You son of a bitch—you're a real pro, huh?

> HY'S VOICE:
> I'm a Boy Scout. Our motto is "Be prepared."

> PATTI'S VOICE:
> How'd you know I was going to let you go up my ass?

> HY'S VOICE:
> I could tell. It's that kind of an ass.

> PATTI'S VOICE:
> Yes, it is, isn't it? The sweet little thing.

> HY'S VOICE:
> C'mere, c'mere.

PATTI'S VOICE:
Easy, baby.

HY'S VOICE:
Let *me* let *me* let—

PATTI'S VOICE:
Aahh!

HY'S VOICE:
What's the matter?

PATTI'S VOICE:
Cold.

HY'S VOICE:
I'll take care of that.

PATTI'S VOICE:
Careful, huh? Don't tear me.

HY'S VOICE:
Don't worry, baby. I'll give it to you an inch at a time.

PATTI'S VOICE:
Wait.

HY'S VOICE:
No. . . .

PATTI'S VOICE:
Here. Let me.

HY'S VOICE:
You.

PATTI'S VOICE:
There. Easy.

HY'S VOICE:
Jesus!

PATTI'S VOICE:
Aaahh!!!

Hy comes out of his chair, tries to stand, fails, and falls to his knees. "Oh, my God," he moans, and begins to retch. "Oh, Jesus. Oh, my God! What's *happening?*"

He breaks down and sobs uncontrollably.

It is all surrealistic. A nightmare. An insane movie. What in God's name am I doing here? Why don't I get out? I can't. Why not?

Hy's double voice in the air. On the machine—moans of ecstasy—through which words float: "Oh, yeah. Oh, good. Good for you, baby? Tell me! Good for you?"

"Oh, *yes!*"

"Oh, good. Hold it. Hold still. . . ."

In the room, moans of another kind from Hy on the floor. And whimpers. And words: "Oh you bastard, you low fucking slimy bastard. The worst. You're the worst. You'll pay your dues someday, you cocksucker. You'll see."

At last at last at last Art shuts off the machine. Hy manages to get back into his chair. He mops the spilt coffee from his clothing with a napkin. I sit there unable to move. I am dripping wet. I hate everybody, including myself. I have no idea how long it is before Hy speaks—a hell of a time, that I do know. When he does, he is surprisingly calm.

"What do you want?" he asks.

"*You* know what I want."

"Say it."

"A rider. I want a rider in our contract—Fred's too. The right to interpolate whatever."

"And what about that?" Hy asks, pointing to the Sony.

"It's yours."

"What about copies? How can I trust a lousy fucking unconscionable swine like you?"

"No copies. You got my word."

"Your word is *shit.* Give me a letter. Indemnify me. If a copy ever turns up anywhere—you owe me a million dollars."

"No," says Art.

"No?"

"Make it I owe you *ten* million."

"Deal."

Art goes over and extends his hand.

"No," says Hy. "I'd rather not touch you. Just draw the papers."

"Here they are," says Art, and hands them over. Hy signs without so much as looking at them. Art gives him another set and says, "And get your daffodil to sign his right away."

Hy is pale—or is it slightly blue? What if he has a heart attack here and now?

He gets up and crosses the room to the door, moving like an old, old man. At the door, he stops. Is he reconsidering?

He turns into the room and speaks.

"Tell me, Art. In all honesty. Was it worth all that? For a lousy couple of songs in a show? Was it really worth it? To *kill* a man? For a *song?*"

No answer. Hy leaves.

"O.K.," says Art. "Here's our copy. Make copies. For Arnold and Larry and Cindy and—"

"I'll be back in a while," I say.

"Why? Where you going?"

"To my room. I have to throw up."

"Do it here," he said.

I went into the bathroom and took his advice.

SHINE ON, HARVEST MOON
Company Bulletin
Wednesday, October 31

HALLOWEEN: All authentic witches and warlocks in the company: Please report to Clay Botsford at midnight for instructions.

THURSDAY AFTERNOON RUN-THROUGH: Please observe the following important rules for the conduct of our run-through of Act I at 3:00 P.M.

1. No clowning on stage.
2. Speak only the text. No paraphrasing, no ad-libbing, no prompting, no apologies, and no going back and starting again.
3. Observe actual performance conditions as far as possible.
4. Speak up, project, sing out.
5. Quiet as possible offstage and in the wings.
6. Please simulate offstage all changes of costume and makeup, making certain you have sufficient time.

COLOR: Today's color is Orange; tomorrow's, Purple.

QUOTE TO REMEMBER:
"Author, director, scene-designer, and actor must become completely the servants of the play. Each must resist every temptation to score personally. Each must make himself a free, transparent medium through which the whole flows freely and without obstruction. No one at any moment can say, 'Ah, this moment is mine! I shall show what can be done with it.' There is no part of the play that is done for the benefit of anyone. It must all be inevitable, impersonal and untrammeled. It requires a complete surrender of selfishness. In fact, it demands of everyone the honest rigidity of the true artist, who will stoop to nothing because it is effective or conspicuous or because 'it goes.' "
Arthur Hopkins,
from HOW'S YOUR SECOND ACT?, 1918

<u>THE COMPANY YOU KEEP</u>: JENNY FLAGG(Choreographer)

I danced my ass off for Jerry Robbins and Bob Fosse and George Balanchine and Gower Champion. I was underpaid by David Merrick, Ray Stark, Herman Levin, Joe Papp (especially), Lester Osterman, Feuer and Martin, The Shuberts, Fryer and Carr, Fryer and Cresson, and just plain Fryer.

When my pins began to complain, I became Everybody's Assistant and worked on hits such as: THE ROTHSCHILDS; JESUS CHRIST, SUPERSTAR; A LITTLE NIGHT MUSIC; and SHENANDOAH. Also no-hits such as: FRANK MERRIWELL; SUGAR; SEESAW; and MOLLY. Finally, a few almosts, among them: COCO; GIGI; and FOLLIES.

I was born in Weatherford, Texas (me and Mary Martin), on January 11, 1940. Don't count. I'm 39. Dancing school from the age of 5. New York at 16, lied re age and got my first job in the chorus of COPPER AND BRASS with Nancy Walker, then replacement in WEST SIDE STORY, replacement in THE MUSIC MAN, lines in THE BODY BEAUTIFUL, and I was launched.

It has all been interesting, educational, glorious, depressing, humiliating, insulting, gratifying, fulfilling, exhausting, sexy, lonely, beautiful, and horrible—and don't ask me if I'd like to do it all again. I might tell you.

I love dancers. I love them better than singers or actors or trumpet players or stage managers or plumbers or cops. Dancers are the best in the world, especially *my* dancers.

There are now 26 days remaining until our Philadelphia opening.

· XVII ·

Clay is a morning walker. So am I. We see each other now and then and wave.

This morning our paths crossed, literally.

"Fate," he said.

We walked together without speaking. Morning walkers understand one another. As we left The Public Gardens and entered The Common, a young couple carrying a blaring, large portable radio passed us. The music was a spirited 1979 version of "Just One of Those Things."

Clay stopped in his tracks, turned, and watched the couple until they and music had gone.

"Cole Porter," he said.

"What?"

"Mr. Cole Porter. My personal God. I was his rehearsal pianist for three and a half years. What years!"

"You're a musician, too?" I asked.

"Was. A spoiled composer."

"Why spoiled?"

"I gave up when I saw I didn't have it."

"Maybe you shouldn't have hung around Cole Porter."

"Hey! You may have something there."

"You should have tried somebody maybe like our little Hy. His music is slick and catchy—but it doesn't wear well."

"He's all right."

"All right isn't Cole Porter."

"Nothing is." We continued our walk. "Mr. Porter was a great professional. Funny how I still think of him as Mr. Porter—I never did get to call him 'Cole.' What the hell. I was eighteen. He was Cole Porter. *Kiss Me Kate.* Lord, I couldn't believe it—what he'd come up with day after day. I suppose I'd call that a perfect show. All the way. And right after that, he did *Out of This World.* Same producers, director. Everything. Even me. And it was leaden. A soufflé that refused to rise. All effort, strain, pushing. As far as I could see—we all worked harder on that one than we did on *Kate.* The result was zero. A complete failure. A few months after it closed he had me up to his place in Williamstown for the weekend. He had some copying he wanted me to do. And one night, I asked him what he thought had happened, and he laughed that sunny laugh of his, and said, 'The book, dear boy, the book. You can't write a good score unless you have a good book. Great book, great score. Lousy book, lousy score.'

" 'But why should that *be,* Mr. Porter?'

" 'Because, my lad, the songs come out of the book. Who's singing —and what are they singing about? And where? And when? "I love you. I love you," isn't a song—it's a platitude—but if the right character sings it to another right character, it can be heaven. The book, remember that. Always the book.' Of course, he was right. Some years later, he said to me, *'My Fair Lady!* I'll never get over it. It is simply the best show I've ever seen. I wonder what *I* might've done with it if they'd asked *me* instead of Fritz. I once told you about the book —didn't I? Well, there's a perfect example. There's a *great* book— result: a great score.' I've had years to observe all this through the years, and believe me. Mr. Porter was right."

"Then why isn't *our* score better? *We've* got a great book."

"No. A pretty good book."

"All right. Is the score *as* good?"

"No."

"Why not, then?"

"Because they're not writing to the book. They're trying for song hits. For Number One on the charts. For showstoppers. They're bringing stuff up out of their trunk. Stuff that didn't work in other shows. Maybe it'll work in this, they think."

"Could they change?"

"If they wanted to, of course. They're extremely talented. But misguided. They want the book bent to suit their stuff. Were you there for the 'Red Cross' number battle?"

"Was I *there?* I'm always there!"

"What? Oh, yes. Of course, you were there."

"The invisible woman, that's me."

He seemed reluctant to leave the subject of Cole Porter.

"I owe him everything—just about everything I know about this business, and I know plenty. Every day, I check what we've got against the principles he laid down. We're getting there—could get there—but it's going to take what I doubt we're going to get."

"And what's that?"

"Unselfishness. Everyone working on the same show. God Almighty, they seem to forget we're all on the same side."

"Another thing," I said. "They seem to be losing the love story."

"Oh, how right you are, and how important it is. Why can't they see it?"

"Tell them," I suggested.

"I would if they'd listen. Up to now, we're all talking different languages. That screamer the other day—when Art shoved Hy right out of his room. Physically?"

"Wasn't that *awful?* Two grown men—like street kids."

"Yes."

"Well, that fight they had," I said, "I heard every word, and I didn't even know what it was about. And I don't know *now.*"

"About the records. The singles."

"Yes—but *what* about the singles?"

"About who to grant permissions to, and in what order, and how many, and so on."

"I'm lost again."

"What do you care?"

We were walking back to The Ritz now, down Beacon Hill.

"I once went up to see him, Mr. Porter—at The Harkness Pavilion —it was toward the end. What style! Even in the hospital. I remember a young Englishman in a beige alpaca jacket meeting me at the elevator and saying, 'Good afternoon, Mr. Botsford. I'm one of Mr. Porter's valets.' And he took me to the lounge, which apparently Mr. Porter had arranged to have to himself. And a tea was served. You know the kind. Grand. Little sandwiches and pastries and cookies. And we talked. Mostly about me and what I was doing. Then later, he wanted to know what was doing on his beloved Broadway. The real dope—not the kind you get in the papers or *Variety*. I told him that Dick Rodgers and Alan Jay Lerner were working on a show. He leaned forward in his wheelchair, and those big eyes got bigger. 'Dick and Alan! Wonderful. A great match. What's the show?' I told him. 'What? Coco Chanel? A musical? Impossible. I knew her. Knew her well.' 'But that's what it is, I'm sure.' 'It can't be done, I tell you. I *knew* her.' 'What's that got to do with it?' He was irritated—not only by me but the whole subject. His voice rose: 'You can't write a musical about Coco Chanel.' 'Why not, Mr. Porter?' 'Because she was never in *love!*' he shouted. . . . I thought he was all wrong. A bit envious, perhaps? But years later, many, it was done—not by Rodgers, and even with the great Hepburn—it just didn't do. That Cole Porter. The things he knew. And what he didn't know, he felt."

We had reached the hotel and I was sorry.

SHINE ON, HARVEST MOON

Company Bulletin

Friday, November 2

PLEASE NOTE: ANOTHER CHANGE TO BE ADDED TO THE
CHANGES DISTRIBUTED TODAY:

On page two of the changes, at the bottom, the
following *is left in:*

BELLE

It's something, certainly, but don't you think
you're making too much of it too soon?

QUOTE TO REMEMBER:

"A good sideshow often earns the expenses of
the entire circus."

John Ringling

November 1 was Gloria's birthday. A belated happy
one and sorry it missed the bulletin.

THE COMPANY YOU KEEP: IVAN KURLANSKY(Sets)

NADIA KURLANSKY(Assistant)

This is me Nadia Kalinin Kurlansky writing down
for both. Ivan Ivanovich Kurlansky is born Tiflis,
August 29, 1902. Father famous big good painter for
portraits andsoforth. Grandfather same. Great-
grandfather also same. Whole family almost same.
Ivan is smallboy wins Prince Igor prize for painting, goes to Conservatory of Art, Moscow. First job
scene painter Moscow Art Theatre. Then designer.
1925 comes America with Stanislavsky and Company:
(LYSISTRATA, BROTHERS KARAMAZOV, CHERRY ORCHARD,
MISTRESS OF THE INN). Likes New York. Goodbye Stanislavsky and Company. But no work. Makes window
displays R. H. Macy Company. In 1928 first show for
Mr. John Golden. Since 88 shows Broadway and regional. Also 6 one-man show paintings. Also 2
churches, 3 temples, 6 Tonys.

In 1939 me Nadia I come here refugee. I am born
Odessa, father and mother photographers. I hate
photography. Study theatre and art. Ad in NEW YORK
TIMES for assistant for stage designer. I am hired
to Ivan. I make models and so forth. Two years we
live together. O.K. Then marry. One daughter,

Basha. She hates stage design. Is teacher retarded
children.
  Happy marriage. I believe Ivan best designer in
all world, he believes me best assistant. Is
enough.

N. K. Kurlansky

THE COMPANY NORA KEPT:

(From THE NEW YORK TIMES, November 14, 1923)
The ACTORS EQUITY ASSOCIATION Announces
E Q U I T Y   A N N U A L   B A L L

"MIDNIGHT JOLLIES"
Staged by Hassard Short
Greatest Midnight Show Ever Presented
The Following Stars Will Appear

FLORENZ AMES	MADGE KENNEDY &
ETHEL BARRYMORE	ALAN EDWARDS
NORA BAYES	CISSIE LOFTUS
IRENE BORDONI	FLORENCE MOORE
FANNIE BRICE	GRACE MOORE
BROX SISTERS	FLORENCE O'DENISHAWN
IRENE CASTLE &	FRANK TOURS and the
WILLIAM REARDON	Equity Orchestra
CORTEZ & PEGGY	FLORENCE REED
RAY DOOLEY	JOSEPH SANTLEY
ELSIE FERGUSON	IVY SAWYER
W.C. FIELDS	VIVIENNE SEGAL
PAUL WHITEMAN	QUEENIE SMITH &
Conducting his	JOSEPH LETORA
Band	LORA SONDERSON
IRVING FISHER	JOHN STEEL
GRANT & WING	FRED STONE &
CHESTER HALE &	DOROTHY STONE
ALBERTINA VITAK	FRANK TINNEY
MAURICE & LENORE	BUSTER WEST
HUGHES	VICTOR BARAVALL
	and Orchestra

George Le Guere, General Manager
Hotel Astor, NEXT SAT. EVE., Nov. 17th
Tickets on Sale at
The Tyson, McBride and Bascom Agencies
Hotel Astor and Hotel Flanders

There are now 24 days remaining until the Philadelphia opening.

· XVIII ·

The "record boys," as everyone seems to refer to them, came down four days ago, saw a matinee, and spent from five o'clock until well past midnight in a secret session with Hy and Fred and Art. Already there are beginning to be vital and dramatic changes in the score. One after another, the character numbers, the germane period songs, and the few comedy songs are being replaced by candidates for the Hit Parade or for Number One Single. Clay was right. I see it now. Hy and Fred are distressed, but don't show it. Larry is furious and shows it too much.

Star and Val are delighted, since their record label deal gives them great opportunities for moneymaking.

I find it hard to understand how and why the record boys should wield such power. How and why are they in a position to dictate what goes in and what comes out? At lunch at the Automat, I ask Hy to explain. He is, understandably, a changed man and has been popping pills like crazy for days. One of his pills—I have no idea which—is apparently the kind that makes one talk without stopping.

"Don't ask me goddam asinine questions like that, for Chrissake! If you don't know, you won't know even after I *tell* you. How the hell did a wet-behind-the-ears amateur know-nothing like you *get* on this show? . . . It's because this goddam production is costing twice as much as it *should* cost because we've got a knucklehead for a producer who knows from nothing, from *less* than nothing. So everybody cons him and rips him off. Holy Jesus, did Clay tell you what's going on in the prop department, for Chrissake, in the prop department *alone?* This property man'll retire to Florida when it's over. Just from *his* rip-off. And *everybody* takes our meathead boss. So the show which should have cost, say, a million, is now going to be more like a million six, or a million seven. So where does it come from? That big boring Cindy Sapiro, she's syndicated a few hundred thou, and the Shuberts are in for a piece, and Art claims some of his is in —more likely his wife's—but the main stuff, baby—the real simoleons, the long green, the shekels, the *gelt*—that comes from the record company because they stand to make more than the producers, more than the backers, if this thing comes off. A million albums at fifteen bucks an album, that's fifteen mil, no matter how you slice it. And you know what it costs them to produce the record? Bubkes. That's all. A few bubkes. They've got the orchestrations, they've got the vocal arrangements, they've got the rehearsed players, so what? They hire the studio and the musicians for scale and we go in there on the Sunday after we open in New York and we cut the whole goddam record in one day. So how much does *that* cost them? And next thing you know, they're raking in fifteen million bucks. So that's why they're interested in what they're going to have on the record, on the original-cast album, on how many singles they can get going, and how many different artists they can get to do every single. I've had numbers in shows where we cut forty-five, fifty different singles. And this is dough on *top* of the album money. That's why these guys are up here! And that's why what they say goes. What's more, they're tough. They're not artists. They don't discuss, they *tell.* They don't ask, they *order.* I'll tell you something else. There's not a songwriter in the business who's prepared to mess around with them. For Chrissake, they *make* songwriters. They make performers, too. They've got power. And they know how to use it."

"But could I ask you something?"

"If it's not stupid, yes."

"Do you think the score is getting better or getting worse, or doesn't it matter?"

"What're you looking for, cookie, a split lip? A knuckle sandwich? You want a punch in the mouth?"

"Why would I?"

"What do you mean, 'better worse or the same'? Who knows? Who can tell a thing like that? It's how it *goes.* It's what grabs them. It's what's a hit."

"I sure miss 'Lights-Out.' It wasn't only the song, it was that terrific way the Everleigh sisters used to do it."

"Wouldn't have gotten us a quarter. Didn't mean a thing. In fact, it's dollars to doughnuts even if it *was* in the show and we cut the record, we'd have left it out."

"So why not leave it in the show and off the record?" I ask.

"So why not stop bugging me and stick to your shorthand?"

"I'm trying to learn," I said.

"Well, the best way to learn is to listen and not talk so much."

He takes three more pills, one blue, one yellow, and one pink. Swallows them without water. He is such an experienced pill-popper that he simply throws them back into his throat and swallows.

"What are those?" I ask.

"Aspirin. I've got a headache."

"Colored aspirin?"

"Colored aspirin. The best kind."

"Could I ask you one more thing?"

"No," he answers.

"Just one."

"I said no."

"A half a thing?"

"No."

He stands up, abruptly, and walks out leaving me with the check. I walk home slowly and think about the bad luck of mixing money and art. Hy knows as well as I do, as well as we all do, that the score is being slowly and systematically wrecked.

At the hotel, I run into Larry. He has been spending some time with AC, trying to get him to control the record boys.

"The best I could do," says Larry, "is a 'let's-wait-and-see.' He thinks as time goes by, we'll be able to make some readjustments, and then later some re-re-readjustments, but I don't know. I think the poison has set in. Especially since we're battling not only those greedy salesmen but they've got Hy and Fred on their side, and her and Val, so the rest of us count for nothing, or at least for very little."

"Does it always happen like this?"

"Always when that kind of power gets to ride herd on a show."

"Is there anything can be done?"

"I'm thinking," says Larry. "Believe me, I'm thinking."

· XIX ·

Larry to the company:

"Play your parts, for God's sake! Or more specifically, let your parts
play you. Everybody still seems too bloody self-conscious. The dancers. All I see is technique. The singers, it's like your vocal coach is
sitting out front. The players, you're like you're at dramatic school
hoping to get a good mark. Let go, for the love of God! Forget about
scoring, forget about making a hit, forget you're on a stage. Be in
Chicago. Be in New York. Be in 1908. Don't worry so much about how
to do what you're doing, just do it! Can I say it any plainer than that?
Do it! Is there anybody here who remembers that famous little poem
from Pinafore Poems? Listen:

> 'The Centipede was happy quite,
> Until the Toad, in fun
> Said, "Pray, which leg goes after which?"
> That worked her mind to such a pitch,
> She lay distracted in a ditch,
> Considering how to run.' "

The company responds with laughter and applause.

· XX ·

A crisis of conscience.

I hope I handle it better than I did the last one. I will.

There is a plan afoot to get rid of Larry.

Is that why AC sent for his wife? For the first time? Apparently, she has some power in the situation and all important moves require her O.K.

Neysa Bayes Clune thinks that she looks like Nora. She is wrong. The only mildly successful nose job did not help.

I have the impression that if Mrs. Clune would leave herself alone, she might be a fairly attractive woman but she is her own principal preoccupation. She and tennis.

She travels with a large Vuitton trunk, which holds a dryer and beauty equipment of every sort.

A hairdresser comes in daily. Also a makeup man, or woman. Mrs. C. changes her clothes three times daily.

She spends two months a year at Maine Chance. One month a year at The Spa, and one in Montecatini. She has had two face-lifts, AC tells me, each performed by the renowned Dr. Converse in New York. She has a daily massage no matter where she is.

Her only activity is tennis, which explains why the Clunes live in Palm Springs and in Palm Beach most of the time. In either place, she has a daily lesson and is said to be comparatively expert. She loves to win, hates to lose—thus her matches are carefully arranged.

She seems manufactured, somehow. Plastic.

When AC wants to rile her, which is too often, he calls her "Gold-berg"—Nora Bayes's real name.

I was working with AC when she turned up with her maid and twenty-two pieces of luggage.

"Jesus!" he said. "I thought I told you *light*. I only got so much room around here."

"So get more," she said, and disappeared into the bedroom.

AC continued to dictate. In view of the fact that they have not seen each other since the day after opening night here—I would say that at the Clunes', the honeymoon is definitely over.

Later, he filled her in.

"The show is on," he said. "He's done the job. Now *fuck* 'im! A fresh son-of-a-bitch from the start! You know what he told me once? I mean in front of everybody? Well, not everybody—but in front of the whole creative team? He told me, 'Shut up!' I didn't make too much out of it then and there but I thought to myself: O.K., you prick, I'll fix you. Just give me time. Well, so I took my time and now *I'm* in the driver's. How about that? 'Shut up,' he tells me. I mean it would be as if Chapman said to *you*, 'Shut up.' "

"What the hell are you gassing about?" Neysa asked. "Do you know? Chapman. Chapman for Jesus' sake is my *chauffeur*. So what's that got to do with a big director? Maybe he *had* to tell you shut up. Maybe you were talking too much the way you usually do. Me, I close my ears off but everybody can't do that."

"Hey, nag. Did I invite you up here? Show me your invitation. Oh, yeah. I did. I forgot. But God Almighty, you show up and right away you're gettin' on my nerves."

"Never mind your nerves so much. All I want to see is you not screw up this show. I've got a stake in it, too, y'know. Or did you forget?"

"Fat chance I get to forget—with a nag like you around."

"So a guy says, 'Shut up.' So don't be so thin-skinned. The main thing is he's got the show on for you, didn't he? And held all these freaks together and out of each other's hair and from down one another's throats. God, the way he operates, he ought to be a Secretary of State. So now you want to fire him."

"Are you . . . What're *you*, bananas? Fire 'im? Who said anything about fire? You realize the bum's got me for three per cent of the gross and five per cent of the profits across the board which means including everything—record and stock and amateur and *movie,* for Chrissake?"

"If you don't stop yelling at me, Art—you know what I'm going to do?"

"Yeah, *what?*"

"I'm going to *stay* here," she said.

"Great! That's all I need."

"You. You don't know *what* you need."

"Yeah? Well, whatever it is *you* can't give it to me."

"You mean I *won't.*"

"Take off, willya?"

"So if not fire him so what *are* you gassin' about?"

"You know, I look at you sometimes and I can hardly believe it. The years you've been around with me—and seen me do business—and you still know from strictly nothing. Only forehand and backhand and that's it. Nothing rubbed off on you, did it?"

"Just a little shit, darling. That's all."

"The thing is, I'm gonna get this bum to quit. Not fire, *quit.*"

"And what if he won't?"

"He will."

"But what if not?" she insisted.

"So I'll have to try something else."

"Like what?"

He turned to speak to me. I could hardly have been more surprised. I would have sworn he had forgotten all about me. He tends to do that.

"Has he got it on with anybody in the company?" he asked me.

"Probably with *her,*" said Neysa, pouring herself a drink. "That'd be a switch for you, won't it?"

He pretended not to hear her.

"*Has* he?" he pursued.

"I don't know."

"Find out!" he ordered. "There's always somebody with these guys. A dancer, a singer—"

"An acrobat," said Neysa. She laughed and went into the bedroom and closed the door.

"Bitch," he said. Then to me, "Look. Find out. Please. Ask around.

One thing. There're damn few secrets around a company. Everybody thinks they're gettin' away with everything and the truth is nobody's gettin' away with nothin'."

"Why don't you ask Eddie?"

"Who?"

"Eddie Convery."

"What's *he* got to do with anything?"

"Oh," I said innocently. "I thought he was your man in there."

"Y'see that?" he shouted. "Like I said. Everybody knows everything. How do *you* know that?"

"Because I heard Buddy beefing to Jenny one night. And he said, 'What's that klutz doing in our chorus?' And Jenny said, 'Ask Mr. Clune.' So I figured. Then I've noticed how he feeds us stuff all the time. Not always accurate, by the way."

"What *is?* You think everything you read in *The New York Times* is accurate, f'Chrissake? You've got to have information in this business. Masses of information. Not just a little squirt here and there. *Masses!* And when you get enough, you sort it out and pretty soon, you *know.* . . . Get 'im up here."

"Eddie?"

"Who do y' think? Walter Kerr?"

Half an hour later, Eddie sat with us, drinking Coke from a bottle. He is small and stocky and wears a toupee that Buddy tells me cost $750. The fact is, I had no idea it *was* a toupee until Buddy told me. He is a good deal older than any of the other dancers, has been around for years, is a professional gossip and an unpleasant personality. His attempts at cosmetic improvement are not successful. He seems often to be on the verge of tears. I feel sorry for him. He is a failure, a loser, a washout. They say that in this business you cannot write anyone off—but I believe one can safely write *him* off, as an artist, that is. So he has to make his way and hang on, somehow, with supplementary activity such as this—spying for the producer.

He listens to Art digging for scuttlebutt, skillfully. Art does not come directly to the Larry question, but in his devious way, pretends he needs to know of the whole company's inner life.

"I don't give a damn what any of them do privately, you understand."

"Me neither," says Eddie.

"But in a company—it starts to affect the work, and the performances, and the whole life—you know what I mean?"

"Thirty-three shows, Mr. Clune."

"What?"

"—I've been in. The same in every one."

"I don't want any cliques in this one. I swear I'll break up every one!"

"Well," says Eddie. "It usually breaks down into the straights and the gays and then the gays break into he-he's and she-she's so that's three and there's always a fourth—the nothings or the *real* marrieds."

Art says, "Like you take a man like Larry—now he's a guy *really* keeps his nose clean. I mean to say—he plays no favorites, he's got no axes to grind, debts to pay, nothing—right?"

"Well," says Eddie carefully. "I really don't know."

I sit there wondering if either of them honestly thinks he is snowing the other. AC is so damned transparent and Eddie an accomplished intriguer. He knows what AC wants and would love to give it to him. Those tiny eyes of his reflect his inner unrest.

"What do you mean, you don't know?" asks Art.

"No favorites—*that's* probably right. But there're some he sure seems to admire more than some others."

"Like who?"

"Oh, several."

"Name me *one.*"

"Well . . . like Gloria. For instance."

"Oh?"

"Sure. Everybody's on to that."

"You think he's got something going there?"

"No, no. I didn't mean *that.*"

"But has he?"

"Oh, I doubt it. He's very good friends with her husband."

"Doesn't mean a thing," said AC. "On the road. What the hell. Who cares?"

"But I don't think so."

"Is he with *anybody?*"

"I don't know. I could check it out."

"Get back to Gloria."

"Yes?"

· 209 ·

"Like what?"

"Like he spends an awful lot of time on her scenes—a lot of people have noticed it. In fact, her Nibs did the other day."

"Go ahead. Keep going."

He points to me and pantomimes a scribble. I am to begin taking it down.

Eddie says, "She asked me to go get her a Fresca—so I did. She never came up with the quarter by the way—"

AC gets out a quarter and flips it to him. He pockets it. Can I believe my eyes?

"—so I bring her the Fresca, and She's sitting there in the wing—and he's working on the scene with Gloria, over and over—and She's drinking that Fresca, and She says to me, 'Maybe I'll ask them to let me switch parts with that chick.' I mean it was a joke, sort of, on account of Gloria's getting all that attention—but I mentioned it to Russ and *he* mentioned it to Larry. So a couple days later, I was playing backgammon with her in her dressing room and Larry comes in with some new pages for her and he says, 'Or maybe you won't need them. I hear you'd like to switch parts with Gloria.' And She plays it *so* cool and keeps playing and says, *'Anything* for a little direction, dearie. Some days out there I feel like I'm going to be picked up for *vagrancy!'* So I laughed and She laughed, but he didn't, and he said: 'Tell you what, dearie. You get rid of your coach and I'll start directing you. Otherwise, it's like trying to carry on a twin affair —no good for anybody.'

"Well, with this, She stopped playing, and She says, 'I don't even know what you're *talking* about.' And he says, 'I'm talking about Harry Silverman, that half-assed mediocrity you made us hire to play the detective—he's inept, by the way—and who coaches you every night and every morning for which like a fool you pay him—and he tells you which part of my direction to accept and which to reject—and gives you phony, idiotic readings, and ridiculous pieces of business—and you have this amateur idea that the more direction you get the better, while the fact is that you are a unique and remarkable and creative talent who just needs to be left alone as much as possible. But you won't even leave *yourself* alone, you're so goddam determined to make it if it kills you and it probably will, you poor brute.' Well. She looks at him for a long time and She says, 'I don't know *what* you're talking about or *where* you get the stupid idea that Harry Sil—' And he stops her and says, 'From *him!* That's where.' 'You're full of shit!' She yells. 'He never talks to you.' 'I never said he did,' he says. 'But he gets stoned every night at Gilhooley's and tells anybody who'll listen. A frustrated genius, in *his* opinion. All frustrated geniuses turn into lushes. So what do you say? A deal? And I'll even keep him in the show if you want me to.' I want to tell you. I've never seen her thrown before. She says to me, 'Get me Harry in here. Right away.' Larry tries to stop her. He says, 'Wait a minute.' But She's off the handle and yelling and yells, 'Don't tell *me* what to do in my own fucking dressing room!' And to me She says, 'Harry. And Val. And Art. And call Dr. Ross, I need him right away.' Well—I don't have to tell you—when Our Little Lady of the Flowers cracks the whip. . . . In about ten seconds flat—her dressing room looked like the stateroom scene in *A Night at the Opera* with The Marx Brothers." He got up and did a really remarkable imitation of Groucho—holding out his hand and saying to the imaginary manicurist— " 'You better cut 'em short, honey. It's getting pretty crowded in here!' And finally, She had poor Harry sitting in her chair and I want to tell you it was weird because her room is so full of mirrors—I mean there's no space that isn't a mirror and one on the ceiling—don't ask *me!*—and so the number of people in the room was multiplied like by about twenty and Harry sat there—he didn't know *what* the hell—and it looked like that scene from *M*—you know?—with Peter Lorre? And finally, She made everybody shut up and She said to Harry, 'Are you my coach?' And he said, 'Of course not.' And She said, 'Have you ever given me any directions or readings or advice on anything?' 'No,' he said. 'Do I pay you anything?' She asked. 'Or does anybody connected with me?' 'No,' he said. Oh God, if She'd only left it there—but no—She had to go too far. No taste. So She kept going and said, 'So what you are is just a lousy bit player. Right?' 'Right,' he said. And then She tore it. She said, 'Say it.' The poor guy turned green. 'Say what?' 'Say what you are. *Say it!!*' She was screaming now—and Harry stood up, I thought he might keel over—and Larry said, 'O.K. That's enough. Let's adjourn.' But once more from her: *'Say it!,* you little shit!' And he said, 'All right, I'll say it. I'm your *coach!*' She was so stunned She couldn't talk for once. *'Not* a lousy bit player. I'm your coach—every night and every morning. *Not* a little shit. Your *coach!* And yes, you *do* pay me. You pay me five hundred a week. And I quit and I hope you bomb out every day of your life from here on in.' As he started out, Val grabbed him by the lapels and Harry belted him right in the mouth and a kind of free-for-all started but it wasn't so much punching as it was pushing and shoving —but Harry got out and nobody's seen him since. I don't know what they're going to do about his part. I'm up for it, by the way. If you could put in a good word."

"A good word? I'll put in a knife, you jerk! When did all this happen?"

"Yesterday."

"Yesterday! And you don't tell me till now, you jerk?"

"I *called* you," said Eddie, whining righteously. "I called you *four times.* Twice yesterday and twice today. You never called me back."

"Who the fuck're you I should call you back—?"

"Then what're you *sore* for? Jesus! I tried to tell you. The way I always. I thought that's why you sent for me *now.*"

He was at the desk going through AC's phone messages. He found all four of his.

"Look! Here! The proof. *Jesus!*"

"O.K., O.K. Quiet down. . . . Anything else?"

"Not right now."

"All right, then. Blow."

Eddie starts out, tearfully. At the door, like a hammy exit, he turns and says cheerfully, "And see what you can do for me about the detective part, willya?"

He is gone. AC stands at the window, looking out over The Public Gardens as though they were the Grand Canyon. I recognize the position of deep contemplation and respect the silence. When, after an extended time, he moves back into the room, I say, "Finished with me?"

He says, "Get me Larry. And monitor."

When Larry comes on, AC does not say hello, nor does he exchange amenities of any kind, although Larry invites them with, "I wish you could have seen the new Scene Three today, Boss. You'd have kissed us all. It's got all the—"

"We've got a problem."

"We've got more than one—but which one is on your mind right now?"

"Gloria."

There follows the longest pause I have ever experienced in a telephone conversation. Finally, Larry.

"Did you say 'Gloria'?"

"You heard me."

"What about her?"

"She's out," says Art.

Another pause.

"I'll be right over," says Larry.

"No—don't do that—I won't be—"

But Larry has hung up.

"Son of a bitch!" says AC. "Let's go."

He gets his jacket.

I say, "Meet you in the lobby."

"Hurry up."

I do the best I can, but by the time I get to the lobby and the two of us get to the sidewalk, Larry is there. How he made it from the theatre in that time is a mystery as yet unsolved.

"Not here," says AC.

"Where then?"

"Come on." AC crosses the street, nearly getting hit by a taxi and ignoring the driver's obscene imprecations. Larry helps me across. We catch up with AC and the following takes place crazily as we walk around the Gardens, sit on a bench, get up, sit on another, and generally attract a good deal of attention.

"Let me begin," says Larry. "O.K.?"

"Help yourself."

"When you said 'Gloria' there a while ago, my first thought was that it was one of your wild jokes."

"No joke," says AC glumly.

"Then on the way over—I got to thinking. I mean—what in God's name could it be? The girl is—right now—the best thing in the show, and everyone around thinks it and knows it. Then it hit me, you heard about the dust-up yesterday—and this is your way of handling it."

AC stops, sits down on a bench. We join him.

"What dust-up?"

"You haven't heard? In her dressing room? The Inquisition?"

"No."

"Well, it's too long to tell—but She made a remark about switching parts with Gloria—"

"No way."

"It was a gag, Art. For God's sake. And I twitted her about it and about her coach—"

"What coach?"

"Harry Silverman—and it turned into a brouhaha. So I figured you figured Gloria was going to be the patsy. But I warn you, Art. If you let this Star Monster start to run the show—"

"Yes?" asked AC, too eagerly.

I saw the quick take on Larry's part. He glanced at me and I could only pray he read me. Probably not. He looked back at AC and said, quietly, "If you let this Star Monster start to run the show . . ."

"Yes?"

". . . She'll never stop. Hand her the power, and She'll use it. This player out, this one in. This number, that line, this scene, that effect. She's a power monkey. We've got to control her as of now."

AC gets up. We walk again.

"It's got nothing to do with *her,*" he said. "Only with Gloria. She's lousy."

Larry stopped in his tracks. I continued walking for a few steps with AC. He turned and moved back to Larry who stood there, dumbfounded.

"What's a matter?" asked AC. "Too fast for you?"

"I'm going mad, Art. Come on. Help me. This is something personal. It *has* to be. And who do you have in mind to replace her?"

"Nobody."

Walking again.

"Nobody?!"

"Chris is writing the part out."

"Impossible."

"She's too expensive for what she's doing in the show. In addition to being lousy."

"Stop saying that, Art. I mean it."

"According to Equity, if the part's eliminated in tryout—we don't have to pay her a goddamn thing. Two weeks. Then later, we put the stuff back in—slowly, in pieces—and spread it around say, two three different girls do it. So the stuff is in—but she's out—and that's the way it's going to be."

"And meanwhile, you ruin about three weeks of performances."

"There's enough show without her."

"But no story."

"Who gives a shit about the story? These yokels up here? They're still trying to figure out what Rhett did to Scarlett—because they didn't see it on the screen."

Larry sits down this time. Art and I stand.

"This is a ghastly mistake you're making, Art. Maybe a fatal one. Would you please reconsider it?"

"I've been considering and reconsidering for a week. That's long enough for that no-talent broad."

Larry stands so suddenly that he collides with AC, who trips backward, loses his balance, and falls.

From the ground he points and yells, "He slugged me! Did you see him? You're a witness. Call a doctor."

Larry moves to him.

"Get away from me!" he shouts.

"Come on, Art. Don't be silly. You tripped. I didn't touch you."

He helps Art to his feet.

Art says, "Just do what I tell you and I won't press charges. You slugged me. I've got witnesses." He looks at me. "A witness."

I cannot take any more of this farce, and say, "I think it was an accident, Mr. Clune."

"You *think?* But you're not sure, huh?"

"Stop it, Art," says Larry. "Look, it's your show, it's your dough— and you'll get what you want—but don't piss on too many innocent people on the way."

We are on our way back to the hotel now—AC ahead of us by about three steps.

"How soon?" asks AC.

"I don't know. I'll have to talk to Chris first."

"*I'll* talk to him."

We reach the hotel. AC keeps walking and without turning back goes into the lobby. Larry and I look at each other. What is there to say? I touch him and follow AC.

Larry speaks to the doorman. "Taxi, Tommy."

Back in AC's room, he says, "Chris. Right away."

I call Chris's room. No answer. I leave a message. Urgent. I have him paged. I try the theatre. He has been there. Not now. Can't be found. Message. Urgent. I try for half an hour without success. AC is in and out of the room.

"Messages all over," I say.

He looks at me with hostility. "You were great out there in the park. Loyal as a mongoose. Remind me to get rid of *you*, too."

"How about right now?" I say and get up. "I'm getting pretty nauseated on this roller coaster of yours."

"Sit down," he says. "Let's have a drink."

And we do.

Is evil contagious?

It all went wrong for him this time. He moved too swiftly, too impulsively, and failed to organize the strategy of his deception. Vartan once sent me a framed Chinese aphorism—with translation—to hang in my room at college. It read: HURRY IS A FUNDAMENTAL ERROR.

What happened was that Larry went back to the theatre, found Chris rewriting in the Men's Room, and questioned him about the changes he had just heard about from Art. Chris, of course, knew nothing of it. Larry did not divine, at this point, that it was the beginning of AC's campaign to make him quit—but he sensed something bizarre. An aberration of some sort. He alerted Gloria, told her not to be concerned, came back to see AC.

"Art," he said. "Listen. I can't do it. I can't fire an actress I admire and respect—"

"—and screw."

Larry took a breath. "Oh," he said. "If only I could. If only."

"I hear different."

"You hear wrong, ol' boy. So *you* fire her. And, by the way, Equity says it has to be in person. Writing does not count. Not anymore."

AC seemed momentarily thrown.

"All right," he said. "Let's leave it a minute. Give me a chance to study it some more. Also. I want to see the rewrites before we take the step."

Larry laughs.

"What's funny?"

"Nothing. Just the way you use the word 'rewrites.' Like most guys in your spot—more in the movies than here, but standard. 'Rewrite' means 'improve' or 'make better' or 'fix.' "

"Well, doesn't it?"

"Of course not. I'd say more stuff is *ruined* in rewriting than improved."

· 216 ·

"You're batty."

"What's that got to do with it? I'm telling you what my experience has been. See, the fact is that writing is hard. It takes a *writer* to write. But *anybody* can rewrite. You, me, Midge, the doorman. All you need to rewrite is a red pencil—or blue. For writing you need talent."

"Chris's got plenty of talent."

"You bet he has. If only we could get him to use it. So far, he just seems to do as he's told—by you, me, Hy, anybody."

"So why don't you leave him alone—all of you?"

"Why don't *you?*"

AC blew. "I've got a million-three tied up in this, you dumb bastard! How much've *you?*" His face had gone beet-red. He took a step toward Larry. I noticed that the veins on his neck had swelled. His voice was someone else's as he repeated, "How much've you?"

"Just my life," said Larry. "That's all, Art. Just my life."

I doubt that he was heard.

"One thing straight," said Art hoarsely. "This is *my* show and *you* work for me, see? *I* don't work for you. You got it straight so far? *You* for *me,* not *me* for *you.* So what *I* say goes, got that? And if you don't like it that way—you know what you can do. You can quit."

"And if *you* don't like it," said Larry, "you can fire me. *I* work for *you,* see? *You* don't work for *me.* . . . Well, I think we've got *that* straight anyway. May I go now?"

"I wish you would," said Art.

"Thank you. . . . And, by the way, I'm sorry I slugged you."

He was gone before Art could think of anything to say. Instead he turned to me.

"Make a note! The date! Four-ten p.m. He said, 'I'm sorry I slugged you.' Write it down. For the record. Got that?"

"Yes."

"What're you smiling about?"

"I don't know. It's either that or bust out crying. Fielder's choice."

"Jesus Christ," he said. "Am I surrounded by weirdos! It's a goddamn wonder *anything* ever gets done. Come to think of it, I'm putting this goddamn show on all by myself! With no help from nobody!"

SHINE ON, HARVEST MOON
Company Bulletin
Thursday, November 8

ROUTINING: On Monday we will try "Was It Wrong?"
after the "Midnight Waltz" in Act II, Scene 3. The
"One-Step" will remain as is.

HEALTH: Dr. Ross recommends *bottled* water while
the company is in Philadelphia.

COURTROOM SCENE: For the "Cantata," we plan to use
2 speakers on the proscenium for sound reinforce-
ment, plus 4 speakers for sound effects in the rear
and sides of the theatre.
  We are going to carry a tape deck for offstage
sound effects: fire bells, trolley cars, church
bells, horses and wagons, cars, street peddlers.
  There will be two speakers backstage.
  The offstage singers will be split into three
groups, with 3 mikes and 3 amplifiers.

ORCHESTRA PIT: We will hang a skirt around the pit
railing in order to contain the sound. In addition,
the floor of the pit will be covered with carpeting.

QUOTE TO REMEMBER:
      "All stage players and players of interludes
   . . . are hereby declared to be, and are, and
   shall be taken to be rogues. . . ."
                        Ordinance of Parliament,
                                     Feb. 9, 1647

THE COMPANY YOU KEEP: FRED MONROE(Lyricist)
      Couldn't help it, born in Philly.
      Most of you will think that silly.
      Went to school with all the rest,
      Never made but second-best.
      Thus it was a slow beginning,
      Then New York and started sinning.
      Rich aunt died and left some dough.
      Wow! You should have seen me go!
      Paris, London, Tel-Aviv,
      Madrid (which I found hard to leave).
      Florence, Venice, then Capri,
      Seeing what there was to see.

Hot Morocco was the best;
Moscow, Yalta, then Trieste.
Started writing stories (punk).
Tried a play (it turned out junk).
Took a chance on serious verse;
Result, I fear, was even worse.
Romance reared its lovely head,
Started writing songs instead.
Published one, a hit! Surprise!
Then none until a dozen tries.
Now Monroe Freedman changed his name
To Fred Monroe, and smelled the same.
Broadway debut—a revue—
(That was *not* the thing to do!)
Finally, a full-scale show:
Friends said, "Yes!" the critics, "No!"
Asked to write a song or two
For a Players Sunday-do.
Teamed up with Hy Balaban,
Soon became his greatest fan.
Players stuff turned out a hit,
Clear we were a perfect fit.
Since—a dozen happy shows
(Except when we are in the throes).
The worst is going, willy-nilly,
Back again to hometown Philly.
Who cares what Philadelphia thinks?
Where one says, "Great!" the other, "Stinks!"
Let's fix and change and sweat and pray,
Forget tomorrow, work *today!*
The end result can be so great,
Or else our show can simply grate.
You are, of course, a perfect Co.
A fact the whole world will soon know.
And so-from Monroe-Balaban:
We love each woman; like each man.

There are now 18 days until our Philadelphia
opening.

· XXI ·

Today's daily surprise is young Saul Clune. I had heard Art talk to him on the phone several times, and could not help but observe the dramatic change in voice, vocabulary, attitude, and personality that overcame him when he did so. Another man.

Afterward, he would wind down by talking to me about his great son. Handsome, lithe, brilliant beyond words, charming of course. Art would become a prototype of the proud middle-class American Rotarian father.

"That Saul of mine? Knows everything, can do anything, on his way to great things—in science. Why do you think I been workin' my ass off for twenty-five years? For him. Because he deserves it."

He goes on and on, usually for twenty to thirty minutes, making that nutty, arrogant assumption that because he is talking, whoever is listening is automatically interested. In my case, he is dead wrong.

There is a photograph of Saul in every room of the suite, including the bathroom.

Today, Saul arrived, turned up again. Everything Art has ever said about him is true—only more so.

Art was downstairs, at a meeting.

"Is he here?" Saul asked.

"Not at the moment. Conference. Downstairs with the record boys."

"Oh, dear!" he said.

"Why?"

"He hates that. He doesn't comprehend their aims or aspirations or motives. It's an esoteric world, isn't it?"

"So they say."

"Will I be in your way if I wait?" he asked.

"Certainly not. Can I get you anything?"

"Such as?"

"The kitchen's insanely stocked," I said. "Almost anything."

"I'll get it."

He went out and returned a few minutes later with a glass of apple juice and a raw carrot. I laughed. He regarded me quizzically.

"Nothing," I explained. "It just struck me how well you'd team up with our Star."

"That so?"

"She's a food nut, too."

"Am *I*?"

"Aren't you?"

He looked at the glass in his hand and the carrot. That smile again.

"I see what you mean."

"She has goat's milk flown down here from New Hampshire twice a week."

"Not me," he said. "I carry my own goat!"

He sat down and nibbled his carrot, looking around the room.

"How's everything going?" he asked.

"Well, now, that's a tough question."

"Why?"

"Depends who you are. Some people think it's all going great and others are in despair."

"Which are you?"

"Patient," I said. "I think it's *going* to be absolutely marvelous."

"If?"

"If what?"

"If what happens?" he asked.

"Control."

"Yes," he said, "I knew you were going to say that."

"You did? How?"

"Obvious. Also, I talk to my Dad every day, almost. Almost every day."

"Either way," I said.

"How's he?"

"Overworked," I said. "But don't tell him I said so."

"I tried desperately to convince him not to do the film simultaneously—but my influence is limited. He only accepts my more outré ideas. You understand, I'm completely out of my depth in this area —but I *could* bring a refreshing note of common sense to the proceedings, if he'd let me. Are you as wild about common sense as I am?"

"I hardly ever run across it," I said.

"Yes, I know. Take me. I'm brilliant—in my own field, I mean— but I have very little common sense. I work nights, don't eat, don't exercise, except on weekends when I *over*exercise. Then I come down here, another world, and I know less than nothing about it— I'm a dolt—but my common sense is in perfect working order."

"Keep going," I said.

"I told Dad when he started that I thought it was terrific—dynamite. I'd read that book by Gene Bowman—a family *scandale,* but enthralling to me. So—the common-sense question is: Why aren't they following the book?"

"Don't look at *me,*" I said.

"Every single element that's come into the show has added something or subtracted something or made changes. Next thing you know—"

Art came in, looking harried. He saw Saul and was instantly transformed.

"Hey, Goofy!" he shouted, as he went to embrace his son.

"Dad."

"How *about* this guy?" Art asked me.

"Yes," I said.

"Yes," he repeated. To Saul: "You see the kind of brains I have to work with?"

"Looks good to me," said Saul.

"Beat it, Midge. Can't you see I've got company?"

I got my things together.

"Tell *him,*" I said to Saul.

"Tell him what?" asked Art.

"He'll tell you," I said.

"Or maybe not," said Saul, enjoying the game.

"Tell me *what,* God damn it?" I heard Art yell as I closed the door.

· XXII ·

Staff meeting. Everyone shows up except Jenny. She sends Buddy. Art is sore as hell and tells Buddy to go get her and don't come back without her.

Larry opens and says he thinks now that Jenny is a definite liability. He admires her and respects her talent, but she has not functioned on this show and what's to be done?

Hy piles in. "I've done more shows than anybody in this room. Twenty-two. Broadway musicals of which nineteen came in and most were hits and I know trouble when I see it and I see it. Right here and right now. This has *got* to be *cruel*-time, Art. We're all sorry for the woman but she's standing still. You wanted an extension of 'Waltz'? I wrote it. I wrote it great and Ralph did an orchestration, for Chrissake—*Ravel* couldn't have done it. Now ten days we're sitting on it and she's just futzing around and won't move."

Russ speaks up. "Why don't you let Buddy take over? Suppose she got sick? Isn't that what you'd do?"

"She *is* sick," says Hy.

"Well, so there you are!"

I look at this little weasel and have to admire his gall. *Three* birds with a single stone. Maybe *four.* He scores with AC by solving the problem easily and cheaply. He gets his boyfriend the Big Break. He lays the groundwork for his own advancement should anything go wrong with Larry. He builds character with Hy, who is Jenny's principal enemy.

· XXIII ·

The trouble with Jenny is coming to a head. According to the record sheet, she has missed four rehearsals completely. Buddy took them, but that was not the point. She has been late for nine of her own calls. Again, Buddy had to stand in for her. The excuse given is that she is "unwell"—said with an inflection that suggests trouble in the lady-works. But no one is fooled. We all know that poor Jenny is a lush.

The night we arrived in Boston, Jenny and Buddy, Clay and I, and Hy and his wife, Rachel, went to Chinatown for dinner. (A word about Rachel Balaban. It isn't just that she is rich—she looks rich, talks rich, acts rich, eats rich, dresses rich. She is a tiny woman and her jewels weigh more than she does. She is surprisingly attractive in a casual, effortless way. Hair dyed an original reddish hue; light-brown, enormous eyes; discreet makeup. Says little. Smiles a lot. Why not? She's got it *taped!*) Buddy is the Chinese food expert and knew exactly where to go. Apparently there is a constant turnover of chefs, and the game is to find out exactly where the top ones are working at any given time. Buddy found out, all right. The place looked like nothing, but the food was superb, nothing like the ordinary Chinese cuisine usually offered in Chinese-American restaurants.

The bar, however, was limited. Jenny, having suspected that it might be, had brought along three bottles of Wild Turkey, and by the time the fortune cookies were being cracked open, had turned into something of a wild turkey herself.

She leaned over to Rachel, apparently admiring her fabulous jewelry, and asked, "Is any of it real, sugar?"

We all laughed, with the exception of Rachel, who shot a look at Hy that shut off *his* laugh as though it had a switch on it. Then she said, "Of course not. *Upstairs* doesn't wear the *real* stuff to dinner with *Downstairs.*" She got up. "Thank you, whoever's paying. It was delicious." She started out. Hy was after her at once, and such was his abashment that he forgot he was carrying a teacup. I assumed that he, or both of them, would be back. I was wrong.

"Cunt," said Jenny. "Good fucking riddance."

"Mistake, ol' girl," said Clay, quietly.

"*You're* a cunt, too," said Jenny. "Where does she come off with that 'Upstairs-Downstairs' shit?"

"She hadn't opened her mouth even *once* till you provoked her," said Clay.

"That was it!" Jenny shouted. "That was just *fucking* IT! Sitting there with that matzo-puss, looking rich. I'd be rich, too, if my old man was a Booze Tycoon. But what the fuck has *she* ever done, except get married four times? . . . My old man was in booze, too. Only he didn't sell it. He *bought* it!" She laughed too hard. "And put it away, too. All-time Pulitzer prize-winning pisshead! And I loved him, the little muzzler." She began to cry, and quenched her tears with a straight slug out of the bottle. She looked around the table blearily, and said, "By the way, who *is* paying?"

"I'll take it," said Clay.

"No, no," said Jenny. "I won't hear of it." She looked at me. "Let's give it to the Rumanian or Bulgarian, or whatever the fuck you are, and have her charge it to the production. He'll never know, the asshole. And doesn't he *owe* us a meal? At least?"

Clay had picked up the check. Jenny tore it out of his hand. She gave it to Buddy, opened her bag, and found a fistful of bills. She gave these, one by one, to Buddy, and said in a choreographer's count, "Four, three, two, *one!*"

Buddy went off to pay the check. We got ready to leave. I was feeling the Wild Turkey myself, and do not now recall how we got to the topless-bottomless bar. It was somewhere in the depths of the celebrated Combat Zone. The minute we walked in, I felt like walking out. The pungent redolence, the acid-sweet fragrance of pot filled the air (if it could be called air). A few kids from the company joined us. I felt like leaving because I was sure I was going to wind up with a contact high. Two things stopped me. One, I was unsteady; two, I was terrified of going out into that hazardous neighborhood. So I stayed and stuck to soda water, with everyone jeering at me. The flesh was in action, mirrored, and revolting. Pot was being peddled as openly as popcorn. ("Loose joint? Loose joint!") I was sitting between Clay and Jenny. She was pretty far gone, and yet deep feelings and thoughts came out. How curious that in this surrealistic atmosphere, reminiscent of Hieronymus Bosch or Gustave Doré, filled with booze and grass and tits and ass and worse, Great Truths were revealed once and for all. That ol' *vino veritas* did its work. Jenny talked to Clay, across me.

"You're a man, Clay. You're a fine man. You're a faggot, but you're a *man.* Damn few around, my boy. *None* in this outfit, if you ask me. Go ahead, ask me. No? O.K. The so-called producer, a ridiculous little Bugs Bunny, who doesn't know his tool from a hot rock. Larry? He *could* be good, but he's yellow. Worried about the job. Needs a hit —or at least, *wants* a hit so bad he can taste it. He'll do anything for a hit. And that's a sure way to have a flop. When you don't give a shit, that's when you get a hit. Hey! Song title!" She burst into song, adroitly fitting the words to the tune of "Big Town":

> " 'When you don't give a shit
> That's when you have a hit!'

"Larry. *He* wants to be *popular,* for God's sake. He worries about if actors *like* him, for God's sake. So at the helm, what've we got? A scared shitless washout. Ivan and Alicia. Christ, what a team! He'd like to redo her stuff, she knows *she* could fix *his.* They'll ruin each other. Which brings us to that poor benighted Chris. Strictly Hasty Pudding. How'd *he* get this job? Who's he screwing?" She turned to me. "If you find out, let me know. Jesus, when I first read the book —I mean the real book, the Bowman book—I damn near pissed myself. I laughed and I cried and I was uplifted, and then I laughed and cried at the same time. And for a couple of days—I guess I went bananas—I thought, Holy shit, here it is! Here's my *comeback!* I *am* Nora Bayes. I can do it—I'll work on the singing with Keith Davis. I can dance it and act it. Can I buy it? Should I call Hal Prince? And

I *did* try—but ICM told me not available, so I figured all right, so what? So it's just one more kick in the twat. I can take it. My twat can take it. Goodbye. See you later. So you can imagine, a year goes by—more—and I get this call from this guy; I swear, I didn't know him, never *heard* of him, even. But when he lays the title on me, I go all gooseflesh. And I say yes. Damn right, yes. Time. I hear the score. All right. It'll work, maybe. It's no *Kiss Me Kate*—but it's a show. Then I get a load of this book, this so-called book, and I damn near passed out. Where are we? What doing? So I told him—I didn't bullshit him. I told him. He says, 'It's in rewrite,' and that's where it's been ever since. I get nothing to take off on—so I'm faking half the time. But the big thing, the main thing, the killing thing, is—SHE is *nothing.* She is a hit record. She is an album. She is a Star. But if She's Nora Bayes—or even a half-assed, cockamamie, reasonable, or even *un*reasonable facsimile—I'll go down on her in Macy's window. In every branch in the country. Got it? So now you see why I'm on the ol' Heimerdeimer morning, noon, and who *cares?* It should be *me,* not She. And me? I'm counting out steps and combinations for a bunch of goddamn gypsies who couldn't care less. Say, listen, Clay. Would you please get me home before I throw up all over these bare asses?"

She was gone, as was Clay. I was with the kids. McDonald's. Hamburgers. A taxi. A hand up my skirt and down my bra. Whose? I am crying. Thank God for The Ritz-Carlton. My own bathroom, my own shower, my *own* nakedness, instead of those strangers'. My own bed. My own sleep and dreams—and my God, *what* dreams! . . . *I* am playing Nora, and doing great, but every time I look into the wings, there is Jenny, wearing the same costume I am wearing, or She, or Debbie Reynolds, or Barbra Streisand, or Shirley Mac-Laine, ready to go on—but I am the one out there, in the spotlight, and doing great, except that I don't know the words, and I hope no one notices. . . .

I am certainly paying for it this morning. I have done it all—everything I know to do: yogurt, fructose, tomato juice with raw egg and Worcestershire sauce, three Theragrans, one Ritalin, and gallons of fruit juice. I'm a fine one to talk about Jenny. I seem to be turning into quite a lush myself—but then, I haven't undertaken a position of importance and responsibility. I could be replaced in five minutes.

One call to The Brook Street Bureau. But Jenny is something else again. She is brilliant and original and wildly inventive. She can dance better than any member of her own company—and they know it and respect her and admire her for it. In spite of all this, it is easy to feel the resentment against her building up. I wish I knew her well enough to tell her, to warn her, to beg her to watch out. But I don't. Does anyone? I doubt it. She is a loner, like most alcoholics. They use the bottle as a friend, company, a confidant. What a sad, sad girl. The hell with it. I am going to tell her.

· XXIV ·

I should have known better. Will I ever learn? Me, with all my advantages and training, to blunder so badly. Anyway.

During the intermission, I asked Jenny if she would like to have a bite with me after the show.

"A bite with you?" she asked. "Or of you?"

"Never mind," I said, and started to walk away. She grabbed my arm.

"Sorry, hon," she said. "But around here, you've got to check everybody out. Me, I'm straight. Was bi for a while, but it got confusing. You know what I mean? Always comparing. Which is the world's greatest drag. So now I'm all the way hetero—which reminds me. I have *got* to get my ashes hauled tonight, whatever else I do or don't do. So thanks for the invite, but maybe some other time."

Afterward, she sought me out backstage.

"Hey! Nothing but strikeouts so far, so if you still want to do that bite thing, let's go. You can bite on whatever you want, and I'll bite on a couple of scotches."

She chose The Playboy Club, of all places.

"I've made a couple of scores in here in my time," she said.

The food was surprisingly good. I had chicken curry and tea. She ate nothing. She drank, but ever so slowly. A small sip, a long pause.

We talked about the show, but her eyes were seldom on me. They swept the room in an unhurried, deliberate way—like a sailor at sea, looking for landfall. From the bar, an overweight young man, drink in hand, dressed so flashily that he looked gift-wrapped, came over to our table.

"How y'doin', ladies?"

"Fine, up to now," said Jenny.

I was looking him over to see if I could tell what it was that made him so instantly unlikable. His untidiness, perhaps. Cigarette ash on his lapel and tie. And he had obviously spilled some of his drink into his lap at the bar.

"You mean you don't want me to join you?" he asked, and burped.

"I don't even want to *know* you," said Jenny.

"I'd like to know *you,*" he said, leaning over us. He winked, badly, and added, "in the Biblical sense."

"Take off," said Jenny, "I don't want to know you in *any* sense."

He straightened up, and looked insulted.

"Why not, may I ask?" he asked with great dignity.

"Because," said Jenny, "you've *pissed* yourself!"

I shouldn't have laughed, but I did. The poor guy looked down, and in a welter of embarrassment, began to splutter.

"No, no—that's—I spilled a little of my— Jesus!—that's a terrible thing to say to—I beg your pardon, I'm sure."

And he was gone.

"I tell you," said Jenny. "This is definitely *not* my night."

We walked back to The Ritz. As we approached it, she said, "One more? In the bar. What a nice bar!"

But the bar was on the verge of closing. I tried to charm the bartender into serving us a single drink, but failed.

"Shall we go back to the Playboy?" asked Jenny, laughing.

"There must be *some* place."

"We could go up to my room—but not only is there no one there, but there is not a drop of nothing up there. I make it a point. My one concession to sense. Drunks are supposed to keep it around, I know. The psychological effect of knowing it's there. Not me. That proves I'm not a real drunk, doesn't it? Say! What about *your* digs— Surely you've got *something*—a bit of perfume, maybe? You *must* have. I can smell it. But of course, I drink only Chanel Number Five."

"Art gave me a bottle of Glenlivet opening night," I said. "I've never opened it. Will *that* do?"

"Will that *do,* my dear! Why, bless your sweet unblended little soul

—that will do until the *cows* come home! So shall we ascend and go from sip to nip?"

"Wait," I said.

"For what?"

I went to the bar and somehow talked the bartender into giving me six splits of Perrier and a bowl of ice. He threw in a box of potato chips. I think I may have promised him a date, I'm not sure.

Jenny swiped a dish of peanuts, and we were off.

In my room, she opened the Glenlivet expertly, something of a bartender herself.

I produced my own glasses, which surprised her.

"What this? These?"

"I always like a few things of my own around," I explained. "Then I don't feel so removed from home."

"You're *something,*" she said. "And how come trading your lily-white body for a few Perrier splits?"

"Well, Glenlivet is scotch, and that means soda, Vartan says. Just as with bourbon, it should be plain water. Branch or bottled."

"Hold it. Who's—Vartan, did you say?"

"Yes. My brother."

"What's *he* doing later?"

"No idea. He's in San Francisco."

"As I said. Not my night."

"You'd like Vartan."

"Baby, tonight I'd like a bull mastiff if he could get it up."

She prepared two drinks, making a lovely ritual of it. We raised our glasses, toasting.

"To whatever happens," she said, cryptically. "What the hell."

We sat down and drank and did not speak until we had finished our drinks.

I spent the time trying to figure out what I believed vital.

I sensed that she, too, was working out some problem in her mind.

She got up, came to me, took my empty glass, returned to the bureau, and repeated the drink-fixing ritual.

We sat again, with our drinks.

"What do you make of it all, my friend?" she asked, suddenly and miraculously sober.

"Of the show, you mean?"

"Of what goes on. Of the scheming and wasting talent and jockeying for position and struggling for power. And the cliques and claques and jealousies and selfishness and unselfishness and sweat and what for? This is your first show, no?"

"Yes."

"It must seem to you like you're Alice in Wonderland now and then, doesn't it?"

"Not quite. I keep doubting if this is the way it *has* to be."

"It always has been."

"But does it *have* to be?"

"Yes. . . . Yes."

"Why?"

"Because it's conception and gestation and birth. It's giving birth, collectively. Listen. It's hard enough to do it *alone!* But in collaboration! So it's full of screwing and morning sickness and worry about what's going to come out eventually—a doll or a cretin. And the pains —worse as it gets closer, and then the agony. And then it's there— whatever it is."

"Jenny," I said suddenly. "I think you're immense. An awesome talent."

"Thank you," she whispered. "But I'm in trouble."

"Yes. You are. That's the point of this whole evening."

"What is?"

"Why I wanted to talk to you. To tell you."

She stood up.

"Tell me what?"

"There's a lot of disaffection around," I said boldly. "Not so much about your work, but about you. About you personally."

"I'm not the only one around here takes a drink once in a while. What the hell is all this? What's behind it? Who?"

"It's the missed rehearsals, Jenny. And the late show-ups. And the pace of the work. Everyone's getting worried."

"And how did *you* get to be the carrier pigeon with the bad news?"

"I didn't. This is on my own."

"You expect me to believe that?"

"Yes," I said.

She stared at me for too long a time before she said, "I believe you. . . . Why?"

"Because you're good. And I'm on your side. And it's not too late to reverse it."

"How?"

"Just do your stuff, Jenny. Go on the wagon for a few days—or until we open. Isn't it worth it? And stop fighting with everyone. Make friends."

"They all hate me."

"No."

"You said so," she said.

"They're disappointed in you."

"All *right!* I'm disappointed in *myself.* And in *them.*"

"That's not the point. You can only be responsible for you."

"Look, Shorthand. Don't Pollyanna me. Don't give me those bromides. I've been around the block."

She looked at the drink in her hand, studying it.

"O.K.," I said. "I've said enough."

"You sure have," she said. "Too much. Everybody wants to get in on the act. On the kill." She moved her glass to her mouth, but stopped halfway. "You've got a hell of a nerve, Missy, Billy Grahaming me. Who the fuck are *you?* You're a goddamn secretary, for Christ sake. What the hell do *you* know about it? About a show?"

"Nothing."

"Nothing is right. So kiss my water closet and get off my back. I'm surprised you found room. Shit!"

Her face was flushed and she was trembling. She turned and walked into the bathroom, leaving the door open. I supposed she was going to be sick. At The Playboy Club, I had counted five drinks—plus two here, well, one and a half. And the emotional charge-up. Should I go in and see if I could help? No. I waited.

"Midge!"

"Yes?"

"Come in here."

I went into the bathroom. She was standing, transfixed, over the toilet bowl. She looked up at me. Her face, red a few minutes ago, was now white.

"Watch this," she said. Slowly and with great ceremony, she spilled the contents of her glass into the toilet bowl. She handed me the empty glass and released the flush.

"Thank you," I said.

"Well, that's that."

We returned to the bedroom. She fixed herself a glass of Perrier on ice, using the same ritual movements as before.

"And now," she said, "let us pray." She laughed. "Hey. Wouldn't it be a gas if it turned out I was just as big a fuck-up dry as wet?"

"Jenny . . ." I began, but could not go on.

She picked up the phone, and a moment later said, "Would you get me the Statler-Hilton, please?" Then to me, "May I?"

"Of course."

Into the phone: "Eddie Convery, please. Three forty-one."

(Eddie! It was all I could do to keep from shouting "Don't!")

"Eddie? . . . Guess who this is? . . . Wrong. It's Jerry Robbins. . . . Yes. I want you for the lead in my new show. . . . Oh, you are? . . . I'm sorry. Well, maybe next time. Hey. What're you doing, klutzie? . . . Uh-huh. So lemme ask you. Would you be interested in a nice piece of ass? . . . What do you mean 'whose'? Mine, of course. You've met it before. . . . Here. Come on over here. . . . Why not? . . . O.K. I'll come there—ha!—pretty good, huh? 'I'll come there'? . . . Now. Right now. I'll drive over in my new wagon I just jumped on. . . . What? . . . Never mind. Nothing. I'll tell you when I get there. Three forty-one, right? . . . Fine. See y'."

She hung up, looked at me and shrugged.

"What the hell?" she said. "Who am *I*?" She started out and added, "Thanks for everything"—but did not look back.

SHINE ON, HARVEST MOON
Company Bulletin
Tuesday, November 13

TRUNKS: All trunks for Philadelphia are being picked up at 9:00 A.M., Thursday morning, November 15. Please have them in the lobby, ready to go.

FOR WEDNESDAY-MATINEE PERFORMANCE: We are going to look at the show without the song part of "Midnight Waltz" and the song part of "Big Town." We are not eliminating the scenes—only the songs, and this will not be a permanent cut.

REHEARSALS: Please check the Call Board Saturday night before leaving. Your rehearsal calls in Philadelphia and the final hotel list will be posted.

THE COMPANY YOU KEEP: ALICIA MARBLE (Costumes)
   I was born on Hampstead Heath, a suburb of London. Besotted by the theatre from my first panto—PUSS IN BOOTS. My father was an editorial writer for *The* (London) *Times,* and a Gilbert and Sullivan buff par excellence. So I was brought up on the very best. My mother was, alas, a frump and my teenage attempts to improve her presentation of herself led me into designing. I owe debts of gratitude to Binkie Beaumont and Tony Guthrie and Larry Olivier and Lew Grade and John Gielgud and Roger Furse and many others.
   I studied at The Slade School, and in Paris at the Conservatoire.
   I believe clothes to be an important integral part of any theatrical production.
   I am happily, no—ecstatically married to John Marble, who is a smasher despite the fact that he is a stockbroker. (Smith, Barney and Company.)
   I garden; also sing Gilbert and Sullivan at parties when sufficiently inebriated.
   I have not enjoyed writing this thumbnail (or is it *toe*nail?) sketch.

QUOTE TO REMEMBER:
      " 'Exactly what is the Abbott touch?' an interviewer asked me the other day. 'I make them

say their final syllables,' I answered. A joke, but with much sense to it. One of the major faults of too many productions is that the actors have sloppy diction. It requires great persistence to get a play clearly spoken, and the actor who swallows his words is cheating. Generally, he doesn't know he is not distinct; he is striving for a certain quality and since he knows his words, he presumes you do. The method actor is a frequent culprit—he has worked so hard for inner feeling that he forgets to bring it out into the light where we can get a look at it. He has struggled successfully at such difficult tasks as pretending that he is a tree in full bloom, but he has never learned to say a final *t*. When actresses come into an audition and take off their shoes before beginning to read, or go to one side to commune with their inner selves while we all wait, I suspect them of being phonies; I fear that they will be fakers who have thought a lot about feeling and little about technique."

from MR. ABBOTT.

Today's color is Blue.

There are now 8 days remaining until our first preview in Philadelphia.
There are now 38 days remaining until our New York opening.

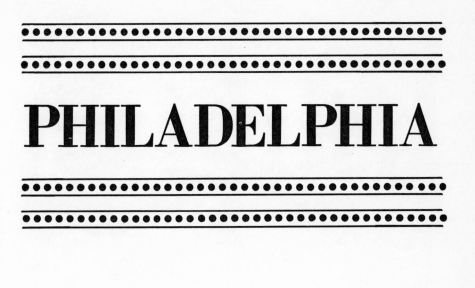

PHILADELPHIA

· XXV ·

Philadelphia.

Relief on the question of the damaged, record-oriented score comes from the most astonishing place—from Cindy Sapiro. She came down the other night, saw what was happening, and raised Holy Hell with everyone. She then went back to New York, dug up some more money, has secretly bought up several blocks of points, so that she and her syndicate are now in control and as she put it, with an angelic smile on her face, "So now those record creeps can go and take a flying fuck at a jukebox!"

Someday I would like to discover the source of Cindy Sapiro's power. She is squat and fat and wears no makeup. Her thick glasses make her eyes look like a pair of mirrors. She never, repeat *never,* stops smoking—which is why she has never seen the show from a proper seat, always from the back of the house, where she puffs and watches, leaning forward, until she is told to stop. Then she says, "Sorry," puts out her cigarette, lights another and puffs until she is told again to stop. But her energy is formidable, and her effectiveness as a fund-raiser immense. Her voice is the most grating, irritating I have ever known. It is dry chalk on a blackboard; a dishpan in a sandy sink; a screeching brake. "In the night," said Larry one day, "I figured out the secret of Cindy's success. . . . She makes her pitch and they say yes right away to stop her from talking any more."

Gene Bowman arrived today and all hell broke loose.

He is a columnist on the Chicago *Sun-Times,* and the author of the book—*Nightingale for Sale*—on which our show is based. He wrote it on commission from the Bayes family, which includes Neysa Bayes Clune (a grandniece), but he (according to them) betrayed their confidence and the mass of material they had put at his disposal. They sued, trying to block publication of the book, and lost. When it was published—not successfully—they quietly bought up most of the copies and destroyed them. There was no second printing, so copies of the book are exceedingly rare.

Until about a week ago, I had a low opinion of this Bowman person, although I had never seen him and had looked at his column only rarely. I don't know why. I usually enjoyed reading him when I did, but the subjects he covered were not often of interest to me.

Around the company his name was Gene Mud. Art saw to that. He lost no chance to throw in a zinger whenever he could. Gene Bowman was synonymous with liar, crook, cheat, deadbeat, incompetent, operator, dangerous.

Last night, talking to Larry, the subject of Bowman came up somehow. I forget what it was—no—now I remember. It was during a meeting with Chris and Larry.

Larry asked, "Did you ever consider, Chris, opening and closing with the funeral, the way the book does? I mean—it would seem to lend itself so cunningly to the stage. For one thing—the shock of it. As an innovation. We come in to see a Broadway musical show and ZOWIE—we're at a *funeral!* But *what* a funeral! Beautiful and glamorous and musical. And from the eulogy—fade into The Everleigh Club and we're off. Then finish the same—from the triumphant finale to the end of the funeral. I mean, I don't know how far I'd dare go—who knows?—maybe the casket carried up the center aisle, even, for a shock finish. Man! Would that be something? And maybe no curtain calls. I don't know. It's something. Of course, in the book, Bowman goes further than we could dare in the theatre—he goes back to the funeral and to the various eulogies a number of times, five, I believe—so that's his whole tent pole, his clothesline, the spine. For the stage, I'm afraid that might get monotonous—but opening and closing. My God! What a frame. Did you ever consider it?"

Chris looked bereft.

"I've never read the book," he said.

Larry stared at him.

"You never? . . . What the hell are you talking about? Your script is adapted from it."

"No," said Chris. "It's the same material as his book, but I never read it because I wasn't allowed to. It was a condition of my deal. I had to promise I wouldn't look at *Nightingale for Sale.*"

"Why? Why not?"

"Because at that time, Art was sure he could freeze Bowman out. And he wanted to be able to say that I had written the libretto for the show independently of Bowman's book. I mean he wanted me to be able to swear to it in court if it came to that. Of course, it never did."

"Then how is it that Gene Bowman's name is on the program, house boards, ads—everything?"

"Because," Chris explained patiently, "Art lost the arbitration. He couldn't beat the one clause in his deal with Bowman that tied Bowman in to any and all subsidiary rights. Art took the position it meant publishing only—not stage or screen or television. But he lost. The arbitrators interpreted it differently."

"But wait, if Bowman *is* in now—and *is* getting his cut—can't we use what we want out of his book?"

"I don't know. I imagine so."

"Well, Christ, if nothing else—we ought to use the funeral frame. Read it. I'll lend you my copy."

"I'll have to ask Art."

"Never mind. *I'll* ask him."

When the meeting was over, I asked Larry if *I* could read the book.

"Of course," he said.

It kept me up all night—first time that's happened since *The Book of Daniel* by E. L. Doctorow. What a writer, this Bowman man. Does it matter that he is—as they say—a reprehensible rat? *Who* says? Art and Neysa and the Bayes bunch. I wonder. I begin to wonder. There is such a vast difference between the Nora Bayes he re-creates and the one we have in the show. What is the main difference? The one in the book is believable. The one in the show is a stage figure. In the book, human. In the show, cardboard. Book: moving and lovable. Show: sentimental and cloying.

I thought our script was all right, but compared to the book, it is pale and dumb.

And Larry is so right about opening and closing with the Bayes funeral.

Further, I now see how whitewashing her, or trying to, has removed power from the show to a distressing degree.

In the book, Nora is one of the Everleigh girls. A prostitute. What's more, he limns such a clear story line that you understand how she got where she did, how it was virtually inevitable. And there she is. The fact that The Everleigh Club catered to class, that John Barrymore would move in and live there during his Chicago engagements, that politicians and bigwigs were the core of the clientele—does not mitigate the fact that Nora was a whore.

Then—from this degrading beginning, she makes her way out and up—through love and talent and aspiration and work, continues up up up until she is one of the brightest stars in the Broadway sky.

But if she begins as a girl who plays the piano, for God's sake, in the club—what's *that?* It simply means that she was an entertainer playing a bum gig and that as time went by, she got better and better jobs.

The tragedy is that this basic change is not going to be made. As I see it now—no way.

Art sent for me.

"This Bowman bastard's arriving. To make trouble, no doubt. I don't want to talk to him—in person or on the phone. Nothing. And I don't want to write to him, either. But I've got to have some communication, so you're it, O.K.? Find out where he's staying. Maybe here, but I hope not. Tell him you're my assistant and—"

"Production Secretary."

"No, no. Don't use the word secretary with this bum. He won't even *talk* to you. A snob on top of everything else. No—my assistant. And tell him we've complied with all contractual obligations, including even a program bio—and if there's anything else contractual he wants to tell me, to tell you. And of course he's welcome to see the show—arrange seats for him, charge to me, but—now here's the but and it's a big one. I would appreciate if he did not, repeat *not*, come to rehearsals at the theatre and not, repeat *not*, talk to Chris or Larry or anybody. Tell him any comments he can put into writing and send to you and you'll take them up with me. In view of our past troubles, he'll understand."

It didn't take me long to find Gene Bowman. He was at The Barclay —on the twenty-first floor! With us.

I called him, told him who I was, said I had a few messages from Mr. Clune, and asked if I could see him.

"By all means," he said. "Anytime."

"This evening?"

"Well, this evening I'm going to the theatre. There's this show in town."

"Yes, I know," I said. "I'm to arrange tickets for you."

"Oh?"

"Yes."

"Surprise number one," he said. "I hope there aren't going to be too many. I'm a man of a certain age. But make that *ticket* not *tickets*. I'm alone."

"Very well. Could we meet before, perhaps? Or afterward?"

"How about dinner? Are you free?"

"Yes, of course."

"Why 'of course'?" he asked.

"Oh. I meant on this job I never have dinner dates. I'm, you might say, on call."

"All right, then. I'm in luck. Where and when?"

"Curtain's at eight—how about six-thirty?"

"Suits me," he said. "And where?"

"Here?"

"Can we do better?"

"Yes. There's a really first-class French place—Le Champignon— but it would mean leaving here at six-fifteen."

"I'm game."

"Lobby, then, six-fifteen."

"Right. I'll be humming a tune and tapping my toe."

At six-fifteen, I went down. There he was—humming a tune and tapping his toe.

He took off his hat and we shook hands. Those perfect teeth. Real? Gray hair, pink face. Rugged. Scar on chin. Tall. Stolid. Athletic. Male as hell. Was he a young-old man or an old-young man? I couldn't tell. I still don't know. My first impression was that here was a man who not only loved life but enjoyed it. In the hours ahead, I was to find that my first impression had been—as it rarely is—perfectly correct.

We stepped out, and I asked the doorman to get us a taxi.

"I have a car," said Gene Bowman.

"Of course," from the doorman.

"Are you rich?" I asked as the limo pulled up.

"Hell, no," he replied. "But I'm going to be."

We got into the car, I gave the driver the address, and we started off.

Gene Bowman was regarding me in the manner of a trained journalist.

"Why didn't you tell me you were a dish? I'd have worn my good necktie."

"Would you like to go back and get it?" I asked.

"Yes, I would," he answered, and rapped on the separating glass. The driver opened it. "We have to go back," he said. "I forgot something."

The driver zigzagged his way through the tortuous Philadelphia one-way–street system until we pulled up in front of The Barclay.

"Won't be a minute," he said, getting out. "Play the radio. News or something."

He did not return for about ten minutes. When he did, I saw that he had changed his clothes completely. Not only necktie—but suit, shirt, and for all I know, shoes and socks.

"There," he said. "One minute flat. And I feel *much* better, don't you?"

"Why?"

"Out with a less disreputable-looking type?"

Routine small talk on the way. After a few "Mr. Bowmans," he said "Gene" would do. And would I mind "Midge"? How was his trip? Uneventful. Had he come from Chicago? Oh, yes. I used to work for Doubleday and we often had meetings in Chicago. Doubleday to *this?* How the come-down? I don't consider it so. I find it fascinating. This assignment, for instance. I explain my mission. He laughs.

"So you're the go-between."

"I suppose you could call it that."

"Remember that beautiful L. P. Hartley book. *The Go-Between?*"

"I saw the movie. Julie Christie."

"The *book* is *my* friend. I'll never forget the opening sentence: 'The past is a foreign country, they do things differently there.' How many times that occurred to me when I was in the throes of Nora."

"They've captured it wonderfully in the show, I think. The period. The look."

"Have they?" he said. "A spy sent me a tape of the music. I thought it pleasant, but nothing to do with nineteen-eight except for two songs."

" 'The Upper Crust' and 'On the Night Boat.' "

"Exactly."

"Well, they've all been working hard."

"Yes. That's why I'm here—to see in which direction."

We said nothing more until we reached the restaurant.

We ordered. He, expertly in French. Then a long chat with the wine steward before making a decision.

"This *is* a good place," he said. "Thank you. Times have changed. Philly used to be such a dull town. When I was covering sports for the old *Sun*, I'd have to come to Philadelphia, P.A., periodically. The sports writers used to call it Philadelphia, P.U."

"Lovely city now," I said.

"Did you say Maghakian?"

"Yes."

"Armenian, then."

"My father, yes."

"I've heard that name before. Where?"

"Me, no doubt," I said. "I've sent you several letters and the schedules and press releases. I was told it was one of the contractual obligations. So you saw my signature."

"Do you know Saroyan?"

"I've met him, yes," I replied.

"We were in the Army together. Well, not together, exactly. I was a nineteen-year-old second lieutenant. He was a thirty-two-year-old private. He wouldn't have it any other way. Didn't want to be an officer—although he could have been in a minute. And got out of any and all promotions. But we were in the same unit in England, and I got to know him. An idol then and now. I'm sure it was his influence that got me through this damn job. I was going along, going along in that pegaway way one does when it's a paid assignment—uninspired —just for the money, really: facts and facts and facts. After a time, I began to get a glimmer of the truth and I got fascinated. Then, God help me, I fell in love with Nora—that kept me going. Finally, after a long time, I had what I thought was the truth—at least, my truth. Come right down to it—the truth is what you happen to believe. Isn't it? That's when the trouble with the family began. They treated my manuscript—thirty-three months of my life—as though it were a piece of cloth they were going to cut and tailor and shape into something of their liking; something to fit their taste. I didn't care, really. What troubled me was my own dissatisfaction with the work —with the vague story I'd found. Then Bill came through town— Saroyan—and we spent a riotous couple of days and nights with Studs Terkel—the three of us. Talking talking talking. And one early morning—we'd been up all night, Bill and I—sitting in an all-nighter, I told him my troubles. Bill laughed and he went into that drawl of his and said, 'I wrote a great line once, kid—explains your predicament fully —I said about this character: "He had found the truth and now he was looking for something better." ' And Bill laughed but I couldn't because it was the nearest thing to a religious conversion I have ever experienced. What they call seeing the light. All at once, I knew that the truth wasn't enough, that I had to go beyond it and not stop and not give up and I put my arms around Bill and he was mortified and the next day he went back to Paris and I went back to work. Another seven months. I pulled out of the deal with them, returned the advance, and went ahead and published. The book bombed. But no matter—I'd written what I wanted to write. Now this. Because of the book, I seem to have an official stake in this show. It was only when they tried to freeze me out and rip me off that I served notice on them. Hence the billing and the money and the situation. What's the message?"

"He says you're welcome to come to the theatre and—"

"Now, *really!* He didn't actually say *that*, did he?"

"Yes."

"Welcome to—Who *isn't*, for heaven's sake? One buys a ticket and goes in. Can he stop me? Ban me? On what grounds?"

"I suppose he means as his guest," I continued, weakly.

"Go on."

"He says he's complied with all the contractual obligations—even the bio in the program and if there's any omission, let him know. *Me* know."

"Yes."

"He'd appreciate it if you didn't come to rehearsals and he'd prefer it if you didn't confer with Mr. Gabel, the director, or with Chris Feller, the author of the book—you know, the libretto."

"I know."

He was no longer eating, but now was clenching his jaws. I could see the ripple on his cheeks. He was a portrait of controlled fury.

"He said that in view of the situation, you'd understand."

"Let's order dessert," he said. "Then I'll give you my answer."

"Nothing for me. Coffee."

"Come on," he urged. "Make it festive."

"Melon."

"Not me. *Mousse au chocolat,*" he said to the waiter. *"Et deux cafés."*

"Bien, m'sieu."

"When I was a kid we used to say, 'If it ain't chawklit, it ain't dessert!' "

We laughed together and I realized that in spite of all the tension, I was having a good time.

He asked me where I had been born and where raised and where school and seemed interested in the answers. He has a way of looking that draws people out. It did me, anyway.

He told me something about himself—a lot that wasn't in the *Who's Who* stuff—and about his wife's sudden death two years ago. Heart attack playing tennis. Son in the army in Germany. Daughter dropout from UCLA married at seventeen and a TV cameraperson in Los Angeles. His new life alone. The good of it and the bad.

We finished dessert, he looked at his watch and said, "Perfect." He called the waiter and without consulting me ordered a white crème-de-menthe frappé for me and a brandy for himself. The drinks arrived, he paid the check and sat back.

"I am, you might say, happily satiated, thanks to you—in more ways than one." He looked at his watch again. "I find that the service in a restaurant is often every bit as important as the food, don't you agree? Bad service can spoil the finest repast. This place is perfect."

"I'm so glad."

"Now. Are you ready for the answer?"

"Just a second." I reached into my handbag, got out my steno pad and my Blackwing pencil.

"What's this?" he asked, amused.

"I'm going to take it down," I said. "For accuracy."

"Can you?"

"I should hope so. I'm the Production Secretary."

"I thought you said—"

"I said what I was told to say. I'm the Production Secretary. What's the difference? Actually—the go-between."

"There are guys—so devious—they'd rather climb a tree and tell a lie than stay on the ground and tell the truth."

"I'm ready," I said.

"Tell him thanks for the free ticket. If I feel like coming to rehearsals, I will—although I doubt it. Rehearsals make me nervous. As to communicating with the writer and the director and so on—I'll use my judgment and not his. If I have anything to communicate to him —about the show—I'll put it in writing. What I'm really here for is to determine whether or not I want my name on it. I'll inform him in a day or two. And whether it is or not, there will be no change in the financial arrangements. Finally, remind him that we went through a long and difficult and agonizing arbitration and that he lost and I won. So he is hardly in a position to call the shots. Paragraph. The weather here is lovely, the first petunias have begun to bloom and if only we could get a little rain, the garden would flourish." I had stopped taking it down, but he went on. "Well, I guess that's all the news from here. I hope all goes well with the show. Love to all. Sincerely. Got all that?"

"All," I said.

I was thinking that I'd better not fall for this man—too complicated, too talented, which usually means too infrequently available. But I was twitching pleasantly down there between my thighs and I resolved that when he came on (why did I think he would?), I would hold back only long enough to make it look respectable. My instinct (infallible in these matters) told me that he was not one who would respond to a predatory female—which I have been on occasion, with lovely results.

We drove back to the theatre. I got him his ticket—fifth row on the center aisle—gave it to him, and started off.

"Oh, Midge!"

I came back.

"You're welcome," he said.

Damn! In the confusion, I'd forgotten to thank him for dinner.

"I'm sorry," I said. "Mixed up."

"Teasing," he said. "You're a peach."

He went into the theatre. I went backstage to look for Art. I found him in the middle of a set-to with Larry.

"I'm not saying it *can't* go in Monday night," Larry was saying. "I'm telling you it would be unwise."

"It's going in," said Art tightly.

"It isn't only the one number, Art. You put a sloppy, half-baked spot in the show and it poisons the whole thing—the players go on frightened—"

"The hell with 'em—they're all overpaid anyhow. Put the goddam number in. That's it."

He walked off. I began to follow him, when Alicia stepped into my path and spoke confidentially.

"Tell Larry to come down to wardrobe. Right now."

I went back, found Larry and told him. He started down and said, "Come along a minute, Midge. I've got a million memos. Mr. Barracuda's striking again. We're putting 'Talking Machine' in Monday night. God help us all. It's nowhere near ready."

Down in wardrobe, Alicia said to her staff, "Take ten, chums. I need the space."

They all went out. Alicia closed the door.

"Safe to talk here, do you suppose?"

"Why not?"

"Lord knows. I'm told he's in the habit of bugging people. Is it true?"

"I don't know," said Larry. "I wouldn't put it past the bastard. He's *weird.*"

"Yes. But in rows such as the present one, he can be knocked for six if we band together—you and Ivan and I."

"How?"

"I was up there for most of your ordeal. He's a bloody fool, that's all. Missed his calling, what's more. He ought to have been a scoutmaster. All that idiot bluster and giving orders. Sexual, probably. He needs to feel manly."

"What's the plan?"

"Don't battle him," said Alicia. "Play along. Rehearse. It's all set for

Monday. No matter how impossible it seems, pay it no mind. Monday it is."

"And then?"

"Ah! There they are—what Max Beerbohm called the two most charming words in the English language: 'And then?' And then, Cockie, the *costumes* won't be ready. Not your fault. Rail at *me* if you like. Scream and yell. But they're not ready, and there's an end of it."

"When *will* they be ready, God damn it—you stupid limey bitch?"

He performed his act so brilliantly that for a moment I thought it was on the level.

"Whenever you say, dear."

They shook hands, ceremoniously.

"Remind me to marry you," said Larry, and left.

"Very nice of you," I said to Alicia.

"Not at all. *Quid pro quo.* He'll do something for me one day. Perhaps. How are you?"

"Fine. I *think.*"

She came over and touched my face.

"You're so *young,*" she exclaimed.

"I'm getting older," I said. "Fast."

"Good," she said. "You'll enjoy it, I expect."

Her staff began to drift back in. I left and went looking for Art again. I found him out in the lobby, talking to Ring Lardner, Jr., and Paddy Chayefsky, friends he had invited down to see the show and talk.

When the overture began, the guests went to their seats. Art and I went into the lounge and sat down.

"Well?" he asked.

I got out my notebook, flipped to the right page and began to read back my shorthand notes beginning with: "Tell him thanks for the free ticket"—Art kept interrupting with comments such as, "Son of a bitch!" and "Let him try it," and *"That'll* be the day!"

When I had finished, he sat still for a full minute (unusual for him) and seemed momentarily not so much defeated as flummoxed.

"I could set *him* up, too, if I wanted," he said suddenly.

"I doubt it." It was out before I could think.

"What? What'd you say?"

"Sorry. It slipped out."

"What did you?"

"I said, 'I doubt it.' But I'm sorry. It's none of my business."

"Sure it is."

"I don't want it to be, Mr. Clune."

"What makes you think I couldn't? With him. Bowman."

"He's awfully smart."

"How do you know? He told you?"

"No."

"Jesus, it's like Sam Goldwyn once kept telling me about how Frank Loesser was a genius. Over and over. So finally I said to him, 'How do you *know* he's a genius?' And Sam said, 'He told me so himself. Personally.'"

"I didn't say Gene was a genius. I said he's awfully smart."

"Wait a second. What the hell's goin' on here?" I said nothing. "Where do you come off calling him 'Gene'? You know him from before? How come you didn't tell me?"

"No. I met him tonight for the first time. He took me to dinner."

"He did, huh? Where?"

"Le Champignon."

"Who paid?"

"He did."

"I'm surprised. One thing I found out about this bird. He makes out how he's one of these high-class above-it-all integrity characters and when you come right down to it—to the nitty-gritty—it turns out the bastard's money-mad. Everything for sale with him, including integrity."

"It was a very good dinner," I said.

"And he told you call him 'Gene,' right?"

"Yes."

"What a character! Right in there. Did he give you a little footsie job under the table?"

"I didn't notice."

"Cop a feel in the taxi?"

"He had a limo."

"A *what!*"

"Yes."

"Figures. With my money. That's great. Just great. Also, him you call 'Gene'—me you call Mr. Clune?"

"I'll call you anything you say, Mr. Clune."

"Call me Snookyookums," he said. "God *damn,* how you got to watch these politicians. He's here ten minutes and already he's working himself into the family where he doesn't belong. No doubt he dripped plenty of that phony Chicago charm all over you. I think I can see some of it. Wipe it off, y'mind?"

"Look, Mr. Clune—"

"Art!" he yelled.

"Look, Art. You gave me a job to do and I did it. I think it's wrong of you to abuse me for it."

"You think it's wrong? Who the hell are *you* to think?"

"I wonder."

"How long is he going to hang around? Did he say?"

"No."

"You didn't ask him?"

"No."

"Why not?"

"You didn't tell me to."

"Well, Jesus—haven't you got *any* initiative?"

"Sometimes."

"What did you think of him?"

"Interesting. Attractive. Intelligent."

"What else did he say? That wasn't the whole everything, was it? What did you read me?"

"Of course not."

"So what else? Or is it confidential?"

"Not at all. What I read you was his direct response to your message. But before that he said—let's see. Not all of it would interest you, but . . . oh, yes. I told him how marvelously the show is capturing the period and he said he didn't think much of most of the score."

He was on his feet. "How'd he hear the score?"

"He got it somehow. A cassette."

"God damn it! I'll *kill* somebody!"

An usher appeared in the arch.

"Sssshhh," she shushed. "Show's on."

"I *know* it's on! I *put* it on! Get outa here!"

The usher retreated.

"Find out who sent him the score."

"How can I?"

"Ask him."

"He won't tell me."

"I'll find out. If it's the last thing I *do,* I'll find out. I'm surrounded by double-crossing parasites." He sat down, wearily. "What else?" he asked.

"Let's see. About his name on the show—I told him that as things stood now, there was very little of his book in it, so—"

He was on his feet again.

"You read the book?" he thundered.

The usher appeared again. He dispatched her with a look.

"Yes," I said, and knew I had blundered.

"How come?"

"I found a copy at The Strand in New York during rehearsals."

"Why?"

"I was interested. No one told me it was the great taboo. I found that out later. After I'd read it. So too late."

He sat down again and began thinking. Thinking? Did he *ever* think. Or was it all plotting and planning and scheming? Meanwhile, I turned my thoughts onto myself. I had just lied shamefully. Why? To protect Larry, of course. But see how the atmosphere infects. A year or two and I'll be like the rest of them. Playing the game. What of it? Doesn't *everyone?*

He was talking to me again.

"All right. So you've read his crap. And you know the show. So what do *you* think?"

"About what?"

"About *what?* About what the hell we're talking about? Which is better?"

"Hard to say—the book is a *book.*"

"A lousy book."

"I loved it." He glanced at me. "As a book."

"And the show?"

"Well, that's still a work in progress, isn't it?"

"Christ, you're slippery. Like everybody else around here. A lot of eels I've got. I ask for straight answers and all I get is goddamn pretzels." He was angry. With me. His finger in my face. "Am I right?"

I thought it best to avoid engaging him, so I simply nodded. He sat down beside me.

"Let me get your opinion on something, all right?"

"Of course."

"About him. Bowman. Knowing what you know—about him and the book and the show—what do you think? Will he want his name on or off?"

"I have no opinion," I said. "But I'll take a guess."

"Yes?"

"Off."

"Why?"

"Because it's not his—not in style or story or character."

"There's something he doesn't know, this wiseass, that if he takes his name off—he can't collect royalties. That's what the Guild says—and don't you tell him or I'll murder you. They made a rule once—it was when directors were always trying to get a piece of the action, and writers were giving it to them. Then the Guild made a rule: If you get royalties, you've got to get credit, too. The whole thing stopped. Because writers, see—they care more about credit than money. That's why they're mostly schmucks. . . . So if you're right about Bowman, that's great for our side—I'll take his name off, sure. Only he's got to put the request in writing. Then I'll have Dan rewrite it in legal lingo, and invoke the no-credit–no-money clause —only he won't know what it is—and get him to sign it and he's out. Keep all this to yourself. *Very* to yourself. Are you going to see him later?"

"I don't think so."

"Do. Catch him on the way out and ask him out for a drink. He took you to dinner, after all. You pay. Put it on your swindle sheet. The Barclay bar. None of our gang goes there, do they?"

"I don't know."

"How could they afford it, the poor bastards? They're all so underpaid! Anyhow, doesn't matter. What I want is a quick reading on his reactions. This could mean a bundle. So do what you can. You won't be sorry. I can be generous if necessary. I'll wait for your call, Midge."

"Call me Snookyookums," I said.

I went out and walked. I think better when I walk. I wondered what would happen if I walked straight to the hotel, checked out, and took a train to New York. Or a plane. Or a bus. Or hitchhiked. I was being drawn into a morass of lies and double-dealing and deception. "Oh what a tangled web we weave/When first we practice to deceive."

What would I miss if I blew this whole thing off? I checked off the various items. The pay. The experience. The excitement. The education. And of the people—whom would I regret leaving behind? The answer, when I finally achieved it, surprised me: Larry and Gene Bowman. Gene Bowman. But you hardly know him. Yes, but I want to know him better. A complex man, the best kind. Funny and sad. Serious and playful. Mature and childish. And, in a strange, esoteric way—sexually attractive. No, not attractive. Magnetic. He had said nothing remotely flirtatious. Done nothing. (The clothes change? A joke.) He had not touched me in any way. Not my arm. Not helping me in and out of the car. Not my back as we left the restaurant (a first, that!). No. He had not touched me. Why not? I began to resent the fact, to feel insulted. This gentleman junk can be carried too far, damn it. Well, it was all new. There was time. I started back to the theatre. What would he be like, lying there stripped on the enormous bed in 2110? Would the gray hair on his head be matched by gray hair on his chest? Elsewhere? Yes, of course. But why should that be so arousing? Why were my nipples hardening? and pressing against my bra? Why was I wearing a bra?

I reached the theatre, went into the Ladies' Room, took it off, and put it into my bag.

I went up into the auditorium to watch the last half hour of the show. All there at the back, standing. Larry, Alicia, Ivan, Art, and the rest. The house was sold out.

I located the back of Gene's head and watched it. A joke from the stage. It moved. A number ended. He applauded. Still it seemed to me that the way he shifted from time to time indicated that he was either bored or restless. As the finale began, I moved to stand at the top of the aisle where his seat was. Art saw me move, patted my behind as I passed him, winked, and gave me a thumbs up. Did he know it was a phallic gesture, indicating a ready erection?

I kept my eye on Gene as he made his way up the aisle, trying to get an advance clue. He was "nonchalanting it"—as I had heard Phil Rizzuto once say describing a catch by Rod Carew.

"Hello," I said as he saw me.

"Good seat," he said.

(That's bad, I thought.)

"How about a drink?" I asked.

"By all means. I could use one."

(Worse, I thought.)

"But I'd like to see Larry Gabel first. Is that possible?"

"Hold it," I said. "Wait right here. I'll catch him before he goes back."

I pushed through the crowd, making instant enemies, and got to Larry just in time.

"Got a minute, Larry?"

"For you, yes."

"No. For Gene Bowman."

"Really? He's here?"

"Come with me."

There was less difficulty getting back as the crowd was thinning out swiftly.

"Gene Bowman," I said. "Larry Gabel."

"Delighted," said Gene.

"I'm honored," said Larry.

"I wanted to say, for what it's worth, that you've done a splendid job—considering the material you've been given to work with."

"Thank you. It's worth a great deal coming from you, Mr. Bowman."

"Let's make it Gene and Larry, shall we? This is 'showbiz,' they tell me. Moreover, I'm not that old and you're not that young."

Larry smiled. "Suits me. About the material. Naturally, we're working to improve it. And now that you're here, I should think we've got a much better chance."

"I'm not sure. There's the question of *modus operandi.* We'll see. For the moment, I merely want to compliment you. Again."

They shook hands. Larry went down the side aisle to the passdoor.

"Ready?" asked Gene.

"You bet. Any special place you'd like?"

"How about one with naked women? They got any of those in Philly?"

(Uh-uh. It begins. There'll be a dirty joke within the hour, no doubt.)

"Not a one."

He snapped his fingers in annoyance and said, "Damn!"

"But I think I know one with naked *men,* " I said. "Would that do?"

"How about the staid ol' Barclay?"

"Why not?"

We walked to The Barclay in silence. Clearly, he was thinking or cogitating or ruminating. Whatever. I thought it wise to say nothing until he did. We stopped for a red light. He looked at me and smiled.

"Thinking?" I asked.

"No," he replied. "Digesting."

"Of course."

The light changed, we walked again. He *still* hadn't touched me. I'd better change fragrance, I thought.

At The Barclay, he asked, "Where's the Men's?"

I pointed it out.

He said, "Chivas and soda for me if they have it. If not, J and B."

I went into the small bar, ordered his drink (they had Chivas) and the same for myself and went to the Ladies' Room. I considered putting my bra back on, decided against it.

He rose as I approached the table. The drinks arrived. He raised his glass, said, "Success," clinked it to mine, and we drank.

"Shall we?" he asked.

"What?"

"To the subject? That's what we're here for, I believe."

"If you like."

"It's a tragedy," he said seriously.

"In what way?"

"It could be so great, and it's so not. . . . I don't claim to know much about the theatre—it's a mighty special craft—but I know one hell of a lot about Nora, and she's not up there, not for a second. And if no Nora, there's no show. It doesn't matter how many great numbers you have—the score, by the way, is much better than I thought. *Much.* I was wrong. . . . The *look* of it—overwhelming. I must write the people responsible—or better yet, meet them tomorrow." He took a stack of three-by-five filing cards from his breast pocket and made notes. "Set, costumes—works of *art.* All the players. And the girls—delicious. But no Nora. It's a great beefless beef stew. The surprise—to me at least—is how that brainless, heartless story they're telling up there doesn't seem to matter that much. The fact that it's a musical, do you suppose? So it's artificial, anyhow. People don't sing at each other in life, so this isn't life—it's a show. I thought I'd *hate* the story—now that it's been so truncated and so stuffed with absolute hogwash—but I didn't care. Mine wouldn't have made all that difference. But *Nora.* Where's Nora? Our little Miss Star could do it,

I suppose. I don't know. If She had it to do. She's all right—having a vicarious love affair with the audience. But She is indubitably SHE. I haven't seen her since Vegas two years ago and—well, hell? I thought I was *back* there. She works and charms and sings and flirts and it's all fine and it's all a waste. As it stands—the show is, will be, a failure. . . . Shouldn't you have taken all this down? Aren't you supposed to report back? You want to get your book out and I'll say it all again? I don't mind."

"No, Gene Bowman," I said. "I'll remember. How could I forget? You've put into words what I've been thinking for a month but couldn't express."

"But that's my *business,* Midge Maghakian," he said.

"I know. Still. . . ."

We were looking at each other, trying to communicate more than we were prepared to put into words. His gaze shifted from my face to my chest.

"Hmm," he said. "I see *you've* changed, too."

"Yes," I said. "I feel so much more liberated."

He looked at me again. "I'm all for it. I walk up and down Michigan Avenue these days feeling grateful to progress. We have loads of lovely girls in Chicago—and the new way of things makes them even lovelier. I'm a feminist, can you tell? I'm for women. And the E.R.A. And beyond. Why aren't they—you—more militant, more active, more demanding? More women than men in the last census—well over a hundred million."

"Too many," I said.

"It's the theme of *Nightingale for Sale!* A girl making it in a man's world. Degraded by men, turned into an object for hire, a chattel, a slave—and by the fact of her personality and the strength of her determination *not* to be any of those things—she goes from girl to woman to, by God, lady. And we should see it—what's more—feel it. That's the great Nora. What you've got up there now is a showbiz cutie, a—to use a least-favorite word—*performer."*

"Would you do me a favor?" I asked. "No, I'm sorry. I didn't mean that. Not me. As someone said to me today—'Who the hell are *you?*' I couldn't answer that question. I'm still moving from girl to woman—"

"Keep going," he said.

"What I meant to say—trying to say—is, would you be willing to

· 258 ·

do the *show* a favor? *Yourself* a favor? After all, it's your show, too. Your name is on it."

"For the moment," he said.

Should I? Do I dare warn him? Careful.

"What's the favor?"

"What you just said here—to me—would you write it out? Let me have it to give him? Maybe he'd see it and if he did would you be willing to work with Larry and Chris and fix it?"

"Waiter!"

He circled a finger over our tiny table, signaling another round.

"Would you?" I asked again.

"Only if requested to. Speak when spoken. The world hates a buttinski."

"But it's yours, in a way."

"A technicality."

"Would you talk to Larry?"

"Of course. But what good would that do?"

"I don't know."

"Has he any clout? Any authority?"

"No, but he can be damned persuasive."

"And what about this Chris guy?" he asked.

"He's a secretary. Like me. Only he doesn't take shorthand, so that makes him a writer."

Gene laughed, lightly. "My oh my. I hope I never get on the wrong side of *you.* You're tough."

"I hope so. It's a tough world."

The drinks had been served without our noticing them until now.

"Well, well, what have we here?" he asked.

"Ambrosia," I said. "Never had it before."

"Stick with me, kid," he said, "I'll show you the goods of life."

"All right."

"One of the reasons I'd like to score for big dough—I'd know what to do with it. Rich people. I can't tell you how many I know. Sad folk, most of them. Fearful. There's something out of joint where the poor know how to use money and the rich don't."

"Some do."

"A few. I'm talking by and large. I know some very rich people who are nice; and some rich people who are very nice; but no very rich people who are very nice."

"Will you? Help the show?"

"I just arrived, dear. Let me think. Sage and pontifical as I seem —I'm not sure I'm sure."

"I *am.*"

"Yes—but in the words of Our Leader—who the hell are *you?* If I'm to get involved—it has to be with conviction. I *could* turn out to be a specious fraud. Further. It may be that what I want done couldn't be done on the stage."

"*Anything* can be done on the stage!" I said wildly.

The waiter came over and said, "Will there be anything else? The bar'll be closing in a few minutes."

"Yes," said Gene. "Two doubles."

"Not for me," I said.

"All right, then," said Gene. "One single and one triple."

"Just for you, please," I said. "No more for me."

"One no more," said Gene. "And one quadruple."

The Greek waiter looked confused. Gene held up four fingers.

"Four," said the waiter. "Four Chivas."

"Right."

"Soda?"

"Soda."

"Thank you."

He went off.

"Too much?" I asked.

"Certainly," he replied. "What's wrong with too much? I should think a nice Armenian girl like you would know that great Saroyan song: 'All I Want Is All There Is and Then Some.' "

"I'm only *half* Armenian."

"Well, then. You ought to know half the song."

The waiter. The check. I reached for it.

"No no," said Gene.

"Art's paying."

"Yes yes!" said Gene.

I signed the check, adding a $5.00 tip.

"Thank you, lady."

He went off.

"There you are," said Gene. "You're a lady."

"A lot he knows."

I finished my drink—was it the second, or third?—in a gulp and looked at the four filled shot glasses lined up in front of Gene like a squad.

"I'll take one of those," I said.

"I knew you would."

We drank and talked and drank and talked and at times it seemed like a record player on repeat. Phrases, whole sentences came through again and again.

I was holding his hand between us on the banquette. When had I taken it? Or had he taken mine? Now at last we were in contact. What we had failed to achieve in words and looks we were—he was —accomplishing with touch. That hand. A man's hand, alive and strong and eloquent and suddenly tender. And this, I considered, was his *left* hand. What would his *right* do to me?

I tried hard to project the next few hours. We leave here. To twenty-one. The same floor. Do I ask him in? No. Brazen. Does he ask me in to his? If so, I say no. No? Yes would be too chippie. No. A short, whispered chat outside my door? I open it in midsentence and move in, still talking as if to indicate that if we are going to finish the conversation it ought to be out of the hall? To make this point, I stop whispering and return to normal speech as I close the door. Then? Then, my girl, it is entirely up to him. Out of your hands completely. This is no time for a wrong move on your part. He is not an ordinary man. He is something special. A man who might easily run a mile if a pass were to be made at him. Another generation. One in which predatory women were thought to be either wanton or emasculating. Let him lead. You follow. And if he doesn't? Then stand still. . . . While we talked, I attempted to convey all this to his hand with my hand. The third drink finished. I could have used another, but it was gone. He, then, had had five. Of course. Eight all together. My arithmetic was exciting me. Not as much as that hand. I had never in all my time been turned on by a hand.

Through the lobby, slowly, "with deliberate speed"—good phrase. I felt unsteady and hoped against hope I did not look it or seem it. A hand—his right one—around my waist. Thank you.

In the elevator, I am troubled by the movement.

In the hallway, whispering.

"Thank you."

"Good night."

"Good night."

Would it be? Was it about to be?

We move to the door of 2104. I continue to whisper. I am in. So is he. I close the door and raise my voice to normal.

"—and you could do it in an hour! Or even dictate it to me."

"I hate dictating."

"I'll lend you my typewriter. Here it is. Look. A beauty. An IBM Selectric with a correction key."

"Useless. I never make mistakes."

A long pause. I look at him—soulfully, I hope; sickishly, I'm afraid.

"Never?" I ask.

"Well, hardly ever. And I'm never sick at sea. . . . I'm going to leave you now," he said. "I don't want to, but I'm going to."

"You don't *have* to," I ventured, making it sound vague. "We could talk some more."

"No," he said. "There's been enough talk."

Another long look. This time he seemed to be considering the purchase of my bosom. "What're you getting for those melons today?" as Pop used to say.

He was still looking there, caught. I wished I could show him the rest of me. That would do it. But how?

His eyes came up and took mine. If he doesn't come here and grab me, I thought, I'll scream. My juices were flowing copiously, my vulva was not only sodden but hot. He moved to me at last. I braced myself for his embrace. He stopped, looked harder and said, "Maghakian."

"Call me Midge."

"Maghakian! Of course. The *San Francisco Chronicle*. Vartan Maghakian."

"Right."

"Your father?"

"No!" I said, furiously. "My sister."

"I know him," he said. "I *know* your sister. A tremendous guy."

"He just *thinks* he's my sister," I said, babbling along. "He's really my brother."

"Of course," said Gene.

The discovery could not have come at a worse moment.

"Good Lord!" he said. "Vartan Maghakian's sister."

A pause as I tried to think of a way out of this wet blanket.

Finally, I said, "Are *you* going to say small world or shall I?"

"No," he said. "I'm going to say good night. And thank you for an illuminating time."

"Nothing at all."

"Perhaps we can meet tomorrow," he said.

"Perhaps."

"And I'll think about your proposal. It's not without merit."

Surely he was coming nearer. A handshake? A hug? *Something!* I was wrong. He looked at me for the longest time, said, "You have the most beautiful legs I have ever seen," and was gone, leaving me in a state.

The cold shower did no good at all. Afterward, I got myself up as though I expected him to come back. Did I think he would, or was it mad hope? I brushed my hair and tied it back—hair can get in the way maddeningly during lovemaking. I put on that subtle skillful bedtime makeup of mine—the merest eye shadow, a suggestion of lips (with Sta-Kiss), tiny dabs of Joy ("The World's Most Expensive Fragrance") here and there—and between my breasts and on my inner thighs. Then my best beige fingertip-length nightgown. What for? Here I was—ready, hungry. And no one with whom to share my longing. What a waste! I got into bed and tried to assess the extent of my inebriation. Not much. The excitement had burned most of it off and I was left with no more than a pleasant, floating little buzz. What made me so sure that the phone was about to ring? I moved it closer to me on the night table. Relax, I kept telling myself. No use. The phone rang.

"Yes?"

"What happened? How'd you make out? Why didn't you call me, for Chrissake?"

Art.

"I thought it could wait till morning," I said. The fact is, I had forgotten him completely.

"Come on up. I wanna hear."

"I've gone to bed."

"Slip something on."

"I was asleep. You woke me up."

"All right, *I'll* come *down.*"

"No!" I shouted, and it came out much louder than I had meant.

"Oh, I see," he said—and if a voice can have a leer, his did.

"Like hell you do!" I said. "It's late, Art. I'll see you in the morning. I assure you I've got nothing to report that can't wait."

I hung up. Almost immediately, the phone rang again. I picked it up.

"Now cut it out!" I said. "I *mean* it!"

"What?" said a beautiful voice. Gene's.

I sat up. "Oh my God," I said.

"Not quite," he said. "What on *earth* is going on?"

"Please," I said. "I'm so sorry. He's been at me on the phone—that damned nerve-tester."

"I'm relieved. At least I didn't wake you."

"No."

"I only wanted to tell you that I *have* thought it over and I *will* write it if you'll lend me your IBM Selectric with the correcting key and keep persuading me—you are a most persuasive girl."

I was being bathed in his voice. I did not want him to stop talking, to leave me.

"What made you decide?" I asked, stalling.

"Conscience," he said. "You may not have intended it, but you made me feel a responsibility to the whole show—beyond the pettiness or the personalities involved."

As he talked, I shifted the phone from my right hand to my left. My right hand went down and I was touching myself. I spread my thighs and raised my knees slightly. My hand was content in the warm and wet. He was talking. In a miraculous way, *he* was touching me. Truly. The vibrations of his voice were coming through the phone, affecting my body.

"I see. What else?" I said softly.

"Showing off, I suppose," he said. "I'd like to impress you—among others. I'd like to impress myself. See if I can do it. It's always a mystery. So far, my ideas are abstract. To make them real, alive—well, that's another matter."

"You can do it," I whispered. "I know you can do it."

What did I mean?

"You sound sleepy," he said. "I'll let you go."

"No," I said. Pleaded.

"Good night. Sleep well."

He was gone. I lay there holding the phone, holding myself. I hung up and knew I had to finish. I put him there—I imagined that fine head there—my hand became his face, my fingers became his tongue —he licked me, lapped me, nibbled me and possessed me. The convulsion came suddenly, unexpectedly and I burst into tears. It lasted —the spasm—infinitely longer than usual, but finally I was at peace.

I lay quietly, resting—and thought of my brother Vartan. Not so much because of Gene's mention of him—but because I owed him so much for having educated and enlightened me in matters of the body, its needs and its uses.

Next morning. Gene Bowman came in a few hours ago, looking cheerful and rested.

I had already prepared the bulletin for copying, so suggested that he stay and do his thing in my room to save the nuisance of moving the heavy machine and table and chair and paraphernalia.

"I don't know," he said. "A lady's bedroom. I feel intrusive."

"No reason to. I have to go to the theatre."

"All right."

"Will you want to go again tonight?" I asked.

"Probably not. But may I let you know later?"

"Of course."

To my surprise, he was still working when I returned at three.

His jacket was off, so was his tie. There were scribblings and jottings and notes all over. He is one of those craftsmen to whom a properly structured sentence is a holy thing.

"Harder than I thought," he said. "One thing to talk it—but when it's down in black and white, there's a danger it may sound didactic or pedantic or plain dumb. Not my field, after all, and I'm not sure of the lingo. Maybe you can help me."

"I doubt that," I said.

"Anyway, here it is." He laughed. "I'm tempted to ask you to do something for me. Sainte-Beuve, the French critic, used to write his essays in longhand and when he'd finished, he would call his secretary in, hand it to him, lean back and say, 'Read it to me—like an enemy.'"

"How could *I* do *that?*"

"Well, try."

He handed me his typed pages and I began to read aloud:

"'A few undigested thoughts on a presently half-baked but potentially extraordinary musical play entitled, *Shine On, Harvest Moon.*"

SHINE ON, HARVEST MOON
Company Bulletin
Monday, November 19

WELCOME TO PHILADELPHIA: Here we are at long last.
You have worked diligently and efficiently and un-
selfishly, and I am most grateful. Moreover, I am
confident that our efforts will bear the fruits of
gratification. Godspeed.

L.G.

OUR STAR has cut four sides for Columbia Records:

"Falling Star"
"Shine On, Harvest Moon"
"Skiddoo"
"Merry-Go-Round"

She has also been chosen Entertainer of the Year by
the editors of CUE Magazine, and a reception is
being held in her honor Sunday night at the Gotham
Hotel in New York at 10:30. Six hundred show business personalities will be present at the ceremo-
nies.

THE COMPANY YOU KEEP: BUDDY RICE
(Assistant to Miss Flagg)
When I was five years old, in Sioux City, Iowa, I
was Fred Astaire. Later, I became Bill Robinson for
six months. After THE RED SHOES I was surprised to
find I had metamorphosed into Moira Shearer and
after HANS CHRISTIAN ANDERSEN into Zizi Jeanmaire.
I would have stayed there had it not been for the
American debut of Rudolf Nureyev. I was Nureyev for
quite a while. But I left him when I left classical
and went Broadway. . . . I had the usual gypsy life:
audition, make it, rehearse, out-of-town, open New
York, give notice, leave, audition, make it, rehearse, etc etc etc (as Yul Brynner says). Sick of it
finally, so I decided to become a legitimate actor.
Two years at The Neighborhood Playhouse did not
help. Back to dance, this time as off-off-Broadway
choreographer. Then off-Broadway. Now on as assistant to Jenny Flagg, who I hope someday to turn
into.

<u>CHRISTOPHER FELLER</u> returns from California on Wednesday and will be at The Forrest Theatre that evening at 6:00 P.M. for anyone who needs to see him about anything.

<u>QUOTE TO REMEMBER</u>:
"We are a part of all that we have met and we've met them all."
Ada Everleigh

Please be aware that additional props are being obtained daily. Check each day to see what props are available for your scenes.

<u>THE COMPANY YOU KEEP</u>: SKIP McCAFFERY
(Vocal Director)
I was earning over $100,000 a year as an art director for Young and Rubicam. Played the piano for fun. Popular at parties. I was a happy man. One party, I met Mary Martin and her husband, Richard Halliday. They introduced me to Richard Rodgers. I nearly fainted. He offered me a job on ME AND JULIET. Quit Young and Rubicam. Into the theatre. Since that time I have earned about a third of my old salary—and am miserable all the time. So why don't I quit and go back to Y & R? Six therapists have failed to help me find the answer, so how can *I* tell?
I was born in New York City at The Gotham Hotel—believe it or not. (I don't believe it myself.) Stuyvesant High. Hamilton College.
I drink (to excess); smoke (like an idiot); chase (slower and slower); and I own the world's greatest collection of Billie Holiday recordings. Would you like to come up and hear them?
I am single and intend to remain so.
I thank you.

There are now 7 days until our Philadelphia opening.
There are now 32 days until our New York opening.

· XXVI ·

I have been working with Gene. Whatever else happens on this job, or has happened, or is going to happen—the experience with him makes it all not only worthwhile but eternally valuable.

He is the very definition of a professional. The work comes first—before any other consideration or responsibility to person, place, or thing. Before himself, even. I honestly believe if I were not around to arrange for food once in a while, he would not eat at all.

He attends every single performance, including matinees. I sit on his right and take his whispered notes in the dark. They are voluminous, often cryptic, always short.

Afterward, I type them up and bring them to him. He is usually already at work, typing steadily. He is a better typist than I am. I put the notes down beside him. He says, "Many thanks," without looking up. I leave and wait for him to call me, which he does after two or three or four hours. He comes over and dictates what he has written. I transcribe it. Now his work begins in earnest. Five drafts, six—more. I note that most of his effort is aimed toward simplification: pruning, condensing, cleaning.

I make no comment about this singular method, but I wonder about it.

This afternoon, he startles me by saying, "Let me explain why I do this."

Apparently, men of his sensitivity read or perceive thoughts.

"Words to be read are one thing, those to be spoken are another. I find I can't dictate straight off, so I have to write it first, then talk it—revising for speech. Do you see?"

"Yes."

"It's a technique I learned when I was on Adlai Stevenson's speechwriting team. Before you were born, I expect."

"Not quite."

"We all used to kill ourselves trying to out-brilliant one another. Then Stevenson would turn it all into his superlative talk."

I remember what Larry once said about "rewriting" being not necessarily synonymous with "improving"—but in Gene's case, it is. Each draft is better than the one before.

He sends me to the library for books of the period and Xeroxed pages from magazines and newspapers. His office sends him a microfilm viewer and three reels of microfilm of the complete *Chicago Tribune* for 1908.

When he is not writing, he is reading. "Looking for the flavor of the time," he explains. And indeed, his stuff has a sound and a rhythm and a vocabulary different from today's.

Chatting about this the other day, he said, "What I'm trying to discover is that foreign country L. P. Hartley wrote about. The past."

"You did it in the book," I said.

"Oh, yes—but that was narrative. I had the luxury of description and explanation and words, words, words. Now it all has to be done like a series of TV commercials, almost. Which, by the way, I admire enormously."

Two women sitting directly in front of us this afternoon are members of that common theatre society, The Talkers. They talk right through the overture and do not stop when the curtain goes up. They comment on the sets, the costumes, the makeups, the hairdos, the shoes. They explain the jokes to one another.

Gene fidgets uncomfortably in his seat. They talk through one whole scene. He clenches and unclenches his fist.

After a while, when they fail to desist, he takes a long, deep breath and leans forward. I brace myself for the explosion. He taps one of the women on the shoulder. She turns to face him, angrily.

Gene smiles at her, sweetly, and whispers, "No one *else* is talking."

He leans back in his seat. To my amazement, his ploy has succeeded in shutting them up. ·

The rest of the performance, by contrast, is a relief.

Last night, he finished giving me the new Scene 3, Act I at 2:15 a.m. I was greatly impressed, but said nothing—which is what I am supposed to say, according to Katharine Gibbs.

I looked up. He was studying me.

"Thank you," he said modestly. "How about a bite and a beer?" He picked up the phone. "Room service, please. . . . It is? . . . Why, what time is it? . . . Oh. Well, thanks." To me: "Did you know it was after two?"

"Of course."

"Why didn't you say so? This is mad. Unhealthy. We need some food. Let's go."

"Where?"

"We'll find somewhere."

"In Philadelphia?"

"Oh, sure. There's bound to be a joint or an all-night diner."

He was right. A taxi driver took us to a place near the main post office. One shift of postal workers coming off was having dinner; the other, going on, was breakfasting.

We took a corner booth. He ordered corned-beef hash and beer. I asked for a chicken sandwich and a glass of milk.

I was astonished by the excellence of the food; he was not.

Away from work now, I felt relaxed enough to tell him how much I admired his discipline and organization. He seemed surprised.

"I don't see how else it can be done—how *anything* can be done."

"I wish you'd talk to our gang about it," I said. "They specialize in chaos. They make schedules only to change them, I think. And as for communication, forget it."

"As a cook," he said quietly, "my wife was a nonesuch. One of my great joys was to see her in action in the kitchen. I used to perch up on a stool—out of her way—and watch. Usually with a couple of newspapers and magazines. She never paid any attention to me at all. Lord, the concentration. And the organization! Every ingredient, every utensil there before her. The measures, precise. The weights, exact. The timing, by stopwatch." He looked away, saw her, I'm sure.

He looked back, tears in his eyes, the tip of his nose suddenly red. "God damn, she was *some* creature."

"Organized," I said (like an idiot).

"Baking a soufflé, building a bridge, getting out the Sunday edition —it all comes down to the same thing, doesn't it? Planning and executing—holding to the plan."

"And someone in charge?" I asked.

"Certainly."

"That's what we don't have. We have a cold war going on all the time."

"Too bad," he said. "Cold war reminds me of the time the paper sent me down to Houston to do a piece on the Doctor DeBakey/Doctor Cooley feud. No wonder they were at odds. You could hardly imagine two men more different. One, cool; the other, emotional. One, daring; the other, conservative. One, humorous; the other, stolid. But. But. In action—precisely the same. Organized, disciplined, no-nonsense. Martinets where their staffs were concerned. Tough. Uncompromising. Come to think of it— that's what I'm involved in here, on the show. Isn't that so? Surgery. And it's delicate. There's an existing show and it's living, breathing—but it's also sick. Surgery is indicated. Little tumors and growths to take out. Medicine and nutrients to put in. The heart made to beat at the proper tempo. But it's tricky. A few wrong moves and it may expire."

"I want to say this, though," I said. "What I *do* like—all the way —with no reservations, is what *you've* done." (Sorry, Katharine Gibbs.) "The book. The story. The words. If everybody respected *that* more it would be better. And I'm not saying that just because you're paying the check. I swear to God—and I *believe* in God."

"I'm glad about that. Not that you believe in God—but that you believe in the book. . . . Finished?"

"Yes, thank you."

No taxis. We walk back to the hotel. It does not seem dangerous because I am with him.

In the hallway of the twenty-first floor, I notice that he looks extremely fatigued.

"Please get some rest," I said. "It's all coming along fine. But you look tired."

I touch his arm without meaning to. He is regarding me with an expression I have never before seen on his dear face.

"Don't worry, Ellen," he says. "I'll be all right."

He takes my hand, kisses it, and is gone.

Ellen? Did he say "Ellen"? Who is Ellen?

(Later. A few days after the foregoing, he said to me, "Were you startled when I called you 'Ellen' the other night?"

"No."

"*I* was. It was the enervation, I expect. And that look of genuine concern on your fine face—so much like Ellen's. Ellen was my wife."

I could hardly contain my joy.)

· XXVII ·

Chris is no longer with us. He did not leave, exactly. He vanished, disappeared, melted into thin air. He said goodbye to no one that I know of, but simply went away.

He is not greatly missed, because most of us are beginning to realize he was not really here even when he was present. He was performing a curious function and maintained a sort of working relationship with Art, but it was one which is apparently alien to theatre practice. In Hollywood, it is common for producers and directors and sometimes even stars, to refer to "my writer." That never happens in the legitimate theatre. But Chris was, indeed, Art Clune's writer. The only one he was trying to please was Art. A mistake. The only person a writer is supposed to please is himself. That's what I've seen Gene doing every day and every night of his time here.

In any event, Chris is gone and there's no point in feeling sorry for him. I doubt that Chris himself is. To him it was simply a job for which he was paid. Now he'll go on to the next job. But I begin to see what was wrong with almost everything he wrote. It was mechanical, constructed, derivative, formula. It seemed to have no passion. He was not speaking in his own voice, or the voices of the characters. He was not writing in the time or the place of the story—thus he was in the wrong key. Anyway, he is gone.

At lunch one day, I mention this whole matter to Gene, wondering why Chris's departure has caused so little stir.

Gene said, "We had a lovely man on the paper some years ago. His name was Lloyd Lewis. A historian, and a sports writer and a drama critic. It was he, by the way, who got me working for Stevenson, his great friend. And he was talking about acting one day, and said, 'You can always tell the size and the importance of an actor or an actress by the size of the hole they leave when they leave the stage.' Well, thinking about it, it's perfectly true, but it affects not only the stage or actors or actresses—it happens all around us, in business, in life, in politics. Don't worry about Chris. He's a perfectly amiable fellow, but unambitious and willing to settle for less in his work, as he does in his life. He'll be all right. Let him live his life. He's probably wild about it."

SHINE ON, HARVEST MOON
Company Bulletin
Tuesday, November 20

LINE REHEARSAL: In the lobby at 5:30 for all new lines in Scene 3, Act I, revised book scenes. Check the Call Board, please.

BIG TOWN: Patti and Sammy 4:30 Ballroom Ben Franklin Hotel.

PRODUCTION MEETINGS: There will be a Musical Staging meeting on Wednesday, November 21, at the Forrest Theatre. Time to be announced.
There will be a meeting on Sound at 10:00 A.M., Wednesday, November 21, at The Forrest Theatre.

NAME CHANGE: The character of "Dan Richards" played by Joey Faye will now be called "Mickey Ryan."

TIME: Our running time is now two hours and forty-two minutes. One way we can cut down is by rehearsing all the scene changes. Watch Call Board for this technical rehearsal.

NORA:
One critic said of Nora that—"with her undisciplined sense of the ridiculous and her mobility of features, she makes herself a handsome woman—more than she has a right to be."

POSITIONS: Again, a reminder to avoid bunching up, and *always* leave as much space as possible between yourself and the other character or characters with whom you are playing the scene.
Moreover, please begin to be aware of large empty spaces on the stage. Use as much of the playing area as you can.

THE COMPANY YOU KEEP: HY BALABAN(Composer)
It's hard to believe, but I was born in Paris. At the American Hospital. July 5, 1912. Who cares? My father (Nathan) was first flutist (please do not ever let me hear you say flautist!) with the old Philharmonic under Walter Damrosch. My mother (Sarah) taught piano at N.Y.U.

She was in Paris, studying with Nadia Boulanger,
when I made my premature appearance. I have never
forgiven my mother, because it means I can never be
President of the United States.

I do not remember any time when I could not play the
piano. I was my mother's guinea pig and all teaching methods were tried out on me.

No college. Straight from Washington Irving High
School to The Eastman School of Music in Rochester,
N.Y. After two years there, a painful realization
that I would never rival Horowitz.

Summer job at the White Roe Lake House in Living-
ston Manor, N.Y. Three afternoon concerts each
week and play with dance band. I began to see that I
liked the band better.

Next summer at Laurel-in-the-Pines. Meet Moss
Hart, who is social director. We write a show together, a musical version of THE SHOW-OFF by George
Kelly. Great. After that, we write a complete musical every week for performance on Saturday night. I
swear to God.

We did: THE ADMIRABLE CRICHTON; TEVYE THE MILKMAN
(later FIDDLER ON THE ROOF); THE INSPECTOR GEN-
ERAL; RIP VAN WINKLE; THE ITALIAN STRAW HAT; LILIOM
(later CAROUSEL); and two originals: THE MOUNTAINS
and THE TRIANGLE FIRE.

I made great contacts during those summers and
used them all.

You all know my other shows so why take up space. 22
Broadway musicals. No wonder I'm tired!

Met and married my wonderful Rachel in 1968.

Met and married (professionally) Fred Monroe in
1971. I hope I never lose either one of them.

Hobbies: Songwriting.

Clubs: Friars, Players, Lambs. City Athletic.

Anything else you want to know—just ask me.

REMINDER: Our midweek matinee here is on *THURSDAY*.

There are now 6 days remaining until our Philadelphia opening.
There are now 31 days remaining until our New York
opening.

· XXVIII ·

I recognize this as a crucial time for the show. And/or Gene. And/or
me. This being the case, it is important to create the right atmosphere and ambience for work.

I had Mr. Armen, the assistant manager, move Gene from his room
into Suite 14A, a two-bedroom arrangement. I had them take the bed
out of the small bedroom and put in a desk. That is now the work-
room. I did it on my own, without asking anyone, because I am
convinced it will be best for the show. The man is working harder
than anyone I have ever known. It is difficult to get him out, and the
minute he is, he thinks of something and wants to go back. 14A has
a fine, small kitchen. Yesterday, I got Gene to go out with me by
saying I had to get some stuff and would not be able to carry it back.

"Won't they deliver?" he asked.

"I don't know."

"All right."

We went to the Vendôme and got everything in one place. Fruits,
vegetables, staples, bread, eggs, and so on. China, utensils, a juicer,
a blender—the works. The bill came to $343.78. I charged it to the
company. Why not?

We lugged it all back to the hotel in a taxi. Halfway home, he
looked at the stuff and said, "What *is* all this?"

"All yours," I said.

"Good God."

But it has worked out well. While he is writing and I am waiting,

· 277 ·

I cook up stuff and have it ready for whenever. I keep the table set at all times.

Also, I have been dealing with his laundry and cleaning and pressing and shoes.

He has not so much as noticed *any* of this activity up to now, but last night, when he had finished dictating, I brought in the *Irablak* (honey chicken in grape leaves) and set it out with pita bread and a bottle of chilled Montrachet.

He moved to the table, began eating absently, became aware of the food, ate slower and slower, tasting it, savoring it. Finally, he looked up at me and grinned. I mean grinned—not smiled. Then he returned to his food. When he finished, he got up, came around to me, and kissed the back of my neck. I thought I might faint. He returned to his chair, took a second helping, looked at me, grinned again, and I realized I was falling in love with him—hopelessly, helplessly.

It makes no sense. He is a man of another world, another time. On what possible plateau could we meet? None. Yet I know that what I feel for him is something I have never known before. I want him. My body and its glands and juices have been telling me that for days. Well, it has often done so in connection with men. It seems to be that kind of body. But as for Gene—I want him inside me and beyond. I want to care for him and have him care for me. I want to know him and help him and grow with him and live forever with him. I want. I want. And no one needs to tell me I am in trouble. I know I am.

Last night, the first sleepless night in years. Thanks to the yoga course, the silly insomnia that plagued me for months had left me— for good, I thought. But last night, none of the exercises worked. I considered a Seconal, but remembering the morning grogginess it brings on—decided against it.

I spent the *nuit blanche* reviewing my damned dumb love life and the mistakes it has been full of.

I have loved (I think), but have I ever been *in* love? No. Why not? Never a man capable of it. And no—I do not believe I have ever loved. I have desired, admired, coveted, had crushes on—but never before have I felt what I feel now for this exquisite man.

I remembered Rich. But that was not love. In either direction. Did he ever say the words? No. Did I? That was Sex, Introduction to.

Thrilling. Exciting. Fun. But I was sixteen, for God's sake. What the hell did *I* know?

And Jean-Pierre. What was that? An affair, I suppose. Romantic in a specious way. And when it ended, the truth is—and it is a truth I have never before faced—I was relieved. I shudder when I think of what the consequences of marriage to him might have been.

Maxie was a brief craziness. An actor in a big hit. It all seemed terribly up-there and with-it and New Yorky at the time. But love? Oh, my God.

How I ever got involved with Fletcher is hard to explain, even to myself. He was wealthy and generous and funny. He represented a New York I had read about and heard about but never experienced. He kept the dilettante side of himself wonderfully hidden beneath the pretense of being an art student. Fletcher was seats in the fourth-row center; The Metropolitan Opera; La Grenouille; black-tie previews at the Museum of Modern Art; trips to Washington (The National Gallery, The Kennedy Center, The Freer Collection, The Madison Hotel); to Boston (The Ritz-Carlton, The Boston Museum of Fine Arts, Lexington, Concord, Walden); weekends in Southampton in the summer and Vermont for skiing in winter. Beyond all this, he paid the rent and all expenses. (God Almighty! Was I what is called "a kept woman"? How could I have been? I wasn't even a woman.) Good ol' Fletcher.

I think of these men and what I shared with them, and then I think of Gene. Our physical contact has consisted of my touching his arm twice, and his kissing me—once, on the hand; once, playfully, on the back of my neck. Still, I feel closer to him than I do to any of the others. I cannot imagine a life with any one of them. I cannot imagine a life *without* Gene. Father figure, I wonder at 4:20 a.m.? Of course not. I *have* a father. Also a brother-father.

What am I to do? Shall I tell him? Declare myself? What if he laughs? I might kill him.

Could I seduce him? I suppose so. All men are vulnerable in that area. And in his case—a younger girl, an older man. If not attraction, then flattery. I could make it happen, I know. Then what? What do I become in his eyes? A tramp, sort of. No. I want him to love me the way I love him. How can I make him do that? Oh, well.

In any case, there is no urgency about the matter. Nothing either sacred or profane is going to happen for some time. The slightest personal involvement would prove to be an irritating, unwanted distraction at this time. He has no energy to spare. His present task is consuming. I shall have to wait it out. Meanwhile, what? Love him, you fool. Love him so much and so hard that it will be in the air around him. When he senses it, he will respond. Or not.

· XXIX ·

"When's Thanksgiving?" Art asks this morning.

"Thursday."

"You sure?"

"Yes."

"O.K. I'm giving the dinner," he says.

"Matinee day, remember."

"You said Thursday."

"Yes."

"Matinee day is *Wednesday. Jesus,* you're dumb!"

"This week it's Thursday because of Thanksgiving."

"It is?"

"Yes."

"Oh. So what do you think? Dinner before—like twelve o'clock? Or between shows? Or what?"

"Between shows."

"Right. So arrange everything. Here, I think. In that big private dining room where I had the lunch for the record guys."

"How many?"

"How should *I* know? Count. Me, my wife if she can get her ass out of Maine Chance West for a couple of days. Anyway, I think I have to ask her. Saul, he's coming for sure, he told me. Now. Hy, Rachel, Fred, Larry, Gene, Jenny, Ivan, Nadia, Alicia, and so forth and so on—and each with a partner I suppose. Oysters, turkey, pumpkin pie, you know, the usual crap. Bar. Good wine but not too much. Cider. What the hell. You know. Oh, yeah. You, too. You're invited."

"Thank you."

As I worked on the preparations, I was overcome by a growing sense of dread. In view of the existing ructions and the continuing devious intrigues, how could this group possibly sit down, all together at the festive holiday board? It was sure to be a frost, and an uncomfortable one at that.

Wrong again. It was a great party, with one or two reservations.

The food and wine and service were impeccable.

The holiday matinee had gone extremely well, so spirits were high.

During drinks, Hy played Gershwin; Clay played Cole Porter; I played my whole Frank Loesser repertoire.

Mrs. Clune got oiled fast. I sat across the table from her and she studied me. After a time she said, "How'd *you* get this job anyway? He usually hires lookers."

Gene, sitting beside her, glared. I thought he was going to sock her.

"*Clay* hired me," I said, and laughed. It took some effort.

"That's the Thanksgiving spirit, Mother," said Art. "Insulting the guests."

"I meant to insult *you,*" she said.

Gene tried to steer away from unpleasantness.

"Neysa," he said. "The only other one I ever heard of was Neysa McMein—the artist."

"You're *so* right," said Mrs. Clune. "Her and me, we're the only two. That's where my wacky mother got it. She liked the sound. Turns out it's no name at all. The original got it made up by a numerologist for luck."

"Did it work?" asked Gene.

"For her, not for me."

Saul rose. "Ladies and gentlemen—"

"Where?" shouted Art. "*I* don't see any!"

Saul ignored the heckling. "As an insider-outsider of this fine and gifted family, I feel impelled to remind you all that you truly do have cause for Thanksgiving in this year of our Lord. In the end, what matters more than playing some part in the creation of beauty? This is a common experience each of you shares and I envy you. I am not naïve, and am aware of frictions and frustrations, of pain and suffering—but I remind you that the process of gestation and birth is ever thus. What transcends all is not the method, but the result. What moves me most is the conviction that my illustrious ancestor would be charmed and pleased by the portrait of her that you present. And so—the toast is to the shining memory of that entrancing spirit, who brought us all together here today—and who lives again because of you. I give you—ladies and gentlemen—*Nora!*"

Everyone rose, clinked glasses, and drank.

Saul was pale and trembling. No doubt that speech had been an effort.

We all sat, then noticed that Neysa was still on her feet.

"Ladies and gentlemen!" She had the attention of the table at once. "Bullshit!" A small, embarrassed laugh.

"Sit down, Mother," said Art.

"Siddown yourself," she replied. "I'm paying for half of this—maybe more, so knock it off! I don't like to disagree with my son—because he's the apple of my eye and a smart son-of-a-bitch, what's more—but about what he said he knows from nothing. Nora would spit all over you if she saw this turkey—not the one on the table here —the one on the stage over there." She pointed to Gene. "You want to believe this peephole artist—go ahead. But he hasn't got the real story, and neither have you. I've got the real story and I'm not telling it. And in closing I can only hope that you all go on your ass. That would make it a real Thanksgiving for me."

A short silence.

Gene rose. "Forgive me," he said. "I suspect writers who talk, and as a rule, I do not. But Mrs. Clune's trenchant remarks call for a reply. Henry Ford once said, 'History is bunk!' and brought upon himself ridicule and abuse. But as the years have gone by—I've begun to wonder if there isn't some small grain of truth in that pronouncement. Mrs. Clune never knew Nora; I never knew her—but I spent almost two years looking for her. I don't claim to have found all of her—but what I did find—I fell in love with. Nora is the love of my life—and telling her story has been its most meaningful experience. She might have been a bit embarrassed by the re-enactment of her courage and aspiration and struggle and triumph—but I doubt she'd have spit. She would leave that to her descendant, who spits very well indeed. I prefer to join an earlier expression." He raised his glass. *"Nora!"*

We all got up again—all but the woozy Neysa—and echoed the toast. "Nora!" "Nora!" "Nora!"

As we sat, we heard music. Hy had gone to the piano and was playing the verse to "Shine On, Harvest Moon." As he reached the chorus, we all began to sing—softly at first—then louder and louder, as if we wanted to make sure Nora could hear us. The song ended.

Art got up. "And now ladies and gentlemen, I am going to make the most beautiful after-dinner speech you ever heard. Ready?"

He called across the room to the hovering headwaiter, *"Check, please!!"*

Laughter. Applause. The party was over.

· XXX ·

Gene has responded. Thank You, God.

The new book went in on Monday night. How the players did it is something I shall never understand. All last week, they were rehearsing one show all day and playing another at night.

But it all went in and was triumphant. For once, there is absolute unanimity. Gene is the hero of the hour. Art had me buy $1800 worth of solid-gold fountain pen from Cartier's. Gene looked at it once, and gave it to me.

"Keep it," he said. "I'll lose it and feel miserable."

Everyone stayed up late. The excitement. A long meeting in Art's suite.

"It's *perfect!*" he kept saying. "Perfect! It's the only perfect show I ever saw in my whole life. *Perfect.*"

When the place had cleared out somewhat, Gene said, "No, not perfect, Art. But immensely promising. I believe in it now."

"I'm not gonna let you change a word. Not a word. Or a comma, even. I love every comma. Every comma is perfect!"

"I'd like Clay to make me a cassette of tomorrow's matinee," said Gene.

"It's done!"

"Then I want to get away for a few days—and get a little perspective on it. After that, I'll be in a position to polish. There are too many odd little warts and pimples still."

"Who notices?"

"*I* do. Can you spare Midge for two or three days? She's been a tower."

"Take her," said Art. "Is one enough? I'll get you *four* Midges!"

"One's enough," said Gene, gently.

I spoke: "Are you sure you can manage, Art? There's so much to do right now."

"Don't worry. We'll use Bruce and Kitty from Paul's office. And listen, if we get stuck, we'll get a couple dozen Kelly Girls! Hey! Philadelphia. I'll get *Grace* Kelly. I'll get the whole Kelly *family!*"

"The only thing—"

"Let me handle it, will y'? Nothing more important now than we all have to get behind Gene and help him."

"Whatever you say."

So it was that Gene Bowman and I left for Atlantic City the following afternoon.

I got an LTD station wagon from Hertz. We loaded, in addition to our bags: two typewriters (each with table and chair), a desk-top copier, a stationery supply, two desk lamps, one Line-A-Time (for me), and the bridge table Gene had been using—he insisted on it— all writers are eccentric, some more than others. A hot-cup. A toaster.

Everything else, we assumed, would be available at the Shelburne in Atlantic City, where I had reserved a two-bedroom suite for him, and a double room for myself—all facing the sea.

He drove—concentratedly and conservatively—but asked me to take notes from time to time as changes about the show struck him.

After half an hour, he asked, "Are you comfortable?"

"Yes, thank you."

"I mean, writing while moving doesn't trouble you?"

"No—except when you talk about cutting out good stuff. Then I get slightly carsick."

He laughed. "But some things will *have* to go, partner. We're still overlong. A visit should go on just so long. A sure way to be a bore is to overstay your welcome."

He turned on the news, listened to it for twenty minutes, then dictated a few more notes. A few minutes later, he turned the news on again. I laughed.

"What?" he asked.

"Nothing. Just all of a sudden I feel like we're a couple of escaping criminals—bank robbers or something—and that's why we keep listening to the news."

"Habit," he said. "We're all creatures of habit, aren't we? Some good, some not so good. News. That's one of mine. I don't know if it's a good one or not—but it's the principal part of my life."

"I was joking."

"I know," he said, and turned on the news.

The quality of the air changed dramatically as we approached Atlantic City.

"How about this salubrity?" he asked.

"Is that a word?"

"God, I hope so."

The Shelburne was perfection. Art had phoned ahead and made the most elaborate VIP arrangements. The manager placed two of his assistants at our disposal to help settle us in. The housekeeper appeared and asked what *she* could do. An engineer. The maids. There were flowers in every room. Baskets of fruit. Steamer baskets. A complete bar. And two boxes full of chips for the casino.

Finally, we were alone. Gene looked at his watch.

"Five-twenty," he said. "What do you think of this? An hour to clean up and change. Then let's have one drink here. I'll make you the greatest martini this side of Heaven, where I understand they have trouble getting good gin—it's all shipped to Hell. Then we walk to Hackney's—it's about two miles down the boardwalk. Will you mind that?"

"Love it."

"Fine. And no dawdling. A brisk walk with lots of deep breathing. Dinner should be smashing if Hackney's is still Hackney's. After that —a trip to the, excuse me, facilities—and walk back. I'm afraid it's still two miles."

"Fine with me."

"But this time—not so brisk and no deep breathing. In fact, you don't have to breathe at all if you don't feel like it."

"And what about dawdling?"

"Nothing but. And looking in all the windows. And bidding at a few auctions—no buying, just bidding. And listening to the pitchmen. If you're not too tired, we can have a look at The Million Dollar Pier and see the horse leap two hundred feet into the water."

"I'd hate that."

"Right. No horse. Also no casinos and no gambling. A scourge."

"I don't know how, anyway."

"That should bring us back here by ten. We can talk for an hour and plan tomorrow and watch the eleven o'clock news. Salt-water tub, and bed by midnight."

"And? . . ." I heard myself ask.

"Breakfast at seven—in here, if you like. Or would you prefer the dining room? Or would you like to have it alone? Many do."

"Yes, but I'm not many. I'm just *one.*"

What the hell was I talking about? I was trying, I suppose, to be sexy and suggestive—but it wasn't coming out that way at all. He was looking at me oddly, apparently as confused by me as I was by myself.

"So," he said. "Six-thirty back here suit you?"

"Yes," I said, but did not move. I was willing him to come to me and . . . And what? Should I move to him? Kiss him, casually? Why was I standing there, like a dumb dummy? What would he think?

"Would you like a drink now?" I heard him ask.

"No, thank you." I walked over to him, slowly. His expression changed. What was it? Apprehension? Fear? Irritation? Close to him, I stopped. A long moment.

"Six-thirty," I said, turned and walked out of the room.

In my own room down the hall, I looked at myself in the bathroom mirror, trying to regain equilibrium. Why did I look so different to myself? And what did I mean by "different"? I had changed. No doubt about it. Something had changed me. Someone. I looked older than the last time I had looked carefully. Why? Because I *wanted* to look older, that's why. And infinitely more attractive. My face—always the least of my attributes—had undergone a change and was now alive and shining. Were those my eyes? Since when? And now I was trembling. I threw off my clothes, found a shower cap, and got under the shower. Hot to scalding to ice-water. What was I doing? I was trying to bring myself back to earth, back to reality by this exposure to a few of the basic elements.

I made up and dressed carefully. I opened the window and breathed deeply.

At 6:27, I went down the hall and knocked on his door. He opened it at once and handed me a martini.

"I *knew* you'd be punctual. How did I know that?"

"No idea."

"I *love* punctual people. They make life so much easier."

He raised his glass.

"To beginnings," he said. "Always beginnings. The secret of life. Don't tell anybody."

"Beginnings," I said, and touched his glass with mine.

We sat on the sofa near the window and looked out at the darkening sky and sea. A tray of hors d'oeuvres was on the coffee table in front of us. We drank and nibbled for a time. I noticed that he did not turn on any lights. Was this a sign of anything?

"Beginnings," he said. "Think of it. Here am I—well past fifty. Life most certainly more than half over—doing something I've never done before, never even *thought* of doing."

"Maybe you should have," I said.

"No. Just an accident. I suppose most of existence is purely accidental. We design a plan, but in the end—a chance meeting, an odd happening—a twist of circumstance determines the course of life. . . . If you want the truth, *I'm* an accident."

"How do you mean?"

"My mother told me so. She was an early champion of Margaret Sanger—name mean anything to you?"

"No."

"Oh, time!" he said. "Time! . . . Margaret Sanger was one of the first of the birth-control ladies when the very *phrase* couldn't be uttered in polite society. Anyway. My mother knew her—believed in her— and of course followed her teachings. No wonder. She already had five. And that was that, she thought. A year. Two. Everything under control. Or should I say, under birth control? Then something went wrong. She's not sure what. There are theories and explanations— but, there it was. And I was born. An accident."

"I'm *so* glad," I said.

He looked at me, but since I saw him only in silhouette, could not see his face. I put down my glass and turned to him in all expectation.

"Let's go," he said.

The next three and a half hours went almost according to plan. The walk, Hackney's, the lounge, the walk back, the auctions and the pitchmen *and* the diving horse! He bought me a beautiful antique cut-glass bowl on which was engraved: WHEN THIS YOU SEE, REMEMBER ME.

Going up in the elevator at the hotel, he looked at his watch and smiled.

"Nine-fifty-six," he said.

"Perfect."

"I don't know." He frowned. "There's such a thing as being *too* organized. I wouldn't want us to become data computers."

"Not a chance," I said.

In the hallway, he took my shoulders and looked into my eyes. I tried to make them say, "Yes!"

"Midge," he said, "you're a dear girl, and I want you to know how grateful I am. It's been grand, and I could not have done it—any of it—without you."

With that, he put his arms around me and held me tightly for what seemed like a long time. He released me, said, "Thank you," and went to his door. I went to mine. I was trembling again, but for other reasons. I stood in front of my door, hand on knob, but could not bear the idea of going in and ending the evening. I could not think of what to do. All at once, I found myself moving toward *his* door—my action preceding my thought. I tried to stop myself. I knew that I was on the verge of committing a blunder, but my brain and my body had severed connection. There I was now, in front of his door. Get away, my brain shouted, but already my finger was on the buzzer. I heard the sound within.

"Yes?"

"Me. You promised me the eleven-o'clock news."

The door opened. I walked in and turned to face him. He was still standing at the open door. I came toward him and pushed him against the door, closing it (as has been done to me so many times). He looked startled, but not surprised. I pressed myself against him, full-length—and then I kissed him. I opened my mouth and placed it accurately over his. I moved about for leverage and thrust my tongue as deep into his throat as I could. He shuddered and grabbed me. Was he going to push me off? No. He hung on and I felt his hands on my back, on my hips, on my bottom. Our middles were pressing hard—one against the other. But why was the kiss still all mine? Why were his lips so passive, his tongue so shy? I devoured him. At last his head came to life. He took charge and returned the kiss in kind. I had kissed him. Now he was kissing me, and all at once, we were sharing it. It was one kiss—a remarkable, thrilling creation. I ended it, pulled away, walked out the door, and slammed it shut.

That was it. The eleven-o'clock news.

I went to my room and got ready for bed.

Did I expect to hear his knock? Did I hope for it, want it? Or was what had happened enough for now? A theme stated.

In bed, I listened, straining. Once or twice I thought I heard footsteps. Later, I was sure of them—they came and passed, going elsewhere.

Hoping, wondering, wanting, I fell asleep.

I awoke, looked at the clock: 6:40. I cannot explain—even to myself —how it happened that at 7:00 precisely, I pressed his door buzzer.

He opened the door.

"Good morning," he said.

"I smell coffee."

"Have some?"

"Please."

There seemed to be a table full of breakfast.

"I wasn't sure what," he said. "So I got one of each."

The news was on the radio, and he listened to it as we talked.

"Sleep well?" I asked.

"Like a baby," he said. "I woke up every hour on the hour and screamed."

"Is that an old joke," I asked, "or did you just make it up?"

"Old," he said. "Old, old."

"I thought so."

"Question," he said. "Did we have a great deal to drink last night?"

"*I* didn't. One here, one there, and a glass and a half of wine. What about you?"

"About the same," he said, and studied me. "Amazing."

"What is?"

"How are you on bicycles?" he asked.

"I was brought up with three brothers," I replied.

"Say no more. The point is that until nine A.M. we can ride bikes up and down the boardwalk. A perfect surface. Glorious air."

"Full of salubrity?" I asked.

"We'll see."

The ride was immense, invigorating, and bracing. We rode and raced ₁ and said little. At nine, we gave up the bikes and walked.

"There's still not enough Nora up there," he said. "What can I do? My feeling is that the show still talks too much—it wants to sing more, dance more. How many numbers does She sing now?"

"Nine," I said.

"Is that about right?"

"So they say."

"I worry about more scenes, but maybe the ones that are there can be deepened. We'll have to look after lunch."

"You want my opinion?"

"Of course."

"You haven't asked for it."

"I'm asking now. Don't be so touchy."

"The fact that there's not enough Nora is because there's too much She. The material's there. It's just that She wants to remain She. She's a performer, not an actress."

"No, no," he said sharply. "Don't lead me into *that.*"

"Into what?"

"Passing the buck. Blaming others. Or the audience. Time enough to do that after I'm convinced that what *I've* done is as much as I can do. My feeling is that they love her when She's a tart—and then they resent her a little when She's a star."

"What's wrong with that?"

"*Everything!* It's ass-backward. I want them to be unhappy about her when She's in the house and then—along with the public, the world—adore her as a star. That gives us an emotional climax, a satisfying end to the evening."

"Why *is* it upside down? Any idea?"

"Not yet. Unless She herself is happier, more comfortable in the first part. Wait. This may be it. She comes on too strong as the star. The real ones—the big ones—are relaxed somehow. Confident. They know they're good, so they don't have to be so goddamn insistent."

"Talk to Larry?" I suggested. "He's a wonder. He can do great things with her. Things She doesn't even know he's doing."

"Absolutely. But let's get the stuff right first."

"Larry could come down here. If you wanted him to."

He stopped and looked at me.

"Do *you* want him to?" he asked.

"Me? What have *I* got to do with it?"

"Do you?"

"Of course not."

We walked again.

"She's too winning in Scene One. That's why She doesn't seem like a real hooker. Winningness is not a common attribute of whores. Strange as that may seem. It's because they hate life. And that's what Nora has to do in Scene One. Is that in the text? Come on, now. Truthfully. You've probably got it committed to memory by now. Is it?"

"Not specifically, no."

"And later, when she makes it—she *loves* life. Is *that* in the text?"

"No."

"All right. There's the job. Lunch at The Shelburne all right?"

"Let's try The Claridge. We had *breakfast* at The Shelburne."

As soon as we had ordered lunch, he asked, "Have you ever been married?"

"No. Never."

"Why not?"

"I'm too good for them."

"No. Seriously. Come on."

"None of your business."

"Of course it is. Human beings are my business. Especially the female of the species. And when I encounter a bright and beautiful girl of well, say—well—whatever. Post-teens, let's say."

"Let's."

"And she's still single, I wonder."

"I've had my share of beaux," I said. "Would you care to see my references?"

"If you're going to turn ugly on me," he said, "I'm going to ask for a table for a party of one. Me."

"Please don't. I'd rather have lunch with you than by myself. Even if I have to tell you the story of my life."

"What makes you think I'm interested in the story of your life?"

"Waiter!" I called out. "I want a table for a party of one!"

"How many serious proposals have you turned down?" he asked.

"None," I said. "Not a one. Can you believe it?"

"No, I can't."

"Neither can I—but it's the God's truth. I have had no proposals —propositions, yes."

"I'll be damned. What a generation!"

We finished our excellent lunch in silence. Crabmeat Louis, Persian melon, coffee. I could not tell if he was thinking of me or of Nora, but whichever it was, I knew it was better not to interrupt him. He smiled now and then, frowned a good deal, winked at me once.

He began rewriting directly after lunch. I went to my room, read, and waited.

At four, he phoned.

"Order tea," he said. "No food. In here. Twenty minutes."

I hated him. So curt, so demanding. Did he ever ask if *I* wanted tea? Was I his slave? I wanted to be.

I called Room Service and ordered one tea, cream and milk and lemon—how should *I* know? And for myself, coffee with hot skim milk and a piece of pound cake.

Half an hour—not twenty minutes—half an hour later, I sauntered down to his room. He was having tea, reading some pages.

"They made a mistake," he said.

"Oh?"

"Yuh. Sent one coffee."

"That's what I ordered."

"You did?"

"Oh sure—I've got quite a little mind of my own. You'd be surprised."

"The operative word there is 'little,' I think. What's this goofy sensitivity you play with? Tea, coffee. What the hell's the difference? We're busy."

"*You* are."

"Well, you're *going* to be. Let's get going on this."

He handed me about twenty pages of manuscript.

"One and one," he said.

"—make two," I said.

He stood up.

"Oh, God!" he said. "I came down here with a girl, and she's turning into a *woman!*"

I moved back and forth from his room to mine all evening. We did not stop for dinner until after nine—and then had it sent up. A charmless meal: steak, baked potato, salad, ice cream, coffee—eaten in silence.

When we finished, he pushed the table into the hall. We went back to work and kept at it until just after midnight.

As I handed him a sheaf of retypes, I yawned.

"Sleepy?" he asked, absently, examining the pages.

"Not at all," I said. "I'm just practicing my goldfish imitation."

"I think you're sleepy. Why don't you go to bed?"

"Why don't *you?*"

"Why don't we *both* go to bed?"

"Why don't we both go to bed together?" I asked.

He regarded me with the kind of tenderness I associate with women rather than men.

"It's been on my mind," he said. "I thought it best to wait for the right moment. I wonder if this is it."

"The right moment," I said, "is when both of us want to." I started out. "I'll be back."

It took me a long time to prepare. My anxiousness slowed me down. How could I be perfect for him? What would he want? Could I provide it? What if I failed? Would I ever get another chance? I kept taking deep breaths.

In my nightgown, slippers, and dressing gown—and carrying one small case—I made my way down the hall. When I reached his door, I did not ring or knock—I walked right in. The door was open. I knew it would be. How?

I closed the door behind me and locked it. I went into the dimly lighted bedroom. He was standing at the window, wearing a robe—and I knew, somehow, nothing else. He turned to me.

"I've been talking to God," he said. "He approves."

I went to him. We embraced. We kissed. I shed every stitch I was wearing and got into bed. He joined me there. Why was the kiss lying down so different from the other? His fingers moved gently on my body. I reached down impulsively and took his genitals into my hand —testicles, penis, pubis, all. His penis, aroused, was hot to the touch. As I held it, I felt a powerful, throbbing pulse beating within it. His face was nuzzling my neck.

"Sleep," he whispered.

"What?!" I was astounded.

"Yes," he said. "Sleep. I'll meet you—right back here—presently."

"Impossible," I said.

"Try. You'll see. Think of what's in store. Float away. 'Hold on tight. And down we went. In the mountains, there you feel free.'"

What on earth was he talking about? The words were vaguely familiar. What did they mean? I was comfortable, too comfortable.

"Listen to the sea," he said.

I did so. It became music. I slept.

I am awakened by a soft kiss and by the weight of his body on mine. My face is caressed by his lips—my ears, eyes, neck, breasts, where he lingers, making friends with my nipples, teasing them wittily and lovingly.

I spread my thighs and lift my knees, inviting his penetration. I feel his stiffness on the inside of my thighs. He raises himself above me —seems to be hovering there, levitated. I feel the tip of him confidently resting precisely where it is wanted. He enters me with reverence, the head of his prick fondling my engorged bud. I am flowing copiously. I hear myself talking. I am saying it all, expressing what I feel, telling what I want. It has never been so. My hands move down his back. I grasp his firm buttocks and press them to me. He goes deeper into me, and deeper still. He is farther inside me than I thought possible. I cry out as I arch to him. He moves from side to side, exploring the cave within me. I try to hold back, to prolong the ecstasy. I fail. I succeed. A paroxysm of joy overcomes me. Only now does he begin a powerful rhythmic thrusting—exciting and agitating beyond imagining my already frantic nerve ends. I want to beg him to stop, but fear that if I do so, he will. His body is moving upward on mine, the pressure of his shaft is precise and maddening. It moves out slowly.

"No!" I heard myself cry.

He plunges back into me. A scream. Mine?

He pulls himself up and out and holds as I move to him, pursuing wonder. Now together we move away—toward—farther—closer— together—meeting, meeting joyously.

I am melting. I am terrified. It is all too much. I explode.

He holds me close, rolls away, and we lie, side by side, still joined. We kiss. In time, I return to earth, to the surface of his bed, and find that he is still inside me, still aroused. Most delicately, he turns again until I am above him. He manipulates my body, my arms, my legs, until we are in perfect physical accord. His hands, behind me, guide me. New parts of me are found and satisfied—I lose track of time and place and space. There is no world other than this.

Later, he is above me once more—senses my need, waits for me, and then pours his warm essence into me.

I feel utterly safe for the first time in my life.

How can I describe the indescribable? How can I convey, even to myself, what the following hours meant? We stayed together, dozed, made lazy love, napped, laughed, talked, played with each other, joked—were suddenly on fire—wild and passionate and seemingly insatiable. Abandoned. Daring. Crazy.

I was discovering love.

Of course, I had done my share of fucking—but this was something else again. I had taken pleasure and given satisfaction. I had done what was asked of me, or expected of me. I had fucked and been fucked—well and clumsily. I had sucked and been sucked—happily and dutifully.

But I had never *shared* lovemaking, never known such joy in it or gratitude or imagination—had never known such heights.

I had known and had boys, jocks, studs, hot-shots, fellows, boy-friends, beaux, sexpots, even a belle, once!—but never before a man, not until now a Gene. A man, a gentleman, a lover, a complete and wise and sensitive and caring and loving and ardent understanding man. How can I hold him, keep him?

The shape and color of our days in Atlantic City changed.

We worked and ate and drank and walked and made love—except that I kept trying to think of another name for it. It was unique. Not what others do.

Then, one rainy afternoon, we decided to take a nap instead of walking. We kicked off our shoes and lay down on the bed. The nap was brief, interrupted by his hand where I wanted it. Shortly after that, he removed my panty hose with skill and care and buried his face where his hand had been. And there he stayed—for hours. I was kissed there and licked and lapped and nibbled and bitten and tickled and teased and sucked and eaten and swallowed. I wanted to return the rapture in kind, and eventually I did. Love at last, Midge, I thought—and knew.

And then, on the ride back to Philadelphia—it struck me. This would end. The show would open and Gene would return to Chicago and to his life. And what would *I* return to? It would all seem pale from now on. A gloom settled over me. I tried to dispel it first with romantic dreams, next with desperate plans. I tried to laugh at myself, could not.

We were back in Philadelphia.

· XXXI ·

Second week in Philadelphia.

Sammy and Patti have begun to stop the show regularly with their number, "Big Town." It has been fascinating to watch the development. It started as a simple little filler that Sammy, as a street-corner food vendor, did to eat up time for a scene change and a complete costume change for Star. Then Larry suggested it might go better as a duet. To this end, he tried several of the girls. They were all good. Hard to make a choice, but Art insisted that he use Patti. Buddy worked out a routine for them; Jenny came in and polished it. Larry gave them some performance pointers. It began to go well, a satisfying moment in the show, if not a spectacular one. Soon I began to notice something. Sammy and Patti rehearsing. In the dressing room, in the lounge, at the hotel, in the lobby, on stage some mornings. They never stopped. They kept doing that number as though nothing else in the world mattered. The performance began to get loose —looser, confident—but more important, it began to achieve precision. They were moving to the music, breathing to the orchestration. I would have bet at times that their hearts were beating not only as one but both of them to the drummer's beat. One night—a Friday —a lively house, they did it and stopped the show. In the wings they hugged and kissed and slapped each other around, I'm told.

I was sitting with Larry. He said, "That's it! They've got it! Now it'll happen every performance."

"How do you know?"

"Because now a magic takes over. How they convey to the audience in some subliminal way I have never understood that this is a showstopper. Something to do with the rhythm of life."

· XXXII ·

The battle of "Big Town" rages. The disturbances began precisely
from the time when the number began to get a nightly ovation.

One could feel first the nervousness, then the tension, and finally
the resentment all emanating from the camp of Star.

A blowup on the subject in her dressing room tonight.

> STAR
>
> I don't give a fuck who gets a hand or who has a number to do.
> Shit, I can't do them all! I'm doing too much as it is!

> LARRY
>
> Then what?

> STAR
>
> The routining, you schmuck. The spotting. What the hell have
> you got that number right in front of my dreariest scene in the
> whole goddam show? I come on, and with, for Chrissake, what
> I've got to do it's like a goddam stage wait.

> LARRY
>
> They're working on it.

> STAR
>
> Oh, for Christ's sweet sake, don't give me that! "They're working
> on it." They've been working on it since Year One. It's *never*
> going to get any better because it's horseshit to begin with. What

do you think they're going to come up with? Chocolate-covered horseshit?

LARRY

It's an essential scene, dear.

STAR

Well, then move it someplace where I can handle it.
(LARRY *laughs*)
What the hell's so funny?

LARRY

How can you move the scene? We're telling the story A-B-C-D-E-F-G and so forth. It's *chronological.* That's where that scene comes.

STAR

(A scream)
Then move the fucking *number,* I tell you! Someplace else. I'm not going to play that goddam scene where it is. Do you understand what I'm saying?

LARRY

Perfectly. Now sit down and let me tell you something. No show means a damn thing to any player if the player doesn't learn something from it. You get better all the time, and it's because you're learning.

STAR

Don't butter me up, buster. I'm not a piece of toast.

LARRY

Let me tell you a story. One of the greatest revues that ever happened in the history of Broadway was a show called *As Thousands Cheer.* By Irving Berlin and Moss Hart. And in it Clifton Webb and Marilyn Miller and Ethel Waters.

STAR

Some show. I never heard of any of them.

LARRY

(Using his inhalator)
Your loss, sweetheart, your loss. But they were big stars, great talents, take my word for it. Now it was a revue, so the question of routining was important. What number followed what, who followed who. A number called "Harlem On My Mind" was done

by Ethel Waters and a real showstopper. Not the mechanical kind, like the manufactured ones we've got around here, but a *real* one. Following that, Clifton Webb had to come on and do a light little patter song and dance. Well, of course, it did seem pale by comparison, and some friction developed, the same kind we have here now. Finally, Hassard Short decided that since Webb was the bigger star they ought to defer to him, so he went to Ethel Waters and asked if she would be willing to put her number in another spot. She wanted to know *what* other spot? The only place it *could* go was following a number that Marilyn Miller and Clifton Webb did that was absolutely sensational. Short suggested that spot, but said, "Unless you think that's too big a number to follow?" And Ethel Waters said, "Hell, no, Mr. Short. There's nothing I like better than workin' on a *hot* stage!"

STAR

Yeah, so what? What's that got to do with me?

LARRY

I'm giving you a hot stage. But you're so tied up in your own ego, you don't see it. You're not taking advantage of it. You're sulking through the scene, so of course it's dreary, and it always *will* be dreary. Why don't you try *playing* it a few performances?

STAR

That's interesting, what you said, you shithead, about not taking advantage. That's the whole goddam trouble around here is I *haven't* been taking advantage. Have you ever seen my contract? Would you like to see my contract? Would you like to see what's in it?

LARRY

Not in the least.

STAR

All right, then, let me tell you. Director approval, that's only *one* of the things that I've got. Director approval. Do you have *star* approval in *your* contract?

LARRY

I wouldn't want it.

STAR

You wouldn't, huh? Well, let's get to the bottom line. The bottom line is that that number gets moved, or else.

LARRY

Would you care to go on with that?

STAR

With what?

LARRY

Or else—what?

STAR

Or else it will be your ass, buddy. If *you* won't move it, I'll get someone in here who knows his place.

LARRY

(Looking at her carefully)

We're not getting along too well, are we?

(He leaves)

Two nights later—the last eight bars of the orchestration were revised. The bing-bang beats were removed. The so-called "button" taken off and although the number went well, it did *not* stop the show.

Sammy was furious, Patti sobbed—but what could they do? Sammy begged Hy to restore the finish; Patti appealed to Art.

"Relax," he reassured her, "I'll see what I can do."

To his credit, he did try at the next conference.

"I know what I'm doing," said Hy. "I don't need anybody to tell me how to handle an orchestration. What's been happening is the worst thing that can happen—when the small part players stop the show—that's like a sucker branch, it weakens the tree."

Larry. "You mean like Stubby Kaye singing 'Sit Down, You're Rockin' the Boat' in *Guys and Dolls*?"

Hy ignored him and went on. "Where you want the strength is in the star. *She's* got to have the showstoppers."

Larry. "Like Stanley Holloway singing 'Get Me to the Church on Time'?"

"We've got a star and we've got to protect her."

In bed that night, I tried to get Gene to intercede. He declined, saying that he believes everyone should stick to his own department.

· 304 ·

Then he added, "And no show-talk in bed. That's a rule! Strictly enforced."

Apparently it was going to take more than mucking up the orchestration to spoil Sammy and Patti. They did something—I don't know what—to compensate, and a few performances later stopped the show again with *no* help from the pit.

Another conference.

HY
Lemme tell you something, fellas. The time has come for drastic. Let me ask you one question.

ART
(Terrified)
What do you mean drastic?

HY
I mean cuts—not trims—y'hear what I'm saying? Cuts! Now's the time we have to begin to cut to the *show*. What's the show? Where's *the show?* We got no time for detours or side trips or mingies. The show! The mainline! What do they want to see? What do they want to hear?

LARRY
That's *six* questions, Hy.

HY
You've been *counting?*

LARRY
That's seven.

HY
So what?

LARRY
So how about a few answers? Or even *one?*

HY
Answers! That's *your* job. Mine is questions. How can we start in low gear, shift, get into high, hit the road, go, and then by God break every God damned speed limit there is? Up the hill over the top. Hit the destination an hour ahead! How can we do that?

LARRY

Call Hertz. They'll send a car. Do that and get in and drive away. I wish you would, honestly!

HY

You don't get me, huh?

LARRY

You *talk*, Hy. Give us some specifics, why don't you?

HY

Fair enough. Right off the top of my head, for instance, in Act One we go good till that dumb filler we got stuck with—"Big Town."

LARRY

What!?

HY

Wait a second! Hear me out!

LARRY

"Big Town," for God's sake, is—

HY

If we didn't have the change there—if She didn't have to go to a bare-ass costume change—would we ever have had that number?

LARRY

Of course not. But it fell in there and it's sensational.

HY

It's a dog. And I ought to know. I wrote it. It's derivative.

LARRY

You like the number, Fred?

FRED

I'm beginning to hate them *all.*

HY

Don't listen to him—he's tired, he's depressed.

LARRY

Amazing—working with such a sunny, upbeat enthusiast like you?

ART

What're you trying to do, Larry, start a whole battle here?

VAL

The number stinks.

LARRY

Let me ask you something, Val. Do you think the *audience* thinks it stinks?

VAL

The audience! What the fuck do *they* know? You give 'em a big finish, with drums and a button and they go bananas. Hy knows what he's talking. He's done twenty-two shows.

LARRY

Jenny?

JENNY

I like it—but if you took it out, who'd miss it? I mean outside of Sammy and Patti?

VAL

Is that who you're doing the show for? A couple of bit players?

ART

We could try dropping it for two, three shows and see what happens.

ALICIA

And what about her change?

ART

Figure out something.

ALICIA

Thank you.

JENNY

We could swipe a trick from *Lady in the Dark.*

LARRY

What trick?

JENNY

When they had Gertrude Lawrence dancing, dancing in the dream sequence, and the lights faded and came on and there she was on the psychiatrist's couch in a complete change.

LARRY

How'd they do it?

JENNY

With a double. Gertie started, then danced through a piece of scenery and a double dancing back-to took her place while she changed.

ART

So could we do that?

JENNY

Not tonight—but in a day or two, probably. We'll need a duplicate costume for the double—and I have some staging—

ART
(To CLAY*)*

And what about the set?

CLAY

Well, if Jenny could do the last part of the dance in front of the street drop—yes.

ART

So let's try it.

I look at Larry, deflated by defeat. It has all been steamrolled through. At least, he knows when he's licked.

The whole company is outraged when they hear of the cut. Sammy quits. Patti gets drunk and misses two shows. Then everything quiets down.

Supper with Gene and Larry at Bookbinder's.
"I miss it," says Gene. "I miss it bad."
"Relax," says Larry. "You'll get it back."
"We will?" asks Gene, brightening.
"Yes, but in a slightly altered form. And probably in another spot."
"What do you mean?" I ask.
"Oh, God," says Larry, "I've been through this sequence so many times, it's sickening. Here's what's going to happen. In a week or ten days, there'll be heat on for one more number for Miss Wonderful. Hy and Fred will come up with two or three. No. No good. Despera-

tion. Then someone—probably Hy—will say, 'Hey! Remember that thing we once had—"Big Town?" Should we try *that?*' Some indecision—some selling—get Sammy back."

"Will he come?" I ask. "He left in a sixteen-cylinder huff."

"He'll come back. They'll tell him the number's back in and that he's now going to do it with Star, no less. He'll come back. *Patti'll* quit. He'll do it with Star and when it's nicely broken in—it'll be decided that it would be better if She did it alone. So Sammy'll be out again, but if he's smart, he'll get a payoff." He sang: "And That's the Broad-way Mel-o-deeee!!!!"

"I can't believe any of that will happen," says Gene.

"Are you a betting man?"

"Ah! My secret is out," cries Gene. "Betting. My downfall. You can't imagine what I went through in Atlantic City."

"Yes," I said. "I watched you suffering. It was pitiful."

"I'll give you odds," says Larry.

"It's too tempting. Stop me, somebody!"

No one did. They made a bet.

The trick change worked marvelously. You could hear the audience gasp at every performance when She danced off and two seconds later came through the big doors in that great formal ball gown.

Gene was goggle-eyed, like a small boy at a circus.

After the show, we went to a jazz joint on Race Street, where I drank too much. I always drink too much in jazz joints.

"It's a real strength," said Gene. "Isn't it? Lord, I love magic. Maybe it's even better than the number. What do *you* think?"

"I think hearts are being broken, and careers damaged, and people hurt and humiliated. I think girls are smiling and dancing while suffering from excruciating menstrual pain. I think health is breaking down along with morale, and a sense of fairness and loyalty and honesty—all for the sake of a goddam musical show."

"What a spill! Finished?"

"No. I think Art Clune is a no-good stinkin' rotten son-of-a-bitch bastard. And some of it rubbed off on me. Clay good but weak. Hy talented but amoral. Ivan a genius. Alicia a mystery. Jenny a tragedy. Larry in trouble. Gene Bowman a great man and I love you and nothing in the world you could ever say or do would change that and

I know it's hopeless and I know I'm not up to you and never will be but I don't care because I've had you in my life and my life'll be better for the rest of my life because of it and I think I'm a goddam mess but it's not my fault and I think I never want to see another musical as long as I live and maybe I'll do what I should have done in 1967 that would have made my mother so happy she wanted me to take vows and become a nun and I should have but then I wouldn't have known you and maybe that would have been better after all. You asked me what I think. Well, that's what I think. What do *you* think?"

"Check, please!" he called out.

He took me home and put me to bed.

In my dream, he became my doctor—a distinguished gynecologist who took care of my cunt beautifully and tenderly. He was dressed in white and wore white rubber gloves and when he decided to operate, did so with gold instruments. The result of the operation was an enchanting four-year-old boy, dressed in a white sailor suit, who looked exactly like the distinguished gynecologist or like me, depending on the angle from which he was viewed. We were all three in a pool, swimming and splashing.

The smell of strong coffee awakened me. Gene stood beside me with a steaming cup in his hand.

"Are you all right?" he asked.

"I will be as soon as somebody gives me the top of my head back."

"Take a sip," he said. "Sit up and take a sip."

I tried, failed.

"Could you turn off the light?" I asked.

"That's not the light, you old souse—that's the sun."

"Well," I said, "would you turn *that* off?"

He pulled down the shade and went out. I sat up, trying to sip the hot coffee and feeling ashamed, remorseful, embarrassed, abashed, and miserable.

He returned, bringing a tall glass filled with a crimson liquid.

"What is it?" I asked. "Blood?"

"I hope so," he said. "Drink it down."

"Not till you tell me."

"Dr. Bowman's Magic Elixir for cramps, pimples, arthritis, female weakness, and slow second acts."

I drank it down in one long draught and could hardly believe what happened next—my hangover was gone within five minutes.

"What the *hell?*" I asked.

"When I know you better," he said, "I'll reveal the secret formula. It was given to me by a millionaire Chicago devout alcoholic about fifteen years ago."

I went into the bathroom, showered, and went directly from the shower back into the bedroom. There he was, wearing a robe only, engrossed in his inevitable newspaper. He looked up.

"You're soaking wet," he observed.

"I couldn't wait," I said, getting into bed.

"You're wet," he said again.

"So are you."

"I think I'd better dry you off."

"Do."

And so the day began.

· XXXIII ·

Gene. I love writing his name. Gene Gene Gene Gene. God, I'm like a teenager with a crush on the football star or a movie actor.

I am trying to be sensible about the whole thing, and practical and reasonable, but it is no use.

The relationship with him goes beyond sexual expression, fantasies of a perfect future, or the sheer joy of being with him. It is a state of being that is utterly new to me.

Lovemaking, at least in my life, used to be a pleasant activity—often more than that. Exciting, intoxicating, stimulating. But it always had a beginning, a middle, and an end. A hunger satisfied. A desire achieved.

Not so with Gene. With Gene Gene Gene there is no beginning and no end. It goes on ceaselessly. It stretches back to always was and goes on into infinity. It is hard to explain, perhaps impossible, but I am trying to explain it to myself.

I am truly more concerned about his health and happiness than I am about my own. A new experience for me, especially in relationships with men.

I think of us as one. He makes me laugh. He takes his work seriously, but not himself.

The physical part of our life together seems to be in the hands of forces beyond our control. There is never any verbalization. It always happens because it is meant to happen—no matter what the time or place.

I compare this circumstance to others I have known.

The overt assault: sometimes bold and sudden and violent; often gentle and suggestive—a thigh touched, a breast considered, an ear brushed with a gentle kiss. In any case—a set of signals to which the response might be affirmative or negative: moves, touches, gestures, looks.

Or words. Some I have encountered have been:

(1) "I want you, baby. I *need* you."
(2) "How about it?"
(3) "I'll *die* if I don't get to fuck you."
(4) "Shall we go to bed?"
(5) "Let's go to bed."
(6) "Here. Give me your hand. Feel this. Want it?"
(7) "I honestly think, Midge, that we're ready for a relationship."

To which the replies might be:

(1) "Not here, honey. Not now."
(2) "Yes."
(3) "Please don't use that word."
(4) "No, I can't."
(5) "All right. If you really want to."
(6) "Get away from me, you creep!"
(7) "The trouble is—I'm in love with someone else."

And in extended affairs I have known, there was generally an approach by either party.

(1) "You feel like it tonight?"
(2) "Let's go home—I'm horny as hell."
(3) "Baby? Want to?"

Or simply a touch in the dark, which might be accepted or rejected.

But in this life with Gene—as I have said, it all happens automatically.

We went for an early-morning walk in the country. The air was crisp and the depth of the fallen autumn leaves made it difficult to walk briskly. But we were breathing deeply and savoring the air. How did it happen? There we were, lying in the leaves, firmly and joyously joined. The scent of the earth around us was overwhelmingly erotic. Love.

I came in late one afternoon. He was working. As a rule, he never even looks up until he is ready—but this time he did and smiled and held his look, and I went to him and knelt before him and unzipped him and took him.

We were watching a performance at the theatre from the back of the house. It was going extremely well. All at once, we moved together out the door, up the alley, through the stage door, up one flight, into the production office. We undressed quickly, spread a mat, and reveled in one another until just before the end of the show.

Gene.
Whenever I talk to him, he listens. Not only that, but he understands—and if he doesn't he questions me. I feel ever in close contact with him.

But it is going to end. Soon. In a matter of weeks. And then what am I to do? Will I be able to accept it for what it was—a lovely, romantic interlude in the heat of the excitement of the creation of the show? Or is there a cumbersome torch to carry waiting for me out there in the near future?

The more I know about his life, the more I see that there is no room for me in it.

Only this strange time and place and extraordinary way of life is making it possible.

One consolation. I will always know that once in my life I was in love, so I know what love is and what it is worth.

I should be sad about all this, but in my present state I cannot find it within myself to be anything but euphorically happy.

SHINE ON, HARVEST MOON

Company Bulletin

Friday, November 30

RUNNING ORDER: Please check the Call Board for running order tonight.

COLDS: That dreaded small epidemic appears to have begun in spite of all our efforts.

Large doses of Vitamin C are suggested; also, if you stay alkaline, your chances of picking up a cold are greatly reduced. This can be accomplished by consuming fruits and fruit juices, fresh vegetables and vegetable juices, particularly unsweetened apricot juice and various alkaline waters, such as Vichy and Perrier, or check for local ones at your grocers.

Moreover, watch the changeable weather carefully and change clothing accordingly.

THE COMPANY YOU KEEP: RUSS KELLY
(Assistant Director)

I owe just about everything to ol' P.A. also known as The High School of Performing Arts. Without it, I would no doubt be a street bum along with the rest of my boyhood pals. Very few of us make it out of the slums. But P.A. did it for me and I went to work at The Long Wharf in New Haven, Conn., as a production assistant directly after I was graduated.

I have done masses of Children's Theatre which I would like some day to make my specialty.

The Big Break for me was, of course, being engaged by Larry Gabel, who has made it possible for me not only to learn but to *unlearn*. So many people in our profession spend years perfecting their mistakes.

I am the only one in my family in the theatre. My father is a barber in the Bronx, two brothers in the used-car business together in Yonkers; one sister, married, who lives in Dayton, Ohio, and has a baby a year. And she's not even Catholic! I do not intend to be an assistant all my life.

BACKSTAGE MANNERS: It is important for us all to cooperate in creating an atmosphere in which creative work can take place. For this reason, it is requested that no card-playing, knitting, cross-

word-puzzling, eating, or drinking take place on the stage *or* in the wings. The above activities should only be pursued in dressing rooms, Green Rooms, or below the stage. *No Smoking* in the wings.
  The management has been instructed to ask you to desist should you forget these instructions.

REMINDER: Joey, please meet with Phil in Our Star's dressing room at half-hour.

DAY OFF: The entire company will be off on Monday, December 3.

UNDERSTUDIES: Run-through will begin at 11 A.M. sharp, Tuesday, December 4.

QUOTE TO REMEMBER:
  "I had worked my way up the ladder always with my eye on the next step—assistant choreographer, then choreographer, then director—but along the way I didn't notice I was losing things. Success is good. It gives you freedom to travel, to have a nice apartment, but it brings certain problems you can't imagine until you're successful. Like the different way your friends start treating you. People don't call you on the phone and if they do they're always afraid they're disturbing you. It can get maddening. What they don't realize is that basically I haven't changed. I'm still that same Michael who danced in the chorus all those years.
  "Those were the happiest years of my life."
                              —Michael Bennett

There are now 21 days remaining until our New York opening.

· XXXIV ·

"Big Town" is back again in the show, as Larry prophesied.

Sammy is back, doing it with Star. It is not as effective as it was, but everyone believes it is going to be. It stops the show all right, but mainly because Hy has restored the razzle-dazzle ending to the orchestration.

Larry hates it.

"It's not a number," he says. "It's a goddam *applause machine!*"

Sammy, delighted though he is to be sharing Star's spotlight, cannot seem to get with her in the way he did with Patti.

He comes up to the conference tonight. He is one of Larry's oldest friends and has done seven shows with him, so there is no danger of a security breach.

"No," he says, "it's not a question of rehearsal—we rehearse all the time. She's a fantastic rehearser—but what She isn't is a team player. What the hell, She's a star—they're not supposed to be team players. Look, *She's* stet—you're not going to change *that*—but is there anything *I* can do? Tell me and I'll try."

"Yes," says Larry, "there is. She's got you psyched. You're performing the number like a supporting player."

"That's what I *am.*"

"In *life*—not on the *stage*, Sammy. Not in the number. In the number, She's a girl who's just arrived in New York—and you're a chestnut vendor—and you're telling her about New York and turning her on, so actually, *you're* the dominant one, or should be."

"Right," says Sammy, thoughtfully.

"Never mind remembering how much *She* gets a week and how much *you* get—that's nothing to do with it. Make believe it says out there on the houseboards your name and her name—side by side, same size—you should be two stars out there knockin' 'em dead. The way you were with Patti. Remember?"

"Patti," said Sammy, with a world of meaning.

"So will you try? It's the only way the number'll get back to what it was."

"What can I tell y'?" said Sammy. "I'll try. But it's tough, y'know what I mean? It's tough to establish a good rappapport with her—nothing against her, She's great—but it's tough to be married to her."

"So they say," said Larry. "But *you* only have to be married to her seven minutes a day—night."

· XXXV ·

The transformation in Sammy, and thus in "Big Town," is extraordinary. He took Larry's direction precisely and began coming on much
stronger—and better. He began to match her in movement and
let-go magnetism. The number was becoming a high spot.

Complaints begin. First from Val, then from her.

"What's he trying to do? Steal the number?" asked Val.

"I don't think so," answered Clay. "It looks better to me."

"Look *again!*"

"All right."

"Y'know, any time She wants, She can blow him off the stage. So
tell him watch his step."

Later. Star: "What's he trying, that little man? To push me?"

Larry: "No, no, just taking my direction."

"Which is what?"

"To make it a duet."

"How can it be a duet? Can he sing like me?"

"Of course not. Nobody can."

"So what's this duet shit?"

"I don't mean vocally."

"Oh."

"I mean number-wise, scene-wise. Boy-girl stuff."

"Boy-girl?! He's old enough to be my great-grandfather."

"A figure of speech, sweetie. Don't jump on me."

"Listen, I'd jump on you in a minute if I thought it would do any
good."

"Now, now."

"Now?"

They laughed a show-business laugh together.

But the situation remained unchanged—or, rather, it continued to develop along the lines planned by Larry. The number became an authentic showstopper—but Val and She were not happy. She could not bear sharing the ovation.

Something began to happen. The number went out of kilter. What was it?

"She's singing too loud," said Larry. "Can you tone her down?"

"I've told her," said Clay. "Twice."

"Tell her again," said Larry. "It's been my experience that if you tell a player to do something and he doesn't or can't or won't— you tell him again, and if he still doesn't—you tell him again, then again and again and again and again and again and again and again—"

"And if She *still* doesn't?"

"You tell her *again.*"

Clay told her again. And again. No use.

Sammy sent for.

"What do you think's the trouble, Sammy?"

"She's singin' too loud."

"That's what *we* think, but we can't get her down."

"Great voice," said Sammy.

"There's only one solution that *I* can think of."

"What's that?"

"If *She* won't sing softer—*you* sing louder."

Sammy looked worried.

"How *much* louder?" he asked.

"To match her."

"You think I can?"

"Try."

"That's some voice," he said. "I don't know *who* could match it. I doubt if *I* can."

"Try."

"When She belts—like on the last sixteen? Sometimes I see the big glass chandelier trembling."

"Just see *you* don't tremble. Sing louder. Get Buzz to help you. Take more breaths. I think if you come up—She'll come down."

Larry was wrong. Sammy did his best. Buzz coached him. He sang louder in an effort to get into the number with her. No use. He was no match for her. Still, Sammy tried gamely to keep up with her—and then a kind of killer instinct took hold of her and She seemed determined, night after night, to do what Val said She could do to Sammy—"blow him off the stage."

Last night, Sammy appeared to go vocally dead in the middle of the number.

In the intermission, Gene found me and said, "Larry says go back and see what happened. Let me know right away so I can tell him."

I hurried backstage, went to Sammy's dressing room. Maurice was with him, helping him. Sammy was leaning over his washbasin, spitting blood.

"I've sent for the house doctor," said Maurice. "I don't like the bleeding."

Sammy looked up, saw me, shrugged, and smiled wanly. He spat still more blood, then turned to me again and ran his forefinger across his throat with finality.

Maurice brought him a chair, and he sat by the washbasin, in trouble.

I went back into the auditorium and reported what little I knew to Gene, who returned to his seat next to Larry.

By the time I got back to Sammy's room, the doctor was there, and Sammy, aided by Maurice, was getting dressed.

"I'll take him," the doctor said. "We don't have to bother with expensive ambulances."

Sammy nodded. He was holding a bloodstained towel against his mouth.

"Where will he be, Doctor?" I asked.

"Jefferson," said the doctor.

"Prognosis?" I asked.

"You a doctor's daughter?"

"No, Doctor."

"Funny way to ask."

"What's the answer? They'll want to know."

"Oh, I think he'll be all right if he doesn't talk for a couple of weeks."

"Weeks!" I said—but it came out as a yell.

"Easy," said the doctor, "—or I'll have two patients with the same trouble."

"What's the trouble?"

"Not sure—looks to me like a broken blood vessel."

I couldn't see Sammy as they left, I could see only his eyes.

Gene and I went out to the hospital after the show. Larry wanted to go—but all agreed it would be imprudent. Who knew? Art—or someone else might turn up.

We found Sammy sedated, a plasma rig beside his bed, blood being fed to him intravenously. He looked small and very old. We waited until he awoke. He smiled and saluted. He looked about, found the little slate board and chalk that had been provided for communication, and printed on it, carefully. He turned it toward us and we read:

SHIT!

"The doctor says you're going to be fine," said Gene.

Sammy erased the contents of the slate board and wrote: "Yes, but too late."

"How do you mean?" asked Gene.

Sammy erased, wrote: "Will miss opening."

Gene. "Maybe not."

Sammy wrote: "My fault. Sorry."

"Not at all," said Gene. "It was Larry's fault. *He* says. Egging you into that screaming match with the world's greatest screamer."

Sammy wrote: "Can I go on? Please? Can handle all but the singing."

"Let me inquire," said Gene.

Sammy wrote: *"Please!* Hate to conk out."

So that's the way it has been settled. Sammy goes on as the chestnut vendor and does all his stuff silently and performs the dance, but as for the song—why, She has it all to herself now and is as happy as a grig, and stops the show regularly.

I find it hard to watch that number, and when I do, I only watch Sammy. Writing this whole history all these weeks, I feel I have become freer with words, and find it easier and easier to express myself and to describe what is going on, but I am *not* going to try to describe Sammy's face every night during "Big Town."

As to the bet Larry made with Gene, they have decided to call it off.

· XXXVI ·

The most violent battle thus far has been concluded. "Big Town" is out. Art and Star and Val and the record boys and Hy are the victors. All others are the losers—including the audience.

I suppose I suspected from the beginning that the number was a lost cause, but Larry fought hard, and indeed was making such a powerful case for it that even the record boys showed signs of weakening.

Art, a past master in noting which way the wind is blowing, yelled louder and louder, with Val providing a stentorophonic counterpoint. This particular round ended with the suggestion by the record boys to leave it in until they could have one more look.

At 5:30 the following afternoon, Art phoned me and said, "Meet me at the theatre in twenty minutes."

"I can't," I said. "I'm in the shower."

"Twenty-five minutes," he said.

"I don't think I—"

That was as far as I got. He hung up.

I got to the theatre at 6:10. He waiting for me backstage.

"You're late," he said. "You wanna watch that. You're not indispensable, you know. In fact, you're *dispensable.*"

"And shall I tell you what *you* are?"

"Not now," he said. "I haven't got the time. Come with me."

I followed him downstairs to the area beneath the stage. No one there except Maurice and Bonnie in the wardrobe section.

Art proceeded to climb through the passage into the orchestra pit. He turned and beckoned me to follow. All at once, there I was, in the pit—where I had never been before. A strange sensation. Claustrophobic. How do the musicians stand it?

"C'mere," said Art.

I joined him. He was going through the piano part of the score, handling the thick folio awkwardly. I worried that he would drop it.

"Careful," I said. "That gets out of order and God knows what—"

"Shut up!" he said. "Here. Here it is—about four numbers after it says Act Two. See it?"

"Yes. What about it?"

"I'm *telling* you what about it if you'll listen instead of talking all the goddam time!"

What was he so angry about? Nerves, no doubt.

"Sorry," I said.

"Now see this number here? The one says 'Big Town'?"

"Yes."

"O.K. We're taking it out of every part. Get going."

"What?"

"Don't ask questions. Just do what I'm tellin' you. And don't forget the *conductor's* part up there."

He started at one end of the pit—the percussion section. I began with the double-basses. It took much longer than I thought it was going to, but just before 7:00, we met in the woodwind section. He grabbed the stack of parts out of my hands, put them with his into an A & P shopping bag and started out. I went with him. In the alley, he stopped and said to me, "Keep it to yourself."

"Of course."

"Never mind the 'of course'—I'm not so goddam sure I trust you —I hear things."

"I don't doubt it—with the bunch of blabs and scandalmongers and gossips and spies *you've* got in your ear all the time. *I* hear things, too, about you."

"You don't say!"

"And if you don't trust me, or if you're not sure—why ask me to *do* stuff like that?"

"Who else have I got?"

"Or why didn't you do it yourself?"

"You want to know somethin'?" he asked. "Your big mouth is going to land you in all kinds of trouble one of these days."

"It already has," I said, and left him.

Keeping this latest caper of his dark was as difficult a thing as I have yet had to do on this whole damned show. But I concluded that bringing it out into the open at this late hour would serve only to complicate matters. As it stood, unless someone discovered the thing —there would be a rough half-minute during the performance and that would be all.

I was wrong. Again. It was only a rough ten seconds. Star and Sammy were ready to go on, She on the prompt side, he on the opposite side. The change music ended. A beat. A sound of confusion in the pit as some of the musicians realized there was a part missing. Phil rapped his baton sharply and I heard him say, "Rack! Play the rack! Now! One, two!"

And they went into the next number. Meanwhile, Clay, thinking an error had been made—simply ordered the set change, which was accomplished in seconds and the show went on, having skipped "Big Town." I could hear noises in the wings—but I doubt that the audience was aware of anything untoward.

Art decided to pass the whole thing off as a great joke. As it happens, he was the only one who thought it funny.

Still, he has accomplished what he wished. The number is out and apparently is going to *stay* out.

I permit myself a moment of satisfaction and say to him, when we are alone, "Now that it's over, may I tell you that I thought it was a nasty, unprofessional, inconsiderate thing to do?"

"You may," he replies smugly. "And may *I* tell *you* that all's fair in love and war and musicals?"

SHINE ON, HARVEST MOON
Company Bulletin
Tuesday, December 4

DISCIPLINE: At this point in our work, we must begin to avoid onstage break-ups and inside jokes. Amateur actors break up—professional actors do not. Errors, accidents, and unexpected occurrences are not humorous in the course of our work. Let us have all our parties, fun, and games offstage and after hours, but onstage in performances, respect the material, one another, and the institution of the theatre.

HEALTH NOTE: Does everyone in the company know about the beneficial effects of Knox Gelatin? Easily obtainable, it provides a quick source of energy through its protein. Many dancers, baseball players, football players, and pole vaulters have proved that gelatin taken in plain water, milk, or fruit juice adds energy and staves off fatigue.

THE COMPANY YOU KEEP: MILLIE KRAMER(Lighting)
    In case you don't know me by name, I don't blame you. I did (am doing) the lighting.
    Chicago-born. Dreamed of being an actress. Imagine it. Me! Went to Goodman, found out I didn't have it. Stayed on as Assistant Stage Manager. Left and went to Yale and studied lighting with Stanley McCandless.
    New York. Fourth or fifth assistant to the great Jean Rosenthal. Saw there was a chance in the field for women. Moved on. Alley Theatre in Houston, Mark Taper in L.A., etc. It *is* a field with room for women: not only Jean but Tharon Musser, Jennifer Tipton—*me!*

ROUTINE: "On the Night Boat" will be relit on Thursday. For all concerned rehearsal on stage in costume 11:00 A.M.

                                            Stu Bender

OUR OWN NORA:
    She once took this ad in the theatrical paper—ZIT'S.

"I, NORA BAYES, being of sound body and in my right mind (open for discussion) do hereby declare my independence by trying to please you, oh you fickle public, in giving you what you think you want. Heretofore, you have complained at the shortness of my programme. Lo!! Your punishment be on your own hands. On the date, and at the place set forth below, I will start to sing, and nothing but the police will be able to stop me." Nora Bayes

QUOTE TO REMEMBER:
"God watches over you, but He won't cash checks."
"Pop" Faye, Chicago newspaperman

There are now 16 days remaining until our New York opening.

· XXXVII ·

Misery. Gene has had to go back to Chicago. If I knew for how long, I could bear it, I suppose. But he couldn't—or wouldn't—say. An editorial shake-up of some kind on the paper.

I clung to him through the night and did not sleep. He did. He sleeps beautifully.

At breakfast, I told him so.

"You're a nut," he said.

"If you don't come back," I said, "I'll die."

"You'll die anyway," he said. "What the hell do you think you are —immortal?"

"But the show," I insisted. "It needs you."

"Right now," he said, "the show needs to be left alone. My mother used to say—'It'll never get well if you pick it.' The show is beginning to have a life of its own. It can use a rest from all us masterminds."

I went with him to the airport and did not cry until the plane took off. He would not have liked it. Then I watched the plane, with my life inside it, become a speck in the sky—then nothing.

· XXXVIII ·

The accident occurred at rehearsal. Thank God. It could easily have happened in performance. One of the boy dancers—Arvin—dropped his partner, Diana, during the big "Waltz" number, just as they reached the top of the staircase. Being a dancer, she knew how to fall, or else she might have been hurt even more badly than she was. She fell flat on her back and broke her coccyx. The doctor who came from Presbyterian Hospital said she might easily have broken her back, her spine, or even fractured her skull. So everyone in the company was relieved and grateful until the police turned up after the matinee and began the investigation.

It turns out that in the course of making a series of routine tests on Diana at the hospital, it was discovered that she had recently ingested a large amount of cocaine.

When questioned, she freely admitted having sniffed some during rehearsal. During the grilling, she was tired and scared and sedated and utterly miserable. Apparently, she didn't give a damn about anything or anyone. Almost anyone. Nothing on earth, apparently, would induce her to reveal her source, her connection. The narcs came in soon afterward, an investigation was launched, and now was under way.

Art responded to the whole affair in his usual hysterical way. Cocaine in the company! His solution was to fire Diana at once.

Jenny, in her present solid position, was able to block this nutty move.

"Listen, you chucklehead," she said to him. "This is old hat to me. I'll tell you how to handle it. Smoke out the connection in the company and straighten him. Or her."

"How the hell can I do that?"

"I don't know. But maybe you won't have to. Maybe the Keystone Kops'll do it for you."

"Nobody in your bunch would give you a hint?" he asked. "After all, it seems to be them that's on it."

"What in Christ's name are you talking about, Art? Do you know? Or are you just beating your gums?"

"Wait a second—"

"Is there any connection at *all* between your brain and your mouth—or is it all short-circuited?"

"I didn't—"

"The dancers, for God's sake, are probably the least of it. The whole *company's* shot through with just about everything there is. Uppers, downers, grass, snow, booze—even—"

"Booze doesn't count."

"Why not?"

"Because it's not illegal."

"Oh, brother!"

"I'm gonna put it up on the bulletin board," he said. "I don't want any potheads in this show. Or acidheads. Or cokies. I'll serve warning. It's bad enough I'm stuck with fags and dykes—but what can I do?"

"You can stop making noises."

"Don't tell me—"

"I said stop, Art. I mean it."

He stopped.

Why did this exchange—and particularly its ending—so delight me? A bully bullied? A monster tamed? A little of each, I suppose. Jenny has this beast tamed, for fair. Odd how it all comes down to the primitive in the end. All roads lead to and from the great male-female game. In work, business, life.

· XXXIX ·

A jolt this morning that has me still reeling this afternoon.

Clay Botsford was arrested at 7:00 a.m. Two policemen and a detective, all connected with the Narcotics Squad, came here to The Barclay, woke him, told him to get dressed, and took him into custody. He was not allowed to make a phone call until after he had been booked and jailed and bail set.

He then, for some reason, called me and gave me the staggering details. I say "for some reason," but thinking on it, the reason is clear. Art would have panicked. Clay's lawyer is in New York. So it was characteristically sensible on his part to phone me. I got hold of Art by eight-twenty. He got Paul Cooley and Joe Block, the theatre manager, to come right over. Then, uninvited, Cindy Sapiro turned up. The things we learn as we move from crisis to crisis. The damnedest people come through in a pinch. I have noticed it before. Strong ones, powers, often collapse under pressure. Diffident ineffectuals frequently rise to the necessity of the occasion.

So it was this morning with Cindy. I have regarded her, up to now —and with justification—as a feckless dilettante with nothing to recommend her or to justify her existence except her money. I have never heard her utter one sensible or practical sentence. Her snobbishness is a proverb. She is the sort of woman who is disliked by her *friends!* Yet, this morning, she proved to be the heroine of the miserable emergency. She is a born take-charge, but has not been allowed to pursue that bent on this show. Too many other take-charges around. But at the hysterical meeting today, she was pragmatic and calm. In three phone calls, she had found a top lawyer with political connections. She had called Washington and New York and held whispered, unintelligible conversations.

I tried to call Gene in Chicago, but could not reach him.

The lawyer, Thomas Edward Atkins, arrived. When I learned that he had those three names, I was instantly relieved. Any lawyer with three names has *got* to be superior. Especially a Philadelphia lawyer.

In the car (Cindy's) on the way to the Municipal Jail, Art kept asking Thomas Edward Atkins if he would make sure, whatever else happened, to get Clay sprung so that he could run the show tonight.

"There's nobody else can handle it," he explained.

"We'll do all we can."

"That's not enough," said Art. "I need the guy in the theatre *tonight.* Will they understand that?"

"We'll do what we can."

"You just said that," said Cindy. "Don't say it again."

"Boy, he sure fooled *me,*" said Art. "Clean-cut, neat, WASP, college man. Son-of-a-bitch turns out to be a pusher."

"You know what you are, Clune?" asked Cindy.

"Certainly."

"You're a Goddamn fool. And a dangerous bastard."

"Watch it!"

"*You* watch it. Where the hell do you come off being judge and jury and hangman all of a sudden? What makes you assume he's guilty?"

"Because!" Art yelled, lamely.

"Oh," said Cindy. "My mistake."

"Why'd they nab him if he didn't?" insisted Art. "They didn't *me.* Or *you.* They got *him.*"

"That doesn't mean a thing," said Cindy. "They like to start someplace. Isn't that so, Mr. Atkins?"

"Possibly."

Art again. "They must have *some* evidence. *Some* witnesses. Wouldn't you say, Mr. Edwards?"

"Possibly."

"But I mean to say—whatever—we can bail him out, can't we? At least for a couple of days? For tonight?"

"We'll do what we can," said Thomas Edward Atkins.

Cindy flicked the ash from her cigarette onto his lap as we reached our destination.

After a good deal of wrangling, most of it incomprehensible to anyone but the judge and Atkins (and I'm not too sure of them, either), bail was set at $10,000 against a hearing one week from today.

"There are bondsmen in the hall," said Atkins. "I know several of them."

"Tell 'em to get lost," said Cindy. "I'll handle this. Who needs *their* rip-off? In the end, it's going to be Clay himself who pays up. So why *load* him?"

"Well," said Atkins, "as a matter of expediency— I thought—they won't take a check, you see, unless it's certified, and that might take — I understood there was a need for speed, since—" He stopped.

"Do you ever finish a sentence?" asked Cindy. "I've got it right here. Who gets it?"

"The clerk," said Atkins. "Are you sure you? . . ."

"Sure I'm sure. I figured something like this would come up so I came prepared. That's the secret of my success. I'm always prepared. Tell you the truth, I thought it was going to be *more.*"

We moved with her, instinctively, to the Court Clerk's desk. No one wanted to miss *this* spectacle.

Papers signed and notarized, then out of Cindy's handbag came a ten-inch manila envelope. She took a bundle of paper money from it and counted out ten $1000 bills. Even the cool, unruffled Thomas Edward Atkins was ruffled for the first time today.

We waited twenty minutes or so before Clay was brought into the room. He winked at us, and proceeded to sign what *he* had to sign before being released.

"That it?" he asked, cheerfully.

"You are free to go," said the Court Clerk.

We started out. I observed that of all of us, Clay seemed the least concerned.

"I need some proper breakfast," he said. "Where's the nearest?" He looked at Atkins. *"You* ought to know."

"Yes," said Atkins.

He took us across the street to a Victorian-type restaurant. He asked for, and got, a large corner table away from the other customers.

Clay ordered a Bloody Mary, steak and eggs, lyonnaise potatoes, rye toast, and Sanka.

The rest of us settled for coffee and Danish.

Art tried to regain control of the situation.

"All right, Clay. Let's have it. What *is* this shit?"

"Please," said Atkins, pained.

"The best thing," said Cindy, "is to tell the truth, the whole truth, and nothing but the truth. That's been my experience. We're all friends here and no finks—so talk up, and then this good attorney here will advise us. You."

"I find it all highly hilarious," said Clay. "I may be the *only* member of this glandular company who's absolutely *clean*. I gave up all forms *years* ago. I don't even drink *coffee*, for heaven's sake. I could sing a song or two if I had a mind to—but no. I'm more interested in getting to the bottom of this sleazy affair. And when I do—"

Two blotches of red appeared on his cheeks, his whole face flushed. He laughed.

Atkins spoke. "If I were you, Mr. Botsford, I'd take this matter more seriously. The charge against you is grave."

"Mr. Atkins," said Cindy, "is one of the finest lawyers in Philadelphia."

"I appreciate that, Mrs. Sapiro. And I appreciate all *you've* done. But listen. All of you. I don't believe in much, but I do believe in justice—and I can't find it within myself to believe that someone completely innocent can be framed."

"It's been done," said Art, darkly.

"Maybe. But it's not going to be done to *me*. This whole silly mess is a crazy mistake."

Art was drumming on the table with the prongs of a fork.

"Are you *sure*, Clay?" he asked.

Clay regarded him, carefully. It was clear that he was ending his personal relationship with Art then and there and for all time.

"The difficulty is," said Atkins, "that as of now, the authorities have a strong case against you. I might say a *very* strong case."

Clay was stunned, his expression incredulous. His lips formed the word "What?"—but no sound emanated.

Atkins took a document from his breast pocket, changed eyeglasses, looked at the paper in his hand, and said, "According to the investigators—who were properly armed with search warrants—

large quantities of cocaine, heroin, marijuana, amphetamines, and barbiturates were found in a locked compartment in a trunk bearing your name in your office at The Shubert Theatre."

Clay could manage only, *"My* trunk?"

"Yes."

"When was this?"

"At eight-thirty a.m. on Friday, November thirtieth—the day after the accident."

"Jesus God!" said Clay.

"You deny knowledge of its contents?" asked Atkins, formally. "This is all quite informal, you understand. There is no oath involved."

"I understand," Clay replied gravely. "Yes, I deny that I ever knew anything about it."

Cindy. "Don't they have to prove he *sold* something to somebody?"

"No, Mrs. Sapiro. They do not. *Possession* is sufficient for conviction under Statute Seven-oh-four B."

"And anyway, for Chrissake," said Art, "you think anybody who bought it or got it from wherever is going to say so? From where? Use your head."

"Don't sass me, Art," said Cindy, sharply. "So far, *I've* done more on this than *you* have. So cork it!"

"Please," said Atkins.

"The question," said Clay, "is who. Who put it there? Why seems clear. But *who?"*

"And how?" asked Atkins. "What sort of lock does it have?"

"A combination."

"Is there anyone who might—in any way—know it? Have it?"

Clay thought hard. "No," he said, finally. "Wait. . . . Yes. An assistant I once had. A girl. But she's not an assistant anymore. She's on a show of her own."

"When did you last see her?"

"A year and a half—maybe two years ago."

"Oh. Well, that's a dead clue, then, isn't it?"

"Yes," said Clay.

"All right," said Atkins. "We have a week to gather information. I'll put two men on it. Can we count on any cooperation from the company?"

"Of course," said Clay.

"I doubt it," said Art.

"Definitely not," said Cindy.

"Oh? Why not?"

"Because," said Cindy, "they're all looking-out-for-Number-One types. They're all going to be looking to save their own skins. What a bunch! Fags, dykes, drunks, hopheads."

"Well," said Art. "That's show business!"

"The hell it is," said Clay, getting up. "I'll see you all later."

He walked out, alone, and we let him go because it was clear that was what he wanted.

We sat for a time, saying nothing.

For some reason, I kept thinking of that one "dead clue." The assistant who knew the combination. Who was she? Where was she?

I called Clay around five and asked him if he would like to have a six-o'clock dinner. He said yes.

At Bookbinder's, we ran into at least a dozen friends from the show. They had turned into other people. They smiled and waved and stopped at our table, but it was all different. A game. A charade. I could see that we were moving into a strange and uptight time.

After we had ordered, Clay took a sip of his vermouth cassis, and asked, "How serious do you think this is, Midge?"

"Depends," I said. "I called my brother and told him the whole everything. Also Gene. He's going to try to get back as soon as he can."

"And what did *he* say?"

"He's worried."

"About *me?*"

"Yes."

"Why?"

"He says anybody with a connection knows that the connection has to be somehow involved with the organization. Otherwise, there's no source. And he says the minute there's a bust, everyone concerned —buyers, sellers—gets the word to clam. Or else. And it usually works, he says. Eventually, someone takes the rap, and it's back to business as usual."

Clay smiled. "And whatever happened to that innocent until proven—*you* know?"

"I *don't* know."

Our soup was served, and we tried to deal with it.

"That assistant you mentioned before," I said.

"Yes."

"What's her name?"

"What's the difference?"

"Tell me."

"Nan," he said. "Nan Arnold."

"Is there anybody on *this* show who was on any of those you did with *her?*"

"God, I don't know."

"Think."

He thought for a long time, reviewing the past. Finally, he said, "No. No one. Funny what a turnover in this business. Every year, almost, a new crop."

"Not exactly. They say Jenny has had practically this same bunch for *several* years."

"Yes, I suppose. But I've never worked with her before. What did the show run last night, do you know?"

I got out my notebook and consulted it.

"Two hours, forty-two, without intermission."

"And how long was the intermission?"

I looked again.

"Twenty-two minutes."

"Too long. We've *got* to cut it down."

I realized that he had deliberately changed the subject. He knew perfectly well what the running time had been and the length of the intermission.

We talked of nothing but the show from that point on.

I asked Jenny out for a drink after the show—and was astonished when she ordered ginger ale.

"Jesus!" she said after the first sip. "I'll bet anybody anything this is worse for you than booze. It's not only chemical, it's *synthetic* chemical. *Cut* chemical."

"Have a drink," I said.

"*You* of all people," she said. "O.K. You talked me into it. Vodka tonic. Russian."

I talked her into four. She became her old loquacious self.

"Well," she said. "That ol' Clay's got his fagotty ass in a sling, wouldn't you say?"

"I don't know. Has he?"

"Damn right. You never know about those smoothies. But wow! You could've fooled *me.*"

"Did you ever get anything from him?"

"Me? What would I get? What is *this?* You diggin', you little cunt? Is that why you're plying me—trying to get me plastered?"

I laughed my best laugh.

"Honestly, Jenny," I said. "You are the most out-and-out neurotic woman I've ever met. Everybody's your enemy, *you* think."

"That's just what I'm going to need before *this* night's out. An enema."

She laughed and slapped the table. The waiter, mistaking it for a signal, came over at once.

"Yes?" he asked.

"Yes!" Jenny said. "One more."

The contretemps sent her into further hysterics. Thank God. She forgot her suspicion.

"Do you know Nan Arnold?" I asked, as casually as I could.

"Do I? I wish I didn't."

"Why?"

"Do *you* know her?"

"No."

"Well, if you did, you wouldn't *ask* why. A real little pisshead. English. *And* a tramp. They used to call her The British Open. She started in the chorus—couldn't dance her way out of a wet paper bag. So pretty soon—choreographer's assistant, assistant stage manager, then with Clay, then stage manager—production supervisor. And now I think she's even getting Associate Producer, the bitch. Well, what the hell. She did what she had to do. Some society jerk once said to Merman, 'Is it true girls in the theatre have to sleep with producers and directors to get anywhere?' And Merm said, 'Sure, it's true—if they've got no *talent!* '"

We were looking at each other, and that thing that happens often with talented people happened again—she knew, suddenly and clearly, what I was thinking: about her and Art Clune.

"Don't say it," she warned.

"Say what?"

"What's going through that slimy mind of yours. That was a crisis. I haven't made it on ass, I've made it on talent. So don't give me that Hungarian look!"

"Nan Arnold," I said.

"You keep *saying* that, for Chrissake. Why? What the fuck're we talking about *her* for?"

"I thought you'd be interested."

"Not in her, I'm not."

"I understand she's coming down here."

"What?!" She set her glass down with a *crack!*, spilling some of her drink.

"Yes," I continued. "To stand by in case we lose Clay. It's all hush-hush up to now—so don't say anything, will you? Or anyway, don't say you heard it from *me.*"

She had turned, before my eyes, into a huge rag doll. She sat there, limp and lifeless, her mouth painted on, her eyes made of buttons.

When, at length, she spoke, it was in an unfamiliar voice: "God help me," she said.

It took a fresh drink to bring her to.

Then she said, "I wonder who engineered it. Not Clay. That's for sure. He loathes her. From way back. They were both working for Merrick when he was doing four, five shows a year—and she tried to leapfrog Clay; but he was too strong, and he had her bounced. A couple nights later, she walked over to him in Sardi's and dumped a plate of spaghetti on his head. With red clam sauce. Eddie told me all about it. In fact, he was there. With her."

An explosion in my head.

"Eddie?" I asked, quietly. I was shaking.

"Our own dear little walking hard-on, sure. I think he had something on with her for a while. In fact, I'm sure."

"Well," I said, "let's hope for the best. What else can we do?"

"We can have another drink," said Jenny.

I could not sleep. There are times when you know something even though you cannot prove it. This was one of those times. I knew for certain that Eddie was involved. I knew that Clay was absolutely innocent—even though Art and Cindy had some doubts—and even though the redoubtable Thomas Edward Atkins did not believe in Clay at all.

I have spent the past two days floating around the company, trying to pick up any scraps of information. It was all meager. The whole gang has clammed up in the most mysterious way. There is still pot around—I can smell it. And still snow—I can sense it. But where it is coming from now, I have no idea.

That Eddie-Nan-Clay triangle haunts me. What can I do about it? Should I take it up with Art? Cindy? Alicia? I'm no good at this on my own. Too involved emotionally, and find myself jumping to dangerous conclusions. What about Atkins? He, at least, is official. Not only that, but experienced. Yes. Atkins it is.

Disaster. I made an appointment to see Atkins, went over, and spent almost an hour with him. I told him the whole Clay-Nan story, and the Nan-Eddie connection, and what I knew about Eddie. I could tell he was only half-listening, his mind on other matters.

Finally, I stopped talking.

"Tell me," he said. "Do you have some personal relationship with Mr. Botsford?"

"No, sir."

"And what, may I ask, is your position with this play?"

"I'm the Production Secretary."

"Secretary," he echoed. And from the way he said it, I knew I was dead. He conveyed somehow that had he known this earlier, he would not have allowed me an hour of his valuable time. He was on his feet now, saying, "I'm sorry, Miss, but your information has no value whatsoever. I appreciate that you are attempting to be of service to your friend and—uh, fellow worker—"

(Fellow worker! "Are you now or have you ever been . . .")

"—but what we are dealing with is an official charge which cannot be countered with gossip or hearsay or unsubstantiated conjecture. I am sorry."

I was out.

I went home and placed a person-to-person to Gene. He was away on assignment. I walked and walked. To whom could I turn? Then it struck me. Alicia. Of all the people in the company, save Clay, she was the only one with whom I had had any intimate contact. Moreover, she is a kind and good person and fond of Clay.

I phoned her, went up to see her. I had not been alone with her since that now unbelievable night.

She poured tea and listened to the story. I was getting quite sick of it.

"Eddie," she said, "is a certifiable rodent. There is nothing I would put past him. Nothing. A wicked weasel. What is ever so painful is the knowledge that there are any number of members of this bloody company who could easily stand up and clear the air—but they won't, you see. Not one. Fear, I expect."

"Is there anything *we* can do?"

"Perhaps."

She moved about the room, going from window to window and looking out. When she had done every window, she turned back into the room. A plant caught her eye—a fern. She put her finger on the soil near its roots, went out, came back presently with a small silver watering can and watered the fern. She then went about watering every single plant in the suite, and there must have been a dozen. When she had finished the last one, she took the watering can out. A few minutes later, she returned, sat down opposite me, lit a cigarette, and said, "Several ways—but suppose we begin with the simplest one."

She then clearly and carefully outlined her plan. I thought it completely nutty, but she appeared to have such conviction that two hours later, we began to carry it out.

While I located Nan Arnold, with the help of Actors Equity membership department, Alicia walked about practicing her imitation of Nan Arnold. She knows her and rather likes her, she says, except for the irritating little-girl whisper she affects in imitation of Marilyn Monroe.

"What a fraud," Alicia had said. "I knew her back in London when we were both still knocking on the door. She's a reconstructed little Cockney, same as I! Still, I must confess—that Monroe pastiche, along with her imitation U-accent, has a certain charm. And it seems to have worked for her. So, *brava!*"

When I reached Nan Arnold, Alicia got on the phone, hooked it to her little tape recorder, and went into a long conversation involving various theatrical shoemakers.

"Of course," she said, "I should have stuck with Capezio—but this chintzy person insisted I take bids, and so I did. . . . Oh, dear me, yes —mean as cat's meat. So here I am. . . . Yes, all period. . . . Who? . . . Spell that out, would you, duckie? . . . I have it. . . . And how goes it with you? . . . Yes, I heard. Many congratters. . . . Oh, the usual tussle. It gets better. . . . Yes, isn't that so? All right then, duckie. Many thanks. Ta."

She played the cassette back several times, talking along with it, until I swear she sounded exactly like Nan Arnold.

"Did you note," Alicia asked, "that she said not a word about our *scandale* down here?"

"Do you suppose she knows about it?"

"Don't be idiotic, there's a dear. Nothing travels as fast as theatrical news—especially juicy stuff, such as ours. I promise you it's all over Broadway. I've had three snooping calls myself today."

"What did you tell them?"

"That I hadn't heard a thing. That I'd let them know as soon as I did."

"Great."

"Well," she said, taking a deep breath. "Shall we have a bash?"

"All right."

I then did what she had carefully coached me to do. I rang the Benjamin Franklin Hotel and asked for Eddie. He came on. I began recording the call.

I pinched my nose, and said, "Mr. Eddie Convery, please. Long-distance, person-to-person calling."

"Who's calling?" he asked.

"Are you Mr. Convery?"

"Who's calling?"

"Who's calling?" I asked.

"Miss Arnold," said Alicia on the extension phone.

"O.K."

"Are you Mr. Convery?"

"Yes!"

"Thank you. Here's your party. Go *ahead*, please!"

ALICIA
(As NAN*)*

How *are* you, loov?

· 342 ·

EDDIE

If I thought you *gave* a pink fuck, I'd tell you.

ALICIA

How's the show?

EDDIE

Same as I told you last week. Only worse.

ALICIA

And how's everything else?

EDDIE

Listen, you cluck! This is a telephone you're talking over. Will you cool it?

ALICIA

You can say yes or no, can't you?

EDDIE

So far so good, now get the hell off.

ALICIA

But have you heard from *You* know?

EDDIE

Who?

ALICIA

You know. *You* know.

EDDIE

I don't know what the hell you're talking about.

ALICIA
(Lowering her voice)
Why don't you fall ill or some such and bugger off for a bit? Y' *know?*

EDDIE

I know you're a cunthead, that's what I know. That would be some sucker shot—to leave here. Christ, they're crawling around like cockroaches. They're all over the place—in everybody's hair and up their ass. So I should blow? I swear to Christ—if you had another brain, you'd have *one*.

· 343 ·

I'm thinking about *you,* Eddie. I'm on your side. And remember,
I'm in on this, too. I mean, if there's a muddle, it wouldn't be too
good for me, either. Would it?
> *(Silence)*

Hello?
> *(Silence)*

Eddie?

EDDIE

Whoever you are, lady—*up yours!*

ALICIA

What?

EDDIE

Fuck you! She never called me "Eddie" in her whole life. Drop
dead, you spying scum!

"Damn," said Alicia.

"What are you talking about?" I said. "We're in! Home free."

"I'm afraid not," she said. "That one blunder botched it."

"Come on, Alicia. Anybody listens to this cassette will know what
we know."

"What do we know?"

"That *he* got Clay's combination from *her,* opened the trunk, and
planted his stash in it."

"That's what we *think,* dear. What we hope. Not what we know.
I'm afraid we're still a long way from the answer."

"Maybe," I said. "But we're a hell of a lot closer to the question.
We know who did it—now all we have to do is *prove* it."

I couldn't imagine why she was so depressed. I was elated.

Drinks with Russ and Buddy.

"Just goes to show," I said. "You never can tell about people. My
father used to say, 'You can't judge a book by the cover.'"

"Your father was William Shakespeare?" said Russ.

Buddy howled.

"No," I said. "I mean about Clay. I mean, I can't believe it."

Acting too hard, I was beginning to sound like Alicia's imitation of
Nan Arnold.

"Can't believe what?"

"Why *would* he?" I asked. "He's successful, and a good job, and a good future. What made him become a pusher?"

"Don't be an asshole, Missy, y'mind? I mean, you *are* an asshole, but try not to show it so much, huh? It's goddam sickening."

I began to cry. That, I must say, I do very well.

Russ to Buddy:

"Now look what you've done. *Another* fine mess!"

"Sorry, Ollie!"

They were into their Laurel and Hardy routine.

RUSS

You've made the lady cry!

BUDDY

Lady? I thought she was a *woman!*

RUSS

You *thought?*

BUDDY

I did.

RUSS

With what?

BUDDY

With what?

RUSS

No. Not with what. With what?

BUDDY

With what *what?*

RUSS

Did you *think?*

BUDDY

Did I think *what?* . . . Ow!!

I stopped crying.

"Dry your eyes, Goldilocks," said Russ.

"And don't wet your pants," said Buddy.

Russ. "It'll all come out in the wash. Clay is clean."

Buddy. "Yes. And clean is Clay."

"What do you mean?" I asked.

"There's been a *ghahstly* mistake," said Russ, with his best British acting accent.

"A foul miscarriage of justice, m'lords!" said Buddy.

I had had enough.

"You two clowns give me a swift pain in the ass," I said.

"Bless her foul little mouth," cried Russ. "She is one of *us.*"

"God forbid," I said. "A cocksucker I'm *not!*" They were well and truly shocked. I went on. "A man's career and reputation and name and everything is at stake—and you two little shits can sit around and joke about it. You ought to be ashamed of yourselves. And I'll bet you are, deep down."

They turned to one another and conversed as though I were not there.

RUSS

Look here, ol' chap. Do you suppose we've stumbled onto an odd affair?

BUDDY

Odd is right.

RUSS

I mean the way Doctor Ehrlich stumbled onto his Formula Six-oh-six? Or was that Doctor Edward G. Robinson?

BUDDY

Are you trying to say, in your stumbling, mumbling way, that Missy Midge and Mister Clay are a *thing?*

RUSS

God! I've never heard him accused of AC-DC, have you?

BUDDY

Heaven forbid.

RUSS

Yuk. Is there *anything* more revolting than indecision?

BUDDY

Than not knowing which way to turn?

RUSS

Watch it, Buddy.

BUDDY

Is that a small 'b' buddy or a big 'B' Buddy?

RUSS

Medium.

BUDDY

Or could it be—look at me, I'm trembling—could it be that Mister Clay has *switched* completely?

RUSS

Are you asking me if Clay has feet of *clay?*

This was too much for Buddy, who went right out of his chair.

They turned back to me.

"What? You still here?" asked Russ.

"Tell all," said Buddy, suddenly matey.

"I will if you will," I said.

"You first."

"All right. You guessed it. Clay and I are in love. And we're going to be married."

"Water!" Russ shouted.

Buddy, for once, was speechless.

"Wait a second," said Russ. "Are we all talking about the same Clay. Or are there two?"

"There's only one I care about," I said, "and he's in trouble."

"He sure as hell is," said Russ, "if he thinks he can make it work with you. It's been tried before, you know."

"I'm talking about his big trouble."

"Oh, that's bullshit," said Buddy. "Those narcs aren't half-wits, y'know. Give them two, three days. They'll come up with it. It's all a movie. Life's a movie. It all comes out even in the end. Hitchcock or whoever. You can't have a whodunit without a who, can you? And it's no fun at all if they get the right guy right off, is it? I mean, you'd have a short, not a feature."

"And anyway," said Russ, "you don't think that the man—oh, God! —you love and are going to marry is *bad,* do you?"

"Yes, I do. But it makes no difference."

"Makes it even better, maybe?" asked Buddy.

· 347 ·

"No. But I can't help it."

"Midge," said Russ, suddenly serious and warm, "Clay Botsford is no pusher. He's clean as a whistle—as your father always said."

"Who, then?" I asked, looking at him hard.

He shifted his glance to Buddy, who said "no" with his eyes.

Buddy spoke. "Look, kid. When I was in the Army, there was an old Army saying around. It goes like this: 'Keep your bowels open, your mouth shut, and never volunteer.' It's good advice around a show, too. Don't go too deep into all this. You might maybe get in over your head."

"You're not going to tell me."

"No."

"But you know."

"Yes," said Russ.

"That makes you God-damned low, the two of you. Even lower than I thought."

"For 'lower,'" said Russ, "read 'smarter.'"

"Don't ever count on me for anything," I said. "And if I can ever do anything to damage you, I will."

I got up and prepared to leave.

"Hey, Midge," said Buddy. "All that about you and Clay. A crock, right? A ruse?"

"Right," I said. "A crock."

"Allah be praised," said Russ.

I went to the theatre. An understudy rehearsal was in progress. In the darkness of the wings, grass was being smoked profusely. I joined a group of three who were passing a stick around. I slipped in, and in turn, took a few drags.

"This sure is lousy shit," I said. "Where's it from? The A and P?"

"Local," said a girl. "You're right."

"Doesn't help me, anyhow," I said. "Anybody know where I can pick up some candy?"

"Why don't you get it where I get mine?" said a boy.

"Where's that?"

"From The Tooth Fairy," he said.

They all looked at one another. They were onto me.

I left the theatre and went straight to the hospital. In the lobby,

I started the Sony, put it, running, into my totebag, and went up to see Diana.

She was sitting up in bed, wearing a pretty bed jacket, and smoking pot.

"How are you, Diana?"

"Well, look at me! And what about all this loot?"

The room was filled with flowers and plants and books and presents.

"Great. I think *I'll* take a fall."

"Do it. I'm the Queen of the Moulin Rouge, for God's sake. I haven't had so much attention since the crib—and *that* wasn't bad, either."

"Have they said yet how long?"

"I've stopped listening," she said. "They change it every day."

"But in time for New York?"

"When's that?"

"Let's see. Two weeks from yesterday."

"God, I hope so! I'm very big in New York, you know."

"Of course."

"Everybody missing me pretty bad?" she asked.

"Desperately."

"Good. And how's everything else around the ol' sweatshop? Any news?"

"Not much. Just poor Eddie."

She sat up sharply, and cried out. *"Aahh!!* God damn fucking back. *Shit!"* She settled back, slowly, tamped out her stick, and looked at me.

"What *about* Eddie?"

"You don't *know?"*

"Know *what?"*

"You haven't *heard?"*

It was cat-and-mouse all right—only I didn't know if I was the cat or the mouse.

"Nothing about *him,* no," she said.

I took a deep breath and said, "Busted."

"Out of the show?" she asked, acting like a dancer.

"Out of life," I said. "He could get ten years, they say. In *this* state."

"What did he do, for God's sake? Rape the Mayor's sister?"

"Worse. Peddled narcotics."

"Eddie?" she said. Her acting was getting worse.

"The same."

"But where? I mean, who to, for instance?"

"*You* to, for instance," I said.

"*Me-ee?*" she yelled, stretching the word out into two or three syllables.

"That's right."

"Who says?"

"*He* says. Not only you. But you're on his list."

"He's a goddam liar. I'd like to see him *prove* it, that little snake. If he says—"

"Easy, Di, easy."

"Why should *I?* . . . "

"Will you calm down? It's not a serious crime to *buy* coke—just to sell it."

"Look," she said, "I don't have to take this shit. My roommate's boyfriend is a terrific lawyer. I'm getting him on the phone."

"You're wasting your time, Di. And his. If he's *any* kind of a lawyer, he'll tell you what all the kids have been told."

"Yeah? And what's that?"

"To tell the truth. When you're called, you'll be under oath. What you've done up to now is not much—but perjury *is.* "

"What kids? Who?"

"Everybody he was supplying. He gave them his list. He's cooperating like a son-of-a-bitch. I guess it's part of some kind of plea bargaining."

"That dirty little bastard! And on top of everything else—he was pushing lousy stuff. Cut. Ask anybody. I think that's what made me so sick. The cut stuff—and whatever he put in it. I've never gotten sick from a little snow in my whole life. Just exhilarated. But how *about* that little bastard? We cover for him and he blows the whistle on us. Little Jew bastard."

"Convery?"

"Oh, for Christ's sake! You believe that? If he's Convery, I'm Liebowitz. He's probably *Cohen.* "

"What do you know?"

"God *damn* what a blast!"

"Poor Eddie. He's going to get it two ways, probably. From the law and from the Big Boys."

"No, no. He's in solid with them."

"How do *you* know?"

"Because. He asked me to do him a favor and date one of them down here—a detective—"

"I know," I said. "Bronzini." (Where did *that* come from?) "He asked me, too. I told him I was too busy."

"No. Not Bronzini. Regan. Mike Regan. Lovely guy. Lousy lay, but lovely guy. He sent me those yellow roses."

I went over and inhaled their fragrance, thinking, I've got enough. More than enough.

I told her about the show, the work being done, the changes being made. I gave her the last two bulletins, and got out.

I thought of going back to Atkins, but simply could not bear the thought of dealing with that snooty, patronizing poop.

Instead, I called Art and Cindy and Clay, told them it was important—very important—and asked for a meeting.

In less than an hour, we were assembled at Art's place.

I told my story, and played both tapes. Alicia-Eddie and Diana-me. The reactions were curious and unexpected.

Art was, first, embarrassed; then angry. (He had not trusted Clay for a moment.)

Cindy sat there giggling. I suppose she was relieved and excited.

Clay burst into tears, and sat bent over, with his face in his hands. Later, he came over to me and kissed me.

The next move was to plan the final strategy. Cindy was all for going at once to Atkins. I was against it, but was outvoted.

Art wanted to send for Eddie and confront him. For some reason, Clay was violently opposed to this idea.

Clay thought we should go to the authorities at once with the new information.

"Not so fast," said Cindy. "All this stuff could be inadmissible. Tapped phone. Secret tape."

"Wrong," I said. "I took down the Eddie call in shorthand—that's not tapping—that's monitoring. And the Diana thing—I'll swear an affidavit. I once worked in a law office, so I know about stuff like that. I remember the conversation. How could I forget it?"

"I still say lawyer," said Cindy. "Let's not be wiseass and outsmart ourselves here."

"She's right," said Art. "We're amateurs. We think it's all open-and-shut. The judge could maybe think different."

Clay spoke. "Anyway, Midge, you did one hell of a job."

"That's what she gets paid for," said Art, larky again. "What d'you think I pay her for?"

"I didn't go to all this trouble for *you*, Art," I said, and made, at last, a really dignified exit.

SHINE ON, HARVEST MOON
Company Bulletin
Thursday, December 6

QUOTE TO REMEMBER:
"Consider, Sir; celebrated men, such as you
have mentioned, have had their applause at a
distance; but Garrick had it dashed in his
face, sounded in his ears, and went home every
night with the plaudits of a thousand in his
cranium. . . . If all this had happened to me, I
should have had a couple of fellows with long
poles walking before me, to knock down everybody that stood in the way. . . . Sir, a man who
has a nation to admire him every night, may well
expect to be elated."
                                    Samuel Johnson

HEALTH: Try to get some rest on the 6:00-7:00
break. Take fructose. Eat glucose. Grapes. Drink
grape juice. Gatorade. Take calcium. Sit still
when not working. Pray.

COSTUME CHANGES: Re "Big Town" elimination: If
anyone in the rerouting to the street scene an-
ticipates any difficulty in making either a costume change or a makeup change, please communicate
this information immediately to Stu Bender.

FITTINGS: Costume, wig, and shoe fittings for the
new numbers are occurring now with greater fre-
quency, so please be prompt for them so that you can
return to rehearsal as quickly as possible.

PRESS MEETING: Please note that the Press Meeting
scheduled for 2:00 P.M. on Friday, December 7, has
been canceled.

                                    Paul Cooley

THE COMPANY YOU KEEP: JOEY FAYE(Mickey Ryan)
   What can I tell you? East Side New York. Amateur
nights. The mountains. Burlesque: The Gaiety.
Floogle Street. Water in the Pants. . . .
   "Betcha five dollars you're not here!"
   "Bet."

"All right. Now, you're not in Cincinnati. . . ."
"No."
"Well, if you're not in Cincinnati and you're not.
in Tallahassee, you must be someplace else.
Right?"
"Right!"
"So if you're someplace else, you can't be here,
right?"
"Right!"
"So I'll take the money!"
"What-the-*HEY!*"
Stuff like that. Finally, a Broadway show. YOKEL
BOY with Phil Silvers, a great man. More shows. Some
movies. TV. Commercials. Night spots. Meantime,
married several times. Not too good. My fault. Why
am I telling you all this? My philosophy? There's No
Business Like Show Business. My advice? Come on
Strong.

There are now 14 days remaining until our New York
opening.

· XL ·

A nightmare afternoon.

I walked over to the theatre with Clay. Although he knew the worst was over and his clearance only a matter of time, he was edgy.

We reached the theatre and started up the alley to the stage door. Eddie and a bunch of the kids were lounging about. Some of them, dancers, were practicing a new combination that has gone in recently. One singer, Johnny, was warming up.

"Hi, folks," said Clay, trying to sound casual.

If only it could have ended there.

Clay's hand was on the knob of the stage door, and that dolt Eddie had to spoil it all.

"Say, Clay," he said.

Clay turned to him.

"Yes?"

"Can I talk to you a minute?"

"You bet," replied Clay, his hand still on the knob.

Eddie came closer and said, "I'm sorry as hell about your hassle."

"Are you?"

"Damn right. Those bums. And listen—if there's anything I can do, just let me know."

Clay's hand came off the knob, and he faced Eddie. Clearly, this was too much. He was pale. Trembling, too?

"Well, Eddie, as a matter of fact, there *is* something you can do."

"What?"

"Come with me tomorrow morning over to Judge Belkin's office
—he's the one's got me under ten thousand dollars' bail—"

"Yuh?" said Eddie, uncertainly.

"—and tell him how *you're* the one's been peddling stuff to the
company—and how *you're* the one got my trunk combination from
Nan Arnold and planted the stash on me." Eddie was frozen. Clay
went on, too gently. "Would you do that with me, please? First thing
tomorrow morning?"

The color was back in Clay's face, but out of Eddie's. It was almost
as if the blood had been transferred from one head to the other.
Weird.

Eddie backed away half a step.

"What're you, *nuts?*"

"I don't think so. Are you?"

Eddie, suddenly emboldened, moved close to Clay, and in a low
and confidential voice, said, "Listen, you fairy bastard. Don't mess
with *me*. Not around here. I'm *connected*. You want to hear more?
You dump on me and you'll wind up with your balls gone! If you've
got any."

"Are you threatening me, Eddie?"

"What do *you* think?"

"I think it's time to stop thinking," said Clay.

He took off his glasses and handed them to me.

Eddie squared off, in the manner of an experienced street fighter.
Stocky and solid. •

Clay, without his glasses, looked weak and ineffectual.

"Please, Clay," I said. "This is ridiculous."

I feared for him in this situation.

He moved toward Eddie.

"I'm *warning* you!" said Eddie.

The action had attracted the attention of the kids in the alley. They
laughed, assuming it to be conventional alley clowning.

Eddie said, "I've got—"

"What?" said Clay. "Who? *Regan?*" A gasp from Eddie. *"He's* in
trouble, too. Just like *you.*"

"You're *dead,* man, you know it? You're *dead!* You can—"

Whatever else he meant to say was stopped by Clay's fist as it
slammed into his mouth. Something went flying out of Eddie's mouth
and clattered to the pavement. His full plate. Upper and lower. With

his face thus collapsed, he looked eighty years old. Clay hit him again, this time on the side of the head. It all seemed unreal.

At one moment, I thought, how can Clay bear to be beating this little old man?

Eddie fought back, but the loss of his teeth had demoralized him.

A girl screamed. Two of the boys rushed in in an attempt to separate the fighters. One got hit in the ear by a flailing blow from Eddie. Blood was flowing. Whose?

Now Eddie began to scream. Looking about for his teeth, he saw an empty beer bottle, picked it up, smashed it on the pavement and brandished the broken half. Clay moved in to take it away from him. As he did so, Eddie's right knee came up hard and caught Clay in the groin. He doubled up with a sickening groan. As he did so, Eddie moved in and hit him a karate chop on the back of the neck. Clay went down. Eddie kicked him. Clay grabbed his foot, tripped him. Eddie fell. Clay got on top of him, grabbed his ears and began beating his head into the pavement. By this time, several stagehands had rushed out into the alley. They pulled Clay off. He staggered into the theatre. Eddie was out, cold.

I went into the theatre and found Clay in his office.

"I need a doctor," he said.

I ran out to the front of the house and asked the house manager to get a doctor right away.

He got to the theatre half an hour later. Clay had recovered. Eddie needed not only the doctor but the ambulance that had been sent for.

He is still in the hospital, on the same floor as Diana.

No lessons to be learned from any of this. All too mad and wrongheaded. No lessons, but a few observations. Isn't it strange how unpredictable human behavior is? Clay. A soft, shy, diffident man. Who would have thought that in a crisis he could turn into a raging tiger, a powerful pugilist, a righteous crusader? And Eddie in all this. Cindy. The only one who ran true to form was Art. I might have known.

· XLI ·

The charges against Clay have been dismissed, and he has received an official letter of apology—or at least, explanation—from the Police Department.

There was some talk, mainly from Atkins, about suing the city for false arrest, or something like that—but Cindy, through her heavy contacts, soon revealed that this was no more than a political ploy. Atkins, a Republican with ambitions, was prepared to do anything to embarrass the present Democratic administration.

He sent Clay a hefty bill. Clay turned it over to Art, who said forget it, he would take care of it. We all thought it a fine gesture until we found he was charging it to the production.

Eddie was replaced by Ted Reid, a splendid actor who came down from New York and went on in two days. Actors are supermen.

Eddie's case is being handled by Diana's roommate's boyfriend, who says it does not look good. There is no way Eddie is going to avoid some time in the slammer.

I hate to write these next paragraphs. The incident is over. While it was going on, the show continued to play eight performances a week, numbers went in, numbers came out, cuts were made, and work went on.

Now everything has returned to normal—or what passes for normal around here. And here is the hateful part: The dope situation is unchanged. The puffing and sniffing and shooting still go on. The supply flows. There is a connection in the company. Who? I do not know. I do not want to know.

The users make up a kind of secret society. The drug culture has its own rules, its own standards and morals and behavior. Gene says the colossal profits in it make it almost unassailable.

<u>SHINE ON, HARVEST MOON</u>
Company Bulletin
Tuesday, December 11

<u>SCRIPT CHANGE</u>: Act II, Scene 1A, and Act II, Scene 2, have been eliminated. The running order should now read as follows:

> Act II, Scene 1—Rector's
> Act II, Scene 2—Nora's Room
> Act II, Scene 3—The Everleigh Club

Please note that the rest of the scenes on the running order will now have to be renumbered.

<u>RESEARCH</u>:
Butterflies in The Everleigh Club were like chorus girls in a New York show in a single respect: Only one out of several ensembles ever stood out. Not that coryphees and courtesans have anything in common, which, of course, they haven't, but few in either walk have that comedy quality or that dramatic instinct which takes them apart from their chosen endeavor. Only one of a hundred in both professions finds her name in lasting print.

The Everleigh Sisters estimate that upwards of 600 girls came and went during their eleven-year reign in Chicago and yet they found it difficult in 1936 to recall more than a dozen who left any sort of an exciting impression.

The comical girls and the villainesses were the featured players. There was no role for the heroine. The ultra-good, ultra-kindly, and ultra-expert made no trouble and are forgotten. Such is the price of sanctity in a sporting resort.

<u>COLOR</u>: Today is Blue, tomorrow is Orange.

<u>THE COMPANY YOU KEEP</u>: PHIL ROSENBERG(Musical Director)
I come from Toronto and if I didn't like this country I'd go back where I came from.

There is nothing in the world I would rather be doing than conducting this great show—no, not even *that!*

I was a child prodigy. (Violin.) I know I don't *look* like a child prodigy but I didn't even when I *was.* Some said I was a midget making out. For the first 15 years of my life I practiced 10 hours a day. The next 10 years, 5. Then 3. Then 2. Then once in a while. Result? I bombed out. Traded my bow for a baton. Band act for years. Then into the pit—first as second fiddle, then second conductor (*that* I practiced). Big chance when Hal Prince tapped me as a replacement. From then on, no more replacement.

Of all the shows I've worked on—this is the best. An honor to be with Star—also the best.

Mazel tov.

RESEARCH: Copies of THIS FABULOUS CENTURY 1900–1910, 1910–1920, are in Mr. Gabel's office. Please look them over at your convenience.

Mr. Clune recommends that everyone read "Concerning," a booklet published by Jack Norworth and Nora Bayes. Midge has copies.

There are now 9 days remaining until our New York opening.

· XLII ·

Larry to the company:

"Today, a word about humor. Humor doesn't necessarily mean jokes or funny lines or double takes or pieces of business. Humor means coming to terms with the nonsense and inequities and chaos and craziness of everyday life.

"Long ago I was on a play and we were out of town—in fact, down here—and that superlative playwright Robert E. Sherwood was a friend of *our* playwright's and came down to see the show. Later, at the conference, after he'd praised everything there was to praise— which wasn't much—he began to discuss the performance of the leading part and he said, 'Unfortunately, the leading character is dull. And when a character is dull, it poisons every scene he's in.' Our playwright was dismayed. He said, 'Well, good God, Bob, it's hopeless then, isn't it?' And Sherwood said, 'Of course not. When you have a dull character, or a dull actor—and in this case you have both—give them a sense of humor. You can help some, Charlie, in the script, and he'll have to do the rest. But once that character possesses and de- monstrates a sense of humor, he won't be dull.'

"Think about that, everyone. You, Star; Gloria, Patti, look how brilliantly Gracie and Ella have made the two Madams so appealing. It's because they have humor. They have humor about life and about themselves. About the situation. Nora, herself, in real life had a *tre- mendous* sense of humor. As you know, we're only telling a part of her life. She and Norworth split up later on. She married someone else, and someone else and someone else and someone else. She was what might be called 'the marrying kind.' They say that once on an Atlantic crossing, the orchestra, in the course of dinner music, played Mendelssohn's Wedding March, and as they hit the opening strains, Nora jumped to her feet and saluted. The other people at the table looked up, perplexed, and she said, 'That's my National Anthem!' "

The company laughed.

"That's a good line," said Star. "Why the hell isn't it in the show?"

"Because, dear, that's only good after she's been married five times, and in the part of the story we're telling, she's only been married once."

"Well, maybe we're telling the wrong story, then," she insisted.

"No, dear, I don't think so. If you examine your part, you'll see that there are many opportunities for injecting humor. Humor in a part is like the seasoning; without it, *any* part can be bland, but humor gives it the salt and pepper and rosemary and thyme and oregano and chili powder and chives. It brings the spice to it all. It provides variety. And by the way, that's the second thing. Every single one of you—Ted, Calvin—look for the *variety* in your parts. The best playwrights in the world err in this matter. They get a concept of a character and write to that concept. The good guys are good, the bad guys are bad. Well, that's understandable. The playwright's trying to make a point, and it's easier to make it if the character delineations are clear, but once that's done, for God's sake, don't fall into the Johnny-One-Note trap. It's been said so often that it's become a cliché that when you play a hero look for his bad side; a villain, for his good side; a powerful man, look for his weakness; an independent woman, look for her femininity, and dependence. Shakespeare understood this. That's why the strongest and most heroic of his men have moments of gentleness and tenderness. His most feminine women—Juliet and Rosalind and Portia—have scenes in which they're as powerful as men. If each and every member of this company will continually seek out the variety in his part, we'll begin to have the sort of multicolored mosaic in front of which a viewer can stand for hours without getting tired or bored."

· XLIII ·

Trouble in an unexpected place—the pit.

Not with Phil this time—although he has already been fired and rehired four times: twice by Hy; rehired once by Art and once by Larry.

Once by Art; rehired by Hy.

Once by Star, and rehired by her after one show with the substitute.

This time the problem is with Ruby, the fantastic first trumpet.

From the first dress rehearsal, it was clear that his overture solo on "Nightfall" was outstanding. Ralph Burns, the orchestrator, has worked with Ruby many times and knows his work, so he indicated an ad-lib trumpet solo for Ruby—and did that Ruby deliver!

Everyone applauded, even the other members of the orchestra. Hy was beside himself with excitement. I suppose for him it was like a playwright hearing—for the first time—Laurence Olivier reading a scene he has written.

Hy raced down the aisle to the pit yelling, "Hold it! Hold it!" The orchestra wound down in a discordant fade. "Stand up, Ruby!" he ordered.

"You think?" asked Phil.

"God damn *right* I think!"

"I don' wanna stand up," said Ruby.

"Why not?"

"Bashful."

A laugh from the orchestra.

"Stand up, Goddamn it! You'll get used to it."

Ruby stood up. Hy turned to the spot platform at the back of the balcony.

"Hit him with a white on that solo."

"What's the cue?"

"When he stands up, that's the cue."

"I can't see him so good from up here."

"You blind or what?" yelled Hy.

Clay appeared on the apron.

"I'll do it," he said. To the spot man: "I'll give it to you on the phones. Warning and go."

"Thanks, Clay."

"Go back," said Hy, "and let's do it."

"From G," said Phil, rapping his baton.

One chorus of "Waltz," then Ruby stood up. The spot hit him and he played his solo of "Nightfall" even more soaringly than before. He sat down. Hy was screaming. "Bravo! Bravo, you bastard!"

So it went. Through the dress rehearsals, the previews, the opening in Boston, the run there, and the Philadelphia opening.

Then, in the middle of the third week here, a note from Val:

"No good the trumpet player standing up like that with a spotlight on him when he plays 'Nightfall' in the overature because after, in Scene Two, when She has to sing it, it's like the whole impack is gone. Also unfair on account of after all, he's got a whole trumpet and all She's got is a voice. So no standing and no spot and also tell him take it easier on the solo. Even sitting. It's like he's reaching for the moon. Or trying for that big hand. Which he gets."

Art read the note, handed it to me, and said, "Give this to Larry for action."

"Larry?" I asked.

"Sure Larry. Why not?"

"Hy put it in, don't you remember?"

"He did?"

"Yes."

"O.K., then. Have *him* take it out."

I gave the note to Hy, who looked at it long enough to read it six times, and said, "God damn son-of-a-bitch bastard! He wants war? He'll get it."

"You think it's him?" I asked.

Hy stuck his finger in my face and said, "Bug out of this, Midge. You're an all-right secretary, but you don't always know your place!"

"Sorry," I said, although I wasn't.

The rehearsal that afternoon was interrupted by loud talk coming from the back of the house. Louder. Louder still. I recognized both voices. Hy's and Val's.

I was sitting in the fifth row with Larry. He looked back once or twice, hoping the noise would come to an end. No.

He turned to me and said, "Tell them to take it somewhere else, will you?"

I walked up the aisle. At the back of the house, Val and Hy stood head to head, both yelling at once, which made it impossible to understand what either one was saying. Only a word or a phrase now and then escaped the shouting match.

"—to talk to her—"

"—your ass!—"

"—fucking *stupid!*—"

"—protect *shit*—"

—and so on.

I moved as close to them as I dared and said, "Gentlemen. Gentlemen, *please!*"

They neither heard nor saw me. Should I touch them? Finally, I did. They regarded me, resentfully.

I spoke. "Larry says would you mind please stepping into the lobby or somewhere else?"

"Get me Art Clune over here," said Hy. "Right away. *Now!*"

He walked into the lobby, followed by Val, who was already picking up the thread of the battle.

"Clune?" he shouted. "*Clune,* for Chrissake. What the fuck is *he* gonna supposed to do?"

"You'll *see* what!"

"He don't own us!"

'He owns the show!"

They were off again. I closed the doors as tightly as I could and returned to Larry. The sound of the argument could still be heard, but with a diminished volume.

"Hy and Val," I said.

"What about?"

"Ruby standing up."

"Come *on!*" he said. "Your humor sometimes."

"No humor," I said. "That's it."

Larry stood up and shouted up to the stage, "That's it for now! Take ten."

He turned back to me.

"Ruby?" he asked, incredulously.

I handed Val's memo to him. He read it, gave it back to me, started for the lobby. I followed him.

In the lobby, the battle had become more intense, and it was clear that Val was winning. I could tell because he was now the relaxed one and they are usually the victors.

"All right, Hy," said Larry. "Take a rest. You too, Val."

"Me?" said Val. "I'm rested."

"Have you heard what this know-nothing greaseball is up to now?" asked Hy.

"Yes," said Larry. "Let me handle it." To me: "Tell Jenny she can run 'One Night at a Time.' I'll be a few minutes."

As I left, I heard him say, "All right, fellas. Let's go somewhere and get a cup of coffee, O.K.?"

I got Jenny started and hurried out of the theatre to rejoin Larry. I had not been invited, but I was fascinated.

Larry had, out of the wealth of his experience, chosen a busy coffee shop, knowing that people are less inclined to shout in public.

I joined the three of them in the booth and ordered coffee.

They sat in silence. I wondered if my presence had turned them off. No. If it had, I'd have been asked to leave. They were thinking, that was all.

After a time, Val spoke. "I'll tell you the truth," he said. "I don't know why I should tell *you* bums the truth, you've always treated me like shit, right from the start you've treated me like shit, so why should I tell *you* the truth? But I'm gonna tell you the truth. I was against this whole thing from the start. This whole show. Who needs it? And it's costing us a fucking fortune. It's an—you know what it is?

It's an ego trip for her, that's all. Broadway! *Broadway,* for Chrissake! It's not like Broadway in the movies. No more. It's a dump. It's a goddamn hellhole. Hookers and pushers and mini-pimps and cotton candy. Filthy dirty. It stinks, for Chrissake. And the theatres are fleabags. But She's always had this thing in her head from when She was a kid—*Broadway!* We get more for one night in Cleveland than She gets for a whole week around here. Eight times. So if on top of all that, it's gonna be aggravation on top of it, She could kiss off fast and why not and no hard feelings. Goodbye and good luck."

"Let me ask you something, Val," said Larry.

"Go ahead. You're payin' for the coffee, so go ahead."

"Are we talking about a trumpet player taking a standing chorus in the overture? Is *that* what we're talking about—or what? *I'm* talking about control."

"What're *you* talking about?" asked Val.

"*I'm* talking about control."

"What's *that?*"

"I'm talking about who's in charge here. I don't care if the trumpet player stands or sits or stands on his head. What's the difference?"

"So what's the problem?"

"The problem is I can't have her calling the shots, mister. I'm an old hand at this game and I can tell you one thing for sure—the minute a director loses control of a show, he may as well quit."

"All right," said Val. "So why *don't* you? Who'd *miss* you?"

"Jesus!" said Hy. "What the hell kind of dumb talk is that? Especially from you. Don't you have *any* appreciation of what Larry's done for her?"

"*Done* for?"

"Fuckin' well right! He's given her elegance and poise. She looks like a star now—an actress—not just a performer. But you don't know enough about anything to *know.* Jesus!"

"Take it easy, Hy," said Larry. "I can handle myself. Thanks, but lay off." He turned back to Val. "Everything in the show is discussible."

"O.K., so I'm discussing."

"Not quite. You're giving orders. Laying down the law. Or She is. And that I can't have. And I'll tell you why. Because once it starts, there's no end to it. If you people start making the decisions—where does it end? She wants something in, it's in? Out, it's out? Fire this dancer, this singer? Get rid of me—"

"Aha!" cried Val. "That's what's your worry, huh?"

"No," Larry replied. "My worry is being stuck with this thing if it should fall into your hands or hers. Then it would be up to Art to decide—me or her."

Val laughed. "They used to say in the Army they have this great dish—a horse and rabbit stew. You know how they make it? One horse and one rabbit. That's like this. You or her. One horse, one rabbit."

Hy. "There've been big hits without big stars, y'know."

"Sure. And big flops."

"Could we stick to the subject?" asked Larry.

Val. "You said discussible, right?"

"Right."

"O.K. So let's discuss. About the trumpet player. Never mind about control and all that bushwah. Just the trumpet player."

"May *I?*" asked Hy.

"Sure," said Larry.

"Look. Ruby's more than a blower. In this way, *he's* a star, too. More than that—he's marvelously supportive. Ask *her* if you don't believe me. The way he noodles around her singing—it's fantastic."

"Who said not?"

"So why cut him down?"

"Answer me this," said Val. "He stands up in the overture with a hot spot on him and he blows this big chorus and he gets a big hand. O.K.? So now, twenty-three minutes later by my stopwatch, She comes on and sings the same number. You don't think that hurts her?"

"Helps her," said Hy.

"How?"

"Sets it up for her. Makes it familiar. Like a reprise. Audiences *love* reprises—it's like they know the number. It's like when I do my club act and I go into one of my songs they've heard, they applaud. Why? Applauding *me?* Of course not. They're applauding *themselves* for recognizing it."

"Hy," said Val. "From my heart I wish to tell you something. You're as full of shit as a Christmas *turkey!"*

"All right," said Larry. "I think we've spent enough time on this earth-shattering question. There's something in what he says, Hy—"

"There's *nothing!* He's a—"

"Hold it. And there's a hell of a lot in what you say. Now. We've done it your way for a while. Let's try a few shows this way, her way. Then we can decide."

"But what about *tonight?*" asked Val.

"Tonight he sits."

"Nothing doing," said Hy.

"Now look, Hy," said Larry. "I don't want them in charge, but I don't want *you* in charge, either. So mind your manners!"

"It's *my* overture, God damn it! The overture isn't the show."

"Oh, come on, Hy. You know better than that. I'm going to try it. Then we'll see."

"See that?" said Val. "Discussible. Why not? So what did we need all the screaming and getting ulcers?"

Larry, to me: "And from now on, all memos—his, Art's, anybody's —all come to me. That was a mistake on Art's part—going directly to Hy."

"My fault," I said.

"How's that?"

"I thought because Mr. Balaban put the effect in, he ought to take it out."

"You were wrong."

"I know. I'm sorry."

Thus the meeting ended. As in the case of most compromises, everyone involved was unhappy, no one completely satisfied. Val knew that his triumph might well turn out to be temporary. Moreover, he had blundered into an organizational rearrangement that might be damaging in the future.

That night, Ruby did not stand up for his chorus, but then, even *I* could tell he was laying way back during the entire performance. His customary bite and crackle were absent, and he seemed to have no contact with Star.

It was reported that directly following Act One, She stormed down to the musicians' room below the stage, found Ruby, and bawled the bejesus out of him. Ruby, the coolest cat in the business, took it all, wide-eyed, claimed complete innocence, insisted he honestly did not know what She was talking about. *Honestly!*

During Act Two, he played exactly as written, submitting to circumstance in the manner of a dutiful but frigid wife during intercourse. The effect of this on her performance was telling.

At the end of the show, She sent for him, but he had already left the theatre.

The next day was a matinee day. Ruby failed to appear. The second trumpet took over his part, with devastating results. Star was well and truly thrown.

"My God!" I said to Larry during the intermission. "I never would have believed one man in the pit could make such a difference. My God!"

"Could you believe," asked Larry, "that one spark plug could interfere with the performance of a Rolls-Royce?"

Clay appeared. "She wants you," he said.

"No, She doesn't," said Larry. "She wants Ruby."

In her dressing room, we faced a livid Star.

"Son-of-a-bitch!" She said. "Hasn't he got a contract? Like me? Like everybody? Where the hell does *he* come off? That prick. I'll report him to his goddamn union!"

"He's sick," said Larry.

"Bullshit!" She said. "What kind of sick? I don't believe it! He's pissed off, that's not sick!"

To me, Larry said, "You talked to him, didn't you, Midge?"

"Yes."

"What did he say? What kind of sick?"

"He said it's his lip. It conks out on him once in a while from blowing too hard and he has to rest it."

"For how long?" She asked.

"A few days, I think he said."

"A few! I'll go nuts!" To Larry: "Go talk to him. Tell him the news. Tell him he's gonna be in big trouble if he tries to pull this on me. Fucking show-off lousy ham."

"I'll tell him," said Larry.

In his room at the Benjamin Franklin, we found Ruby lying on what appeared to be a bed of newspapers and magazines.

"How are you, Ruby?" asked Larry.

"Lip," Ruby answered, and tapped it with a forefinger.

"Hurt?"

"Stiff. A real mother. Almost ready to crack. I've got A and D Ointment all over it. See?"

"Yes. Should you see a doctor?"

"Naw," said Ruby. "They don't understand, doctors. Not unless they happen to have been trumpet players. In fact, there was one once—in Chicago—guy blew his way through medical school—good man—he understood. Trouble is, he turned out a proctologist—so even though he understood, he couldn't help me. Wrong-end specialist, see? In Chicago, this was."

"Ruby, could I ask you something? You mentioning a proctologist sort of threw me a thought. Does the lip hurt more standing up or sitting down?"

"Oh, sitting down, definitely. It's unbearable. Standing up, it's bearable. Barely."

"I see."

"Why do you ask?"

"Well, it's this new idea struck me—just now, in fact. That standing up for an overture chorus—Hell, that's cornball. That's Guy Lombardo.

"I thought it was nice."

"But I've got something much nicer."

"Speak."

"Suppose we leave out the overture—I know it hurts to sit, but try—"

"Well—"

"Wait! Instead, when She *does* the number—*then* you stand up in the pit—and you do it *with* her, like a specialty. . . ."

"*With* her?" asked Ruby, suspiciously.

"Right with her!"

"And what about the spot?"

"One on her and one on you."

Ruby got off the bed and moved about the room, rubbing his lip thoughtfully.

"Good," he said to himself. "Yeah, good." Then to us, "Good!"

"Tonight?" asked Larry.

"Got to rehearse, though. I don't wing in public."

"Say seven?"

"I'll be there."

"Bring your lip," said Larry.

Walking to the theatre, I asked, "What makes you think he'll go for it?"

"Who? Val?"

"Yes."

"He's got nothing to do with it, you know that. This is all Miss Missy's doing. She's the one I've got to see."

"Do you think you can?"

"I don't think anything anymore, ol' pal. I just let the winds blow me around. Nature follow its instincts. Does an ant think? Or a sea gull? What about elephants? They respond, but I doubt they think. That's me."

At the theatre, we waited onstage. She customarily stayed in between shows, had a hot dinner sent in, an hour's sleep, a massage—before beginning to make up for the evening performance.

Bonnie came out and said, "Just finishing the rub. Be maybe five, seven minutes, no more. He ain't here, though. Just She."

"Good," said Larry.

He put it to her beautifully, I thought. He has a marvelous way of transferring enthusiasm. He sold the idea with excitement and humor—acting it out, creating the scene—selling, selling.

"I don't know," She said, frowning.

"Please?" he begged. "A try? One show?"

"What if I say no?" She asked.

"I don't know, but I'll give you a guess."

"No Ruby, right?"

"That would be *my* guess."

"So he's got me by the balls—is that it?"

"I wouldn't put it quite like that."

"O.K. We'll try it. One show. When? Tonight?"

"Fine."

"But I've got to rehearse. Otherwise, no."

"Seven?"

"I'll be there."

They rehearsed—tentatively at first, but before long they were caught by the music, by the subliminal exchanges, by instinctive understanding, by the witty back-and-forthing, and were clearly enjoying themselves and each other.

They ran through the number six times, then She asked, "Enough?"

"Fine for me," he said.

"How's your lip?" She asked.

"Great. How's yours?"

She walked off. Ruby blew a juicy fart on his horn. Either She did not hear it or She ignored it. I suspect the former.

However good the number seemed in rehearsal, in performance it was a revelation. She and Ruby became a team in passionate action, worked carefully, skillfully, to a crashing climax, and stopped the show cold. The number had always gone well, but never before had it been a literal showstopper.

Later, backstage, there was nothing to discuss. All were agreed that the show had acquired still another strength.

"Greatest thing I ever saw in show business," said Hy to Larry.

"Thanks."

"But how come you put it in without consulting *me?*"

"Ask Val," said Larry, and walked away.

· XLIV ·

I finished reading the Bulletin to Boss. He is one of the very few people I have ever encountered who actually likes being read to. I wonder why? Perhaps because it frees him to move about and pack or unpack or eat or drink or arrange things on his desk or play with his money. Who knows? Russ told me once—well, "told" is not the word. Russ once *conveyed* to me in that ventriloquist style of his— talking without moving his lips, the sound emanating from his nose —that AC is literally illiterate; that he cannot read or write. I found this impossible to believe, although I must say I have never seen him do either—other than sign his name to letters and checks.

"Take out the thing about opening-night tickets," he said. "I don't want everybody thinkin' about opening night. Not yet. What's it their business? So far, how do we know there's gonna *be* an opening night? Y'know what I mean? I mean, *I* know there's gonna be an opening night—but the rest of these cruds— I don't want 'em to think it's a sure thing. Let 'em worry. Once they know we're goin' in, it's all over. I want everybody on their toes—and not only that— I want 'em scared shitless, then they'll make an effort. If not, no. So take out the thing about opening-night tickets."

"Very well. Anything else?"

"Yeah. Stick around."

"You've got a four-o'clock with Jenny."

"I *know* I've got a four-o'clock. What am I? A half-wit?"

"Just a reminder."

"I notice you didn't answer my question."

"Oh. I thought it was rhetorical."

"Sure."

He blushed. A characteristic, I note, when confused.

"Do you want me back here before show time?" I asked.

"No. I want you to stick around now. Like I said."

"Now?"

"That's right." He began moving about the room, nervously. "I don't know what's gonna happen here with her. She's a bottle baby, after all. If it gets noisy, I want a witness. Also, make notes. For the record. But that I guess I don't need to tell you, huh? Notes. Jesus, you make notes like a handicapper. I mean, they never stop and neither do you."

"Part of my job, isn't it?"

"If you say so, sure."

"Remember I have to run these bulletins before six," I said.

"Hey! Right. Do it while."

"But you wanted notes."

"So what? You can't do both?"

"I don't see how."

"Holy Christ! What cooperation. Notes, I said. Did I say word for word, f'Chrissake? *Notes.* Here and there. The general idea."

"All right, all right."

"You'd think I was asking for—"

"I said *all right,* Mr. Clune."

"And don't call me Mr. Clune. I haven't done anything to *you!*"

I went to the typewriter and began to revise the bulletin.

He picked up the phone.

"Mr. Balaban," he said. "Fourteen-ten. . . . Hy? Me. . . . Fair. Listen, I'm seein' her here in a few minutes—so what I need to know is like this: Anything better? . . . When? She *did?* . . . Why the hell didn't you call me right away? I'm here. What am I here for? . . . But where the fuck does She come off making a cut without? . . . You *did?* . . . Fine. . . . Look, Hy. Calm down. *I'll* tell her. You don't have to tell her anything. *I'll* tell her. You stay buddy-buddy. Let *me* be the son-of-a-bitch. . . . That's not funny, Hy. What the hell's the matter with you? That's a shitty thing to say. I'm breaking my balls for you and you insult me. . . . Yeah? It's as good as yours, my sense of humor. . . God damn it, I only hope *you* try producing a God damn someday and see how *you* feel surrounded by a lot of God damn—"

The door buzzer stopped him. He glanced at his watch. He dropped his voice.

"That must be her. Talk later." To me: "Get that, will you?" Into the phone: "And save that smart-ass shit for your songs."

He hung up as I opened the door. Jenny, looking adorable.

"Hi!" she said.

"Come in, Jenny," he called out. "Come in."

As she crossed the room, I realized I had never before seen her in a dress; therefore had never seen her legs. They could be described only one way: Leggy. Long, slim, elegant dancer's legs. They seemed to want tights or silk stockings or a net leotard. The rest of her wasn't bad, either. She was so adroitly made up that an inexperienced eye would see no makeup at all. Her hair tied back. A loose-fitting, swirling skirt. A white white blouse. No bra. Had she had her neck lengthened? And would she reveal the name of that fragrance if I asked her to?

She sat down on the sofa and crossed her legs, unsettlingly.

AC's blush again.

"A drink?" he asked. "I've got everything right here."

"I don't drink," she said.

"Yeah," he said. "I heard that."

"Tea?" she asked.

"We got any tea?" he called across to me.

"I think so," I said. "Anything with it?"

"Not a thing," said Jenny. "As it comes."

I went out to the kitchen to get the tea and worried for a moment about missing what I was supposed to be noting—but only for a moment. To hell with him, I thought. He can't have everything. I took my time.

I brought in the tea, and found him sitting in the armchair, facing her.

I put the tray down on the coffee table.

"Thanks, hon," she said.

"Anything for you?" I asked him.

"Vodka-tonic," he said.

I went to the bar to get it.

"But I've *always* worked this way, Art," she said. "Nothing new.

The job is to marry the movement to the music—that takes adjustments. Sometimes a change in the moves, sometimes a snip in the music. What's the panic? It's not Beethoven's Fifth, after all. It's Hy Balaban's Fiftieth. Utility music. Or am I wrong?"

I served his vodka and tonic. He said nothing.

"Thanks," I said as I returned to the typewriter.

"O.K.," he said absently.

Jenny laughed.

"Look, kiddo," he said. "You've got *your* job. I've got *my* job."

"Wanna trade?" she asked.

"Boy, *would* I!"

"Let's."

"Trouble is, I've never understood dancing. All that jumpin' up and down. What does it mean? Like Harry Cohn used to say about ballet—'I don't like it where everybody chases everybody and nobody catches nobody!' "

"A profound man," said Jenny.

"Could I ask you one thing only? A favor?"

"You bet."

"If you have to make a cut or a trim or a change or an anything —would you ask first, please?"

"Certainly."

"Thanks."

"If he's around," she said.

"If who's?"

"Hy. Isn't the beef his?"

"No."

"Whose, then?"

"Mine. I'm trying to keep this thing organized. And everybody happy."

"And some more than others."

"What? No."

"Tell him for me" said Jenny, "that if he wants to protect every precious bar of his deathless composition, the way to do it is to *be* there. I can't hold up my work to get a clearance on every teensy-weensy—"

"Hold it."

"No, I'm telling you—"

"Hold it, I said!"

Jenny stood up, abruptly, and moved to him.

"Art?" she asked, concerned.

"What?"

"Are you all right?"

"Sure all right. Why?"

"You're flushed," she said.

"So what? Happens all the time."

"It shouldn't. And those *neck* muscles! They worry me."

"They do?" he asked vacantly.

"Yes. Look here." She went around behind him, put her left hand on top of his head, and began to feel his neck with the fingers of her right hand. "Feel that?"

"Feel what?"

"The tension? Do you have headaches?" she asked.

"Doesn't everybody?"

"*I* don't."

"I know. You let *me* have your headaches."

"Relax," she said. "Let your head fall forward." He did so. I could not help looking over at the action. Jenny caught my eye and winked impishly. "That's good. Let go. More."

I went to the copier and began to run the bulletin.

She grasped his shoulders beside his neck and with her thumbs firmly in place on his upper spinal column, began to massage the base of his neck column.

"My God!" she exclaimed.

"What?" he asked, not without alarm.

"Like steel wires," she said.

"Yeah, I know," he said modestly, as if responding to a compliment.

She threw her forearm across his throat, steadied him, and continued to massage his back.

"Good," he said hoarsely.

"What?"

"Feels good," he said.

"That doesn't matter," said Jenny sternly. "What feels good isn't necessarily what's good for you. There's a whole tyranny of what feels good. Take off your shirt."

"No, that's all right. That's enough."

"Don't be silly. You're in trouble."

He stood up, removed his shirt, threw it onto the sofa, and sat down. She resumed her ministrations from behind. They became more vigorous, more complete.

"What you need," she said, "is a good osteopath."

"You'll do," he said dreamily.

"No, no. This is just first aid."

"Sensational," he whispered.

She placed his arms at his sides, hanging down.

"I could use some oil of some kind," she said.

"Let me see," I said, and went out to the kitchen again. It took me a while to find a bottle of safflower oil. When I returned with it to the living room, AC was stretched out on the sofa, face down, and shoes off.

I went back to the copier, wondering if I should make notes on *these* goings-on.

"I mean it," he said. "You're a goddam *professional.*"

"Watch your language," she said.

"I mean it."

"It's nothing," she said. "All dancers know all about it. God, we spend half our lives with osteopaths and chiropractors and trainers and yogis and healers and foot-fixers. If you're a dancer, you *hurt* all the time. Sprains and strains and bruises and welts. You get to know. Your body is your instrument. You learn to take care of it."

"Yeah," he exhaled.

I was trying to keep my attention on the copier, but some magnetic force was impelling me to take in the scene. I looked over and shuddered slightly. The magnetic force was Jenny's eyes. She had apparently been trying to get my attention for some time. Now that she had succeeded, her eyes held mine for an instant before she motioned me out of the room with one swift throw of her head.

I picked up the copies, my few belongings, and got out of the room as fast as I could.

I had to go out and walk. The scene upset me. Would *I* have done what *she* had done? Doubtless she believed her job was at stake, but I have begun to see that with these people, it is not so much a question of the job or the activity or the money involved—it is a question of the credit, the career, and in most cases, career means life.

Vartan used to say: "We're not here to pass moral judgments on one another. Just see that *you* behave well, and leave the others to their own devices."

I walked and walked, and at length came upon the little Rodin Museum I had often heard about, meant to visit, never have. I went in and wandered about the wonders. Works of art. One man's vision. Is that what is wrong with what is happening over at our place? That it does *not* represent one man's vision? Of course, I know that the aim over there is a million light years from the work of Rodin. Still, in its way, it aspires to creation.

More questions. Is every show done in the same way as this one? Is there always this amount of deviousness and scheming and politicking and backbiting and perfidy? It is difficult to understand how beauty and magic and wonder can be born out of such a revolting morass of human behavior. Then I remind myself that birth is not altogether beautiful. It is surrounded by nausea and discomfort and eventually intense pain—some say the worst in the world.

What troubles me most of all about that lovely girl back there, putting her body on the line—whoring—to hold on to her job, is that she is not a fraud, not a relative. She is a truly talented artist. I can understand someone humping their way up the ladder. The routine is not indigenous to the theatre, despite all the snide jokes about casting couches and so on. Using the fundamentals is common practice in all businesses—and (do I dare put it in writing?) even in the academic world. We all know some who made their grades on ass alone. But they were the dummies, the ones who could not make it legitimately. Jenny is different: able and imaginative and inventive. Why does *she* have to put out? Or *does* she? Or does she want to? No. In this case, I believe it is her only route. If it works. He is such a reprehensible, amoral man that he might easily cross her. How I wish Hy were taping *him* through the wall! But as someone said the other day—"If you're looking for justice, don't look in Shubert Alley." It has been a wildly disturbing day. Should I resign? I feel poisoned—but it is all too fascinating to leave behind.

I return to The Barclay and find three messages from him in my box. I am tempted to ignore them, but then I imagine the consequences, so I sit down in an armchair in the lobby for a few minutes and collect my thoughts—such as they are.

I ring his room from the lobby.

"Where've *you* been, f'Chrissake?"

I say, "Walking"—but "Working" comes out.

"Who on?" he asks with his charmless vocal smirk. "Come up here. Right away."

I use my key to open the door of his suite. He is not in the living room.

"That you?" he calls from the bedroom.

"Yes."

"In *here!*"

I go into the bedroom, and it is all I can do to keep from collapsing into laughter.

He is sitting up in his bed, under the covers, bearing a striking resemblance to Vivien Leigh in the morning-after scene from *Gone With the Wind*. He is (for him) relaxed, content, satiated, smug.

"Took a nap," he explains. "Doctor's orders. He says I'm on the verge of exhaustion. Boy, do I hate a nap! Look." He throws a sheaf of proofs to me across the bed. "Have you seen these Sunday ads that pisshead put together?"

"No."

"What do you think?"

I look over the ads. They seem like all Sunday ads. No better, no worse.

"I don't know," I say. "Don't ask me. I don't know the first thing about ads."

"That's why I'm asking you. You're not *supposed* to know. You're just supposed to react. Like the dumb public."

"All right." I look at him again. "No good." The line of least resistance.

"See that?" he shouts. "You *do* know. Tell 'im get his ass over here so I can chew it out."

"All right."

I call Paul Cooley and tell him he is wanted.

"Memo," says Art. "Strictly confidential in caps   Hy Balaban from AC   Re Choreo   I have given this matter a great deal of thought and have come to the conclusion that any change in the present set-up would be disruptive and counterproductive   Para

However I have had a long serious and satisfactory conference with JF and have explained your point of view   I suggest you attend as many dance rehearsals as possible so you can be consulted on any necessary changes in the score   Successful work in this area depends completely on cooperation and collaboration   A question of marrying the movements to the music   I know I can count on you to do your part in achieving it."

Thus endeth the First Lesson.

She times it perfectly. Her choreographer's instinct, I suppose. The whole plan had a kind of grand design. Had she made this liaison earlier, it might have been worn out by now and our lover might have been ready to move on. Had she waited, it might have been too late and he might have been too deeply committed to dropping her overboard. No—she hit it bang on. The right day. Even the right hour. She is in the strongest of positions now, and unless she makes a major blunder, seems destined to hold it to the end.

What it does for her work is to free her from anxiety and make it possible for her to function without overhanging fears. It will be interesting to see what she does in the next few days. She has been trying to please everyone. Now she needs to please only herself.

SHINE ON, HARVEST MOON
Company Bulletin
Wednesday, December 12

TO ALL PLAYERS WITH LINES: Please do not fall into the common and very bad habit of interpolating the expression "y'know." In the attempt to achieve naturalism, you will only succeed in repeating a cliché. Look at your scripts. Our musicians do not add or subtract notes; we should respect our text just as they do the score.

PERFORMANCE ROUTINE: Please do not cross over at the rear of the stage during Scene 3, in Act I. Always wait until the scene is over before crossing over. From the front it is enormously distracting. We are aware of the smallest movement of the drops and we hear your footsteps.

REVIEW: The performance on Tuesday was the best yet, although we still suffer from a lack of projection. Please speak up and *sing* out. The great Frank Loesser had a musical-theatre maxim he often repeated: "Loud is good. Louder is better."

HEALTH: Mrs. Eleanor Roosevelt once recommended garlic tablets as an aid to memory. We have experimented with this idea across the years with some, although not total, success. Garlic tablets are available at all health-food stores in various forms. Some of them are honey-mint flavored and some are marked "odorless." *What* a good idea! Try them.

THE COMPANY YOU KEEP: GLORIA FULLER(Cathy)
    I'm the one from Seattle. (Applause.) Stagestruck from the crib. A born show-off. Strangely, encouraged (spoiled?) by both wonderful parents.
    Lousy in grade school, worse in high school, except for cheerleading.
    At 15, a break. Scholarship to study at the San Francisco Ballet School under William Christensen. I have since appeared on Broadway in FOLLIES (love Hal Prince!); MUSIC, MUSIC!; and SMITH.

Also road tour of CABARET. On TV, I did LIZA WITH A Z;
Ed Sullivan's COMEDY YEARS; and ON BROADWAY.
I am looking for a husband. I am single.

MENTAL HEALTH: Visit the Rodin Museum. Midge is
organizing a group for tomorrow afternoon. Sign
up.

QUOTE TO REMEMBER:
    "There's no way of knowing how it's going to
come out. But I do know I'm taking my shot and
it's great. I was never much for screaming at
people or having hysterics, but with this cast
there is such a feeling of love and cooperation, it has never been necessary. . . .
    "The show's almost ready. Sure, it needs
tightening, but I save that for the last minute
in order to keep the spontaneity and spirit intact."

Patricia Birch

There are now 8 days remaining until our New York
opening.

· XLV ·

Hectic days. The tour has been extended and the New York opening postponed for five weeks.

The mass of detail which this decision has engendered is staggering.

But more important. All important. *Only* important. GENE IS COMING BACK. GENE GENE GENE.

What happened was that a rival musical, meant to go into The Kennedy Center in Washington, closed unexpectedly in Chicago.

Roger L. Stevens of the Kennedy flew from Chicago to Washington and met with Art, offering him what is said to be the most desirable booking in America. Business is always good there: the audiences superior, sophisticated, and cosmopolitan.

The Shuberts had to be consulted, but they agreed after making the financial arrangements.

Some of the members of the company are less than thrilled with this development. There is talk of neglected apartments, husbands, pets, wives, children. Also missed TV jobs and commercials, in addition to simple testiness. The chronic complainers now have a new object on which to vent their never-ending supply of spleen.

Others, myself included, are delighted. It gives me an extension of life with Gene—which means an extension of life—although he is not yet sure he can get a new leave of absence for another month. What he hopes to do is compromise with his paper and get them to accept his column from Washington. He says it is the newsiest and most interesting in the United States. He thinks he will be able to give us at least half his time there. What the hell. Half a life is better than none.

The creative team is overjoyed. Hy and Fred and Larry, as well as Alicia and Ivan, feel that even if no extensive changes are made, the show will benefit greatly from playing in.

Accommodations are a problem. The Watergate complex right next to The Kennedy Center is ideal, but they have only a few suites available (the other show's cancellations) and in any case, it is too expensive for most of the company.

However, this morning it seems set for Art and Gene to have suites there. And a room for me.

Hy and Fred are going to The Madison.

"It's not so convenient to the theatre," Hy explained, "but I like it because it's so much more *expensive* than The Watergate."

Ivan and Alicia will not be staying in Washington, coming down only when and if needed.

Meanwhile, the ructions here continue. Art still seems determined to provoke Larry. Their relationship has deteriorated further. Now that the show is so good, Art feels he no longer needs Larry, so he baits him. Larry insults him openly, often going too far, I think.

"I like you, Larry," I said to him yesterday. "But I can't say I always approve of you."

"Who does?"

"Why do you have to exacerbate the situation? Why don't you make peace with him?"

"For the same reason we didn't make peace with Hitler," he said. "This guy's a menace. He wants me to quit—he's trying to make me quit—but there's not a chance. Of course, I could drop dead, and I would, except that I'd hate to give him the satisfaction. Even if I did, he'd owe my estate my royalties and percentages. My lawyer says so. And he knows."

From this, I flew back to Art. Shuttle diplomacy. Little Miss Kissinger.

"Art, would you allow me to express an opinion?"

"If it's about how I'm the sexiest man around, yes."

"It's about something more important than that."

"What could be more important than that?" he asked.

"The show."

"The show's great. *Time* and *Newsweek* have scouted it already and the feedback is smash."

"Then why do you hector Larry all the time?"

"Hector? That's a word?"

"Yes."

"I thought it was a name. Since Hector was a pup. Hector Berlioz. I hector him because he's a no-good arrogant bastard with a big mouth. Remember way back when he told me to shut up?"

"No, I don't."

"You were there. *Everybody* was there. In front of everybody he tells me to shut up."

"I don't remember," I said.

"So what? *I* remember."

"It seems an age ago, and what does it matter? Everyone connected with the show has said and maybe done things they'd like to forget."

"So how come he doesn't apologize?" asked Art.

Shuttle.

"Apologize?" said Larry. "For *what?* For putting on a hit for the bloody idiot who doesn't know a scene from a number? He ought to be showering me with bonuses."

The shuttle has broken down. I give up.

Odd how infrequently right and wrong are cut and dried. Both these men are right and wrong. They could admit this and even find a way to compromise, but they have grown to dislike one another with such intensity of bitter feeling that they don't make sense on the subject of one another.

What worries me is what would happen to the show if for any reason, Larry *did* leave.

<u>SHINE ON, HARVEST MOON</u>
Company Bulletin
Thursday, December 13

<u>REMINDERS</u>:

1. Sunday, December 16, the company will travel to Washington. The train will leave from 30th Street Station at 10:00 A.M. Everyone should be at the Information Booth no later than *9:30 A.M.* The scheduled arrival time in Washington is 11:35 A.M.
2. Monday, December 17, the entire company will have the day off.
3. We intend to work with all understudies while on the train. Please have your scripts with you.
4. The call in Washington on Tuesday, December 18, will be at the Watergate Hotel, next door to the Kennedy Center, promptly at 6:30 P.M. This will be for the entire company.

<u>RUN-THROUGH</u>: There will be a dress rehearsal on Wednesday, December 19 at 2:00 P.M. Half hour at 1:30.

<u>THE COMPANY YOU KEEP</u>: CALVIN SHARP (Jack)
A terrifyingly ordinary early life, I'm afraid. Born Nashville, June 20, never mind the year. Father Coca-Cola executive. Dumb school, dumber High School. Freed at last at Princeton. Glee Club. Weekend trips to New York. Broadway! How long has *this* been going on? A FUNNY THING HAPPENED ON THE WAY TO THE FORUM; PORGY AND BESS; Ethel Merman, Bert Lahr, Mary Martin; HELLO, DOLLY!; BEYOND THE FRINGE; FIDDLER ON THE ROOF. Decide on stage career. Drop out of Princeton mid-sophomore year. Excommunicated and cut off without a shilling by F. W. Sharp who had had high hopes for me in Coca-Cola. Starved one year. Second year on bread and spaghetti. Third year joined flop rock group: THE BITTERENDERS. Then original off-Broadway HAIR. Same on Broadway. Constantly employed since: 1776; MINNIE'S BOYS; 70 GIRLS 70; VIA GALACTICA (oi vey!); GIGI; HOME, SWEET HOMER (1 consecutive performance on Broadway); ROBBER BRIDEGROOM. Also Reno Sweeney's, The Bottom Line. Dreams of glory: a mo-

tion-picture career a la Gene Kelly, Fred Astaire, Dan Dailey. Have tux, will travel.

COLOR: Today is PURPLE. Keep an eye out for Ruby's tie!

A WORD FROM AN EVERLEIGH SISTER:
"A girl in our establishment is not a commodity with a market-price, like a pound of butter or a leg of lamb. She is much more on the same level with people belonging to professional classes, who accept fees for services rendered; she charges in accordance with the client's means. She doesn't 'sell herself' as these eggheads keep shouting. Such statements are unfair and unjust. As for the moral and the aesthetic standpoint—who knows! They write books about it, but get nowhere.
"The plain, commercial, fish-face reformer, from the time of Charlemagne onwards, has over and over again brought his hooks into the evils of our generous catering to nerve-racked males and he has always made matters worse. It is only by wisely working around the issue that we can hope to lessen its sorrier side. A saner and truer conception of womanhood and of the responsibilities of women is the only way I know of that we can expect to take the sting out of 'slipping.'"
Minna was always the one to avoid the uglier words.

COME INTO MY PARLOR
Charles Washburn

There are now 5 days before our first preview in Washington.
There are now 8 days before the Washington opening.
There are now 50 days before the New York opening.

WASHINGTON, D.C.

· XLVI ·

Washington.

Is this the raunchiest group with which I have ever been associated? Probably.

I have debated a long time whether or not I should set down my most recent happening. Who knows who may be reading these notes someday? And even though they are in shorthand, I have found that others can often read my scrawls.

Anyway. It all began when Val Belmonte, Star's husband, asked for a meeting with Art. It had to be private, personal.

Art told me later he had turned up with four pages of notes. They talked them over. Art then suggested to Val that he dictate them in detail to me. I would then transcribe them, and they would be forwarded to the proper departments for action.

So right after lunch, he came up to my room. He is a short, fat, bald-headed slob, who usually reeks of garlic, and on this day, since it was directly following lunch, the fumes were intense.

I opened the window.

Also. He smokes cigars.

"You mind I take my coat off?" he asked. "This is a big job we got here."

"Go ahead."

"I'll go slow. I know about dictation's speed. If I go too fast, you tell me. Right?"

"Fine."

He began. Some of his notes were too silly for words.

"In 'Waltz,' Belle is now doing her hair exactly like Star. She didn't used to. Now she does. This should be stopped right away as it is very annoying to Star. The way She does her hair is her way and belongs to her. Not some low-pay showgirl.

"Paul rushes too much the tempo on 'Nightfall.' Which makes the dancing very hard on her. Tell him take all tempos from her. All he's got to is watch her right and She will give him the tempos.

"Whoever is on the follow-spot for her should be fired and a better follow-spot man should be put on. And the same guy or man should be the same one for each and every performance. If they change, every guy follows the routine but She changes her positions all the time so routine means nothing. There should be an intelligent electrician up there (if there is such a thing) and tell him stay with her, to keep that spot on her always at all times and change the gels the way the sheet says. Also tell him if he makes one mistake he will be out.

"The battery for her body mike—the one taped to the inside of her right thigh—is hurting her something terrible. We have heard there's a new kind—made by some company in Cambridge, Mass., that is a whole lot smaller and better. Somebody better look into this right away. It's the same one Shirley MacLaine used in her club act and why should she have anything better than us? Check this out right away and stay on top of it with follow-through and let us know when are we going to get ours. And no stalling on this."

And so it went. On and on. And on. In its charmless, illiterate, and selfish way.

There was hardly a point that took cognizance of the show as a whole, or of anyone else in it. I do not know why it should have surprised me, but it did, somehow. It all stems from Star, of course. A Queen Bee in the classic sense. I think of those years in Saint Helena when Pop kept beehives in the big apple orchard. How fascinating we found that world! Why does it remind me of the one I am living in now? The Queen Bee mates only *once* in her whole life, but she has a few hundred males (drones) who work for her, clean and defend the hive, feed her, and care for her until they die. Well, that is pretty much what we have here. Why would anyone want to *be* a Queen Bee?

Val had dictated for an hour, dizzying me. Then he said, "How long will it take you for the typing up?"

"Not sure. An hour or so. I'll call you."

"No, no," he said. "I'll stick around so I can read the pages as you do 'em. Wouldn't that save time?"

"Well—" I began.

"Sure it would. These are important stuff. Y'mind I use your ladies' room?"

"Help yourself."

I began to type, faster than I had ever typed before. I had no idea I was capable of such speed. The sooner I got him out of here, the better. For some reason, I was tightly ill at ease in his presence.

He returned, got on my phone, and made six or seven calls. I tried not to listen, and concentrated as hard as I could on my work. Then, sudden silence jolted me—like Vartan's story of the lighthouse keeper who is accustomed to hearing the bell go off loudly every fifteen minutes for years and years. One night, the bell fails to ring. The lighthouse keeper jumps out of bed and yells, "What was *that?*"

I kept typing. Then it came upon me—that awful, terrifying, sickening sensation I experience whenever someone comes up behind me. It stems from that attempted rape I lived through when I was nine. Nothing will erase it. I have tried just about everything: psychotherapy, hypnosis, even specific analysis. No use. The trauma of terror is there, too deeply imbedded to be removed.

So there I sat. The typing stopped, although my hands were still on the keys. My heart was pounding and I seemed to be sweating from every pore. In addition, nausea was taking hold. I wanted to speak, could not. My mouth was too dry and my tongue immovable. God *damn* this ridiculous phobia! All right. Now. The words came at last.

"Please . . . don't . . . do . . . that."

For a crazy, irrational nut, my voice sounded surprisingly normal.

"Do what?" he said, behind me.

"Stand there like that. It makes me nervous."

"What'm I doing? I'm reading your typing," he said.

"Yes, I know," I said, still in control but ready to scream.

I began typing again, furiously, and finished the page. I tore it out of the machine and stood up. I turned to face him, handed over the page.

"Here," I said. "Sit down and read it. And here are a few more." I handed him three more pages.

He sat down and began to read. I went back to work, but could not help noticing that already he was making penciled corrections on my copy. Who cares?

The work took all my attention since it was not easy to make sense out of the nonsense he had dictated. I was pondering a long, involved, mindless suggestion, trying to dope out possible punctuation, when I froze *again!* I closed my eyes in a fierce attempt to collect myself. A tightness in my chest, and all at once, pain in either breast —no, not pain—*hands!* His hands! I opened my eyes, saw them, leaped to my feet, and rushed into the bathroom. Cold water—brush teeth—why?—take a Dalmane—pee—there, that's better.

I came back into the room and found him sitting in the armchair near the window, reading my pages.

I said, "I think the best thing would be for you to go. O.K.?"

"No," he said. "I better stay and work with you here. There's a lot of mistakes."

"You bet there are," I said. "And they're all yours."

"What're *you*, mad or something? Insulted? What? I touched you? So? You should be insulted only if I *don't* touch you. Right?"

He came toward me. "All right, so you don't like it from the back. Fair enough. How about from the front?"

"Keep away from me," I said.

"But look what I've got for you," he said. "Look!"

There it was, in his hand, an outsized erection—phenomenal. His secret weapon, I suppose. He had precious little *else* to recommend him. For the life of me, I could not remove my stare. It was like seeing a hand with six fingers.

The room turned upside down. Was I falling? Had I fainted? No. My panty hose were being torn from my body, and here he was desperately trying to position me for penetration. I tried to scream, and realized that my mouth was covered with his hand. I bit as hard as I could. He pulled it away with a cry, and struck me in the head. I blacked out for a moment, and the bastard almost made it. *Jesus,* he was strong! Vartan to the rescue. Vartan, who insisted I take that self-defense course. I hated it. So unfeminine. But oh, did it come in handy now! I reached down, grasped his testicles with my right hand and squeezed with all the strength I had. His attention shifted at once from me to himself, as he struggled to get free—but I hung on and added the eye thing with my thumb.

"Christ Almighty!" he gasped. "Fuck off! You crazy? Or what?"

I let him free. He turned away, modestly, and adjusted his clothing. I picked up my torn-to-shreds panty hose and threw them into the wastepaper basket. Now, to my astonishment, he sat down and began to read my pages again. I would have laughed if I'd had the energy. Instead, I said, "God damn you—out! I mean it. Get out! *Now!*"

He looked up at me, a man wronged. "You hurt me," he said. "You know it?"

"I hope so."

"A little pass. What the hell? You make a federal case?"

"Out," I repeated. "Or should I call Art?"

"*That* schmuck. I'll flatten him if he opens his dumb kisser to me. I'll have him worked over."

I went to the door and opened it. We stared at each other. I won. He got up, put on his jacket, and started out. At the door, he stopped.

"I owe you one pair of panty hose," he said. "Lemme know what size, what color, O.K.?"

He was gone. I closed the door and locked it. I took a shower and changed my clothes. I called Vartan and told him what had happened.

"Should I quit?" I asked.

"Of course not. Why should you let a filthy criminal like that interfere with your life and your work?"

"Tell Art?"

"What can *he* do? No, tell the skunk's wife. That'll *really* squeeze his balls. The picture I get is of a pathetic little parasite. Tell her. That'll tear up his meal ticket."

"I'm not sure."

"All right, don't. But listen—whatever you do, don't do *nothing*. Do *something*. Otherwise, it'll stay with you, live with you for always, like the time on the picnic."

"All right, I'll think of something."

He made a kissing noise and was gone. I was alone again with my shock.

A big think.

At the theatre, I asked Bonnie, her maid, if I could see Star in her dressing room after the performance tonight, privately. Important.

The word came back. Yes.

I waited in the outer room while She changed. From within, rock music blared. I looked around. Two refrigerators. One to hold the celebrated bottles: acidophilus, Kefir, yogurt, and goat's milk. The other, fruit and vegetable juices, and a supply of saltless, sugarless, chemical-less provisions. On the dressing shelf: an Acme juicer, a Cuisinart, a Waring blender, a crock pot. She was determined, this little lady, to live forever. So far, She was making it, too.

She came in, wearing one of her beautiful dressing gowns—they are all pretty starry, this one was especially so—pink with marabou feathers. A champagne glass in her hand was filled with carrot juice. She was still in her sensational stage makeup, and dripped charm as She greeted me. I felt like a stage-door Johnny.

"Problem?" She asked, coming right to the point and wasting no time on anything so mundane as "Hello."

"Yes."

"Yours or mine?"

"Hard to say. *Both,* probably."

She sipped her carrot juice, but held my eyes with hers.

I decided to be as brusque and as businesslike as She was, coming to the point at once.

"Your husband tried to rape me this afternoon," I said.

She laughed. "Y'mean to say he didn't make it?"

"He did not."

"The jerk-off must be slipping. Usually he doesn't miss."

She laughed again, infuriating me to the point where I fantasized slapping her, or grabbing *her* by the balls. I did not doubt She had a pair.

"You find it funny?" I asked.

"What? That he did it? That he tried?"

"Yes."

"No."

"Then what are you laughing at?" I asked.

"At your telling me. *That* I *do* think is funny."

"Why?"

"Why?" She echoed. "Because what the hell am *I* supposed to do about it? Spank him? Or what? I can't. I'm busy."

I got up and said, "I thought you ought to know. I see I was wrong. Sorry."

"Sit down," She said. "I've got time. When you said important, I blocked out a whole half an hour."

I sat down, surprised, but I must say, impressed by her remarkable sense of organization.

"I really don't see the point," I said. "Obviously, there's something else I should do about it."

"Like what? Spread it around?"

"No, I thought of going to the police and filing a complaint and having him arrested. I believe rapists ought to be stopped."

God, I sounded idiotic.

She looked at me for a long stretch, and suddenly yelled, "Bon-*nie!!*" using her full pharyngeal voice, and damn near blasting me out of the room.

Bonnie stepped in.

"Yes, hon?"

"See if Mr. Clune's around."

"Sure, hon."

She went out. Star and I sat together, waiting, saying nothing.

Bonnie returned.

"Gone," she said.

Star pointed a warning finger at me and said, "Wait here."

She and Bonnie went into the dressing room, left the door open. Working expertly with Bonnie, She changed in about two minutes flat—like a quick change in the wings between scenes.

She strode through the room where I sat, and without stopping, said, "Let's go."

I followed her across the stage, out the stage door, through a gauntlet of fans whom, for once, She ignored, into her waiting limousine.

As we drove off, She said, "Good show tonight. You see it?"

"Not tonight, no."

"Too bad. Real good."

We reached The Watergate. She phoned Art from the lobby and told him we were on the way up. What if he hadn't been there? I suppose She'd have waited with me until he turned up.

Whoever had been with Art was gone by the time we got upstairs. His door was open, and he stood in the doorway, clearly aware that there was big trouble.

We all sat down.

"Get me a carton of skim milk," She said.

Art looked at me and said, "Milk."

"What about it?"

"Get it."

"Get it yourself," I said.

"I mean order it on the phone. From downstairs. From Room Service."

"Order it yourself," I said.

"What's goin' on here?" he asked, confused and worried.

Star was already on the phone raising hell with Room Service.

"Lousy dump," She said, returning. To me: "You want to tell him, or you want me?"

"You."

"All right. Here it is. My beloved, according to this one, tried to jump on her bones. That's his way, y'know? He does that once in a while. So I don't know what's her angle, but she's set to blow the whistle. So what do you say? You want that? You want to do that? She's *your* employee, not mine, after all. So what do you say?"

Art looked at me.

"Why?" he asked.

"Because I don't think a man who does that should be allowed to get away with it."

"Come on," he said impatiently. "Get back on the ground, willya? So a guy makes a pass, so big deal, so what? Listen, didn't I make a pass at you myself back there in the beginning? So you said no, so that's it. Curtain."

"You didn't throw me around and tear my clothes off and belt me."

"And *he* did?"

"Yes. He did."

"But don't worry," said Star. "She fought him off because she's bigger and stronger, so her cherry's still intact."

"I don't know why I'm sitting here," I said, and got up.

"No," She said. "You stay. *I'll* go."

She got up, I sat down.

"Here it is," She said. "The bottom line. I don't need aggravation, I've got plenty, so I'll tell you this, any more shit about this—talking, blabbing, complaining, law—and it's going to make me so sick I'm not going to be able to *talk,* let alone sing. I'm going to be in a state of shock. My doctor's going to order a complete rest. Complete. Six, seven months probably. Got that? Oh. If that milk ever gets here, which I doubt, stick it up each other's ass."

She was gone.

We sat without talking for five minutes.

"Once out of the well," said Art.

"What?"

"You don't know that one? Richard Harding Davis was writing a serial once for a big magazine. One episode ended with the hero looking for the heroine in the middle of a Central African jungle, and he falls eighty feet into an abandoned well filled with snakes and rats and lizards, and he breaks both legs and faints. End of episode. Now Davis gets into a big money hassle with the editors and walks out. They get every writer in town to try and continue the serial, and nobody can—so they have to come to terms with Davis. O.K.? He sends in the next episode and they can't wait to read it. It begins: 'Once out of the well—' "

"I see."

"Whenever I get into an *impossible* situation—that's the story I think of. I mean, what's the use? You know I'm with you—why should you be harassed by this louse? Why shouldn't you stand up for your rights? Y'know? But She's not bluffing, this bitch. She'd hang us, like She just threatened, in two seconds."

"Couldn't you *prove* She was faking?"

"Come on," he said. "You want me to get you a certificate signed by *four* doctors saying you have to have complete isolation because of a nervous breakdown? I'll have it for you in the morning."

"Well, then *what?*"

"A drink," he said.

We had several, and talked of other things.

"Let's sleep on it," he said.

So that is what I am about to do. Sleep on it.

<u>SHINE ON, HARVEST MOON</u>
Company Bulletin
Friday, December 21

<u>COMPANY</u>: I have long believed that it is the principal function of a director to create an atmosphere in which creative work can take place.

Moreover, I find that to accomplish this, it is necessary to have the cooperation of all members of the company, stage management, and the crew.

We are professionals and not amateurs. Oscar Hammerstein once defined the difference as follows: "A professional works while an amateur hopes."

Congratulations on a smooth and highly professional opening-night performance at the Kennedy Center.

My thanks to you all.

L.G.

<u>TICKETS</u>: If you are going to need tickets for any of the performances in the next four weeks, you are advised to put your request to Henry Wadsworth in as soon as possible if you want choice locations. Do not wait till the last minute and then be disappointed when you can't get good locations.

<u>THE COMPANY YOU KEEP</u>: SHARON VAUGHN(Ginny)

Born in the heart of Harlem. Tough kid. Lena Horne my absolute all-time idol. My room plastered with her photos. Did everything as much like her as possible: Hair, eyes, clothes, walk, mannerism, singing. Saw JAMAICA 55 times. One day an agent said to me, "You remind me of Lena Horne." I kissed him right on the mouth. . . . I am a graduate of The High School of Performing Arts. . . . My mother and father are divorced and both have remarried so I am in the fortunate position of having two mothers and two fathers—all wonderful. . . . My real father is a newsfilm editor for CBS, the other one is an English teacher at Martin Luther King. My mother runs the most beautiful dress shop in Harlem and my stepmother is a dentist which explains my *beautiful* teeth. (Free, what's more!) I have not yet decided whether I want to be a singer, a dancer, or an actress. The trouble is, I do them all so brilliantly.

I love my part in this show but wish I had more to do. In addition to flirting with all the powers to this end, I go every morning to the Baptist Church and take it up with them there.

<u>HOLIDAY</u>: The Christmas tree and grab-bag are on stage left. The company party will be in Georgetown on Sunday, December 23, after the evening perform-ance. Check Call Board for details tomorrow.

<u>QUOTE TO REMEMBER</u>:
> "I've been a bad girl all my life,
> I've drank my share of booze,
> But you've got to give me credit, boys,
> I never wore white shoes."
> An Everleigh Girl's Epitaph

There are now 42 days remaining until the New York opening.

· XLVII ·

Reviews here excellent, especially Richard Coe in *The Washington Post*, who said, "A sure-fire, gold-plated hit in the grand tradition."

Gene is back. I have not told him about the Val incident. Maybe I will someday, but as of now, what's the point? He's back and that seems to be all that matters in life.

The Christmas party was run by Saul who came down especially to do it. Everyone connected with the show is too frazzled to think in terms of celebration.

But Saul did it perfectly, as apparently he does everything. He took over The Foundry in Georgetown and invited *everyone:* cast, orchestra, crew, front of the house. Informality was the order of the evening. No one dressed up. Blue jeans, turtlenecks, sweaters, ponchos. We made a colorful group. Two bands. A conventional dance orchestra and an all-girl rock group alternated. The food was grand after-theatre stuff: Lobster Newburg, Welsh Rarebit, hamburgers, hot dogs, chicken curry, Japanese and Chinese specialties. Wine from barrels and beer from kegs. A wild event. The dancers danced all night, the singers sang, the principals talked.

A tree. Presents. Art Clune, padded and dressed as Santa, presided. At the appropriate moment, he gave out boxes and bundles.

Neysa hovering. She has decided now to love the show.

With the party in high, Saul joined Gene and me at a corner table somewhat removed from the noise.

"Terrific," said Gene. "I wish *I* knew how to give a party."

"Money," said Saul.

"And imagination," said Gene.

"What about Dad as Santa? Is that something?"

We say nothing. He goes on. "A misunderstood man, my father. Tough. Tougher than he has to be, I know—but toughness was forced on him early on and became ingrained. He took me down to show me where he was born once—it was appalling. I'd forgotten there were such places in New York. A slum. How do you get out? He did by *working* his way out. The jobs he had—newsboy, messenger, stockboy, runner for a numbers man. Petty thievery. Busted. Reform school—about the only schooling he got. Finally into the agency as a mail boy and—well—you know the rest. So if he wants to be Santa Claus—it's all right with me. If he believes it's all money—it's because that's what the world taught *him* and it worked out that way. For him."

"There's another side, Saul," said Gene. "But this is hardly the time and place."

"Of course," said Saul. "I understand. But remember—he may change. We all do. Won't success help?"

"It might," said Gene. "And it might make things *worse!*"

Saul laughed. "Oh, no! Oh, please *no!*"

Suddenly, a fistfight in the middle of the dance floor. Saul rushed in to deal with it.

"Shall we melt away?" asked Gene.

"With pleasure."

"Oh. By the way."

"Yes?"

"Merry Christmas," he said.

"Merry Christmas."

· XLVIII ·

Larry has fallen ill. I am not entirely surprised. The pressures to which he has been subjected in the course of the past several weeks would be enough to wreck anyone. But he has had the additional load of Art Clune's determined effort to grind him down, using whatever methods he deemed necessary. These included scoldings, humiliations, 4:00-A.M. phone calls, threats, nit-picking, petty criticism, personal criticism, interference, rudeness, deliberate provocations, memos by the score, planted rumors and scuttlebutt and gossip, to say nothing of his assigned spies (Russ and Buddy and Paul), who report to him every move Larry makes, every remark, every meeting. He sends for big-name directors and choreographers to come down and look at the show, provides them and their parties (of four or six or eight) with limousines and suites and dinners or lunches or suppers, or all of them, plus extravagant presents. They are innocent and have no idea of what he is up to. They come down, he parades them around the lobby during intermission, introducing them to anyone he can—preferably press people and New Yorkers. The rumor mill begins to grind. Thus far, he has had Bob Fosse, Gower Champion, and Michael Bennett down. He hopes to get all the rest.

Larry, seasoned and experienced as he is, knows the score and hangs tough, but now and then I see it wearing him down. His inhalator is working overtime.

In addition, Art, by various means, has begun to build a sort of political party based on the principle: If you are not for me, you are against me. He doles out favors and presents and money and invitations. Thus far, he has won to his side Hy Balaban and, by extension, Fred Monroe, Russ and Buddy, of course; Phil; surprisingly, Clay; and, not surprisingly, Jenny.

Ivan and Nadia and Alicia and Gene remain steadfast and refuse to play Art's game.

Star is unpredictable, as are most of the members of the cast—except for Calvin Sharp, the so-called leading man, who believes Art's snow about his next show—a musical based on *Ruggles of Red Gap*. The fact that Art does not own the rights does not deter him from discussing it as though he does.

A few weeks ago, I noticed a red splotch on Larry's forehead and thought it might be a bruise of some kind. Later, it developed into a rash. He treated it with drugstore ointments and lotions and took my suggestion of witch hazel, but the rash spread and continued to spread. A week ago, the area around his eye began to swell, and I insisted on making an appointment with the hotel doctor, who came up and had a look at him. A diminutive man in his eighties, brusque, self-assured, no-nonsense. He hands us each a card as he comes in. I have never before met *anyone* with three initials. It reads: A.M.W. Hall, M.D., Ph.D., FASP.

"Any allergies?" he asked.

"None that I know of."

"Anyone hit you?"

"No. Some would like to, but no."

"Well," said Dr. Hall, "it could be nothing, and it could be herpes zoster. I hope not."

"Spell it," said Larry.

"H-e-r-p-e-s z-o-s-t-e-r," said the doctor. "Commonly known as 'shingles.'"

"I thought shingles hit around the middle," said Larry.

"You thought wrong," said the doctor. "Where'd you take *your* M.D.? You'd better see a dermatologist, fast. I know a good one. In the morning all right?"

"I have a rehearsal."

"What time?"

"Ten."

"No matter. I'll ask him to see you at eight. Can you make that?"

"If you think I have to."

"It's up to you. I know what *I'd* do. I'd find out for sure."

I went with Larry the next morning to see Dr. Kantrowitz, because I thought that left to his own devices, he might blow it. It did not take long for the specialist to confirm Dr. Hall's suspicion. Herpes zoster. Shingles. Painful and potentially dangerous. Daily treatment required, by him and by an ophthalmologist, to protect the eye.

"What is it, actually?" asked Larry.

"A virus."

"Contagious?"

"Rarely."

"Do you two sleep in a double bed?" asked the doctor. "Share a bathroom? Towels? Things?"

"I would," said Larry, "but my wife won't let me."

I was blushing.

"We're not married," I explained. "I'm Mr. Gabel's secretary."

"Oh," said the doctor. "I'm sorry."

"So am I," said Larry.

A new morning routine began. I would meet Larry for breakfast every morning at 6:45 in the dining room, and we would proceed: first to Dr. Kantrowitz, who unbandaged, treated with radiation, and rebandaged Larry's head; then to Dr. Wilford's office for attention to the eye.

Even with this extraordinary amount of ministration, the condition grew worse. Larry's head bloated alarmingly. He began to resemble a prizefighter after a losing bout.

In a matter of days, Larry's left eye was unusable, swollen shut, although Dr. Wilford assured us that the eye was still safe.

"It's not infected," he said. "Not yet."

Larry and I exchanged a look. He sighed.

Not long afterward, Larry asked Dr. Kantrowitz for a painkiller.

"It's pretty bad," he said. "Wakes me. I need the sleep."

"Trouble is," said the doctor, "anything effective in this line, say Demerol, tends to be addictive. But I know how excruciatingly painful the condition is, so—"

"How did it happen, Doctor? Any ideas?"

"Usually the result of massive emotional pressure or strain. Overwork. Frustration. Anxiety."

Larry laughed. "Story of my life," he said. "But I thought you said 'virus.'"

"Yes," said the doctor, "but a virus needs a nonresistant field. We're all exposed to viruses and bacteria and bugs all the time, but a healthy body fights them off."

"I see," said Larry. "In the circumstances, Doctor, I suggest you send your bill to Mr. Art Clune."

Art on the phone to his lawyer in New York: "Stubborn son-of-a-bitch, I tell you! Me in his shoes, I'd go lay in a hospital someplace. Not him. But listen, he's going on one eye now, so maybe with a little luck, the other eye'll close up on him and then I've got 'im, right? I mean, a guy can't see can't direct a goddam show, can he? . . . Act of God, my ass! He's supposed to be ready, willing, and able—right? So how is no eyes able? . . . Get a second opinion. Ask Roger. You don't know everything. You know how many lawyers in New York? Thousands!"

He hangs up in a temper, has me get his doctor in California on the phone. Dr. Hy Engleberg.

"Hy? . . . Me. So what did you find out? Contagious or not? . . . But what does that mean, 'possible not probable. . . .' Yeah, but is it possible enough so it'll stand up in a suit? It ought to be. I got a company here all together over a hundred and fifty people. What if it starts going through the company? Isn't that dangerous? . . . What do you mean 'measles'? Who said anything about measles? . . . Oh, it is? . . . No, no. I *can't* wait. It'll be too late then. And what if it *doesn't* happen? You don't think I could take the position now that he's a potential danger? . . . But you said *possible.* . . . All right, all right, Hy. Thanks."

We meet with Larry in his room. Art makes a great point of staying as far away from him as possible. He has also put on a surgical mask.

"I just got a medical opinion, Larry, from California, from a man who's the greatest expert in the world on shingles—"

"I know. The greatest expert on everything is always in California —according to Californians, that is."

"Look, cookie, just because you never made it out there, don't give me that wise-ass New York snot shit."

"What did you come down here for, Art? Just to plague me?"

"No. To ask you for Christ's sake to be sensible. You're a sick man. You can't function. So why hang on?"

"Truthfully?"

"Yeah."

"I hang on, yes—knowing I ought to resign—I hang on because I don't want to give you the satisfaction of getting this whole show out of me for free. You don't deserve it. You're a fucking fiend. If you want me out, you can get me out early. You know how. Fire me."

"Sure, you'd like that, wouldn't you? I fire you and pay you for the next three years, huh?"

"Exactly."

"You got a dream, baby. You're Dr. Martin Luther King. You got some dream, baby."

"Why not?"

"What if I took you off right now—today—because you can't function? You're not functioning."

"Of course I am."

"Not *good.*"

"—your opinion."

"And I stop paying you. Then what?"

"Arbitration, and you'd *lose.*"

"I would?"

"I'd stake my life on it. You'd lose."

"All right, we'll see," said Art, tightly. "I got more friends around here than *you* have."

"The kind of friends *you've* got, Art, you don't need any enemies. Friends! What you've got is a bunch of sycophants and whores and parasites and kiss-asses—that's what *you've* got."

"Yeah? Well, we'll see."

He left, and I followed, after exchanging a wink with Larry.

A bad break for Larry. Late this afternoon, he fell asleep at rehearsal. Damn. Already, I make it sound worse than it was. He was actually watching Jenny restage the "Delmonico" number. I was sitting with him. Actually, he didn't *have* to be there, but that's Larry. He is dedicated and diligent and never stops. He even goes to understudy rehearsals.

"Would you be an angel," he said, "and get me a cup of coffee? Black?"

"Of course."

"Did a dumb thing," he said. "Took an extra Demerol. Stupid. But damn—I was on the brink. Coffee'll help."

I went off to get it. When I returned, an awful sight greeted me: Larry in his seat, fast asleep—surrounded by Art and a group he had assembled. The rehearsal had stopped. The kids stood on the apron, peering into the auditorium and laughing.

With Art: Buddy, Russ, Jenny, Hy, and Paul.

I made my way to Larry's side.

"Coffee!" said Art. "This bum needs more than coffee. He needs a blood transfusion! He's out cold, f'Chrissake."

I woke Larry and gave him the coffee. He looked up, took in the scene, and was clearly mortified.

"Your round, Mr. Clune," he said, and left the theatre.

Art, to me: "Got that? Put it down. And who's witnesses. Four twenty-five. The director is sleeping at rehearsal."

Clay. "There's only one trouble, Art."

"Yeah? What's that?"

"It wasn't his rehearsal."

"So what? It's his show."

"He may be right, Art," said Jenny. "Don't go off half-cocked—oh, sorry!"

Hy said, "The way I see it he was like a drop-in. Not his responsibility."

With the tide turning against him, Art lost his temper.

"Look, you assholes! Don't f'Chrissake mastermind *me*. What am I, some dummy? This isn't my whole case—a guy corks off. We're talkin' maybe a half a million bucks here. I know no arbitration's gonna charge a guy a half a mil for a nap, f'Chrissake. This is only *one* thing—one *more* thing—I got a whole *list*. That's how you build a case, with lots of points—not just two, three. Everybody mind their own business, O.K.? This is *my* business—and I'm minding it!"

Roger Mannering, another of Art's lawyers, is not happy to have been summoned to Washington. It is clear he considers it infra dig. He is accustomed to having his clients come to *him*. He is pissed off, although I am sure he would not put it so. He would more likely say "perturbed."

"I'm not in the habit of making house calls, Art. And certainly not to Washington. Are you sure this could not have been done by telephone?"

"I'm sure. I want to know about arbitration."

"What about it?"

"How does it go?"

Mannering. "Your contract with him provides that in the case of a dispute, the matter is submitted to arbitration. A system set up to relieve the courts of unnecessary burdens. *You* choose an arbitrator. *He* chooses one. Together they choose a third—usually a lawyer—from an official panel. Then it's very much like a lawsuit. Witnesses, depositions, affidavits. Under oath. Penalty of perjury and so on."

"But if one guy is mine and one his—so it's the third guy really counts, right?"

"Precisely."

"All right. So from what I've told you so far—say you were the third guy—how would it go?"

"Well—"

"That's enough. *Shit!*"

"I beg your pardon?"

"A guy says 'well' the way you said 'well' just now like that, I know I'm in trouble."

"Why?"

"The answer is supposed to be, 'You'd win hands down, no contest, game over!' "

"I couldn't say that, really,"

"You could if you were any good," said Art. "You're supposed to have confidence. You're supposed to be on *my* side."

Mr. Mannering stood up.

"Sit down!" Art yelled.

Mr. Mannering clenched his fists and took a step toward Art.

"How *dare* you!" he said, hoarsely.

(I don't think I have ever heard anyone use that expression in real life.)

"What?" Art was stunned.

"You misapprehend our relationship, Mr. Clune."

"I'm sorry."

"I am not an employee."

"I apologize."

"I no longer represent you."

"Come on, Roger!"

"I shall have your files prepared for transfer."

"What're you doing to me? I'm in the middle of a production here!"

"Goodbye, Mr. Clune. And now, as a disinterested party, I can tell you—based on the present evidence—you would most assuredly *lose* an arbitration."

He was gone.

"Schmuck!" said Art. "To tell you the truth, I never liked the creep anyway. Big pompous windbag. Get me Cindy. She'll know a lawyer —a real one. *Without* a vest."

The new lawyer is Alfred Nardino. No vest.

Life has become a series of depositions and affidavits. Some true, some half-true, some false—and all sickening.

From Jenny's:

Q: And did you ever see Mr. Gabel asleep during the course of an official rehearsal, Miss Flagg?
A: Yes.
Q: More than once?
A: Many times.
Q: How many times?
A: I can't say. I didn't count.

· · ·

Q: Did you find him professionally cooperative?
A: Anything but.
Q: Would you call him *un*cooperative?
A: Yes, I would. And even worse.
Q: What do you mean by that?
A: I mean actually disruptive and hostile. He caused arguments and needless long discussions that used up endless time. And money.

· · ·

Q: Would you characterize Mr. Gabel as an alcoholic?
A: Oh, no. Absolutely not. I happen to know something about

the subject and I would say he is more of a problem drinker—definitely *not* an alcoholic.

Q: To your knowledge, did his excessive consumption of alcohol ever interfere with his work?

A: Well, that's a hard question because who knows what he might have done if not, but—well, now that I think of it, yes—I would have to say yes. Yes, it did interfere.

(May God forgive you, Jenny, since He knows that *I* won't.)

From Buddy's affidavit:

Q: How would you rate the morale of this company?

A: Lousy.

Q: How many companies have you been with?

A: Fourteen.

Q: On a list of all fourteen, where would you rate the morale of this one?

A: Fourteenth. The height of the pits.

Q: What would you say is the principal cause of its poor morale?

A: I didn't say poor, I said lousy.

Q: All right. Lousy. And the cause?

A: Same as always. Soft at the top.

Q: What does that mean?

A: Well, like take in our department—choreography—we've got Jenny on top—so a tight ship—no horsing around—discipline—schedules—rest periods—everything works—so the morale is good—the *dancers'* morale, I mean.

Q: But the company's—lousy, I think you said.

A: Right.

Q: And for this you blame—

A: Larry Gabel. Who else?

Hy Balaban's defection to management surprised me. Larry has handled his score with loving care from the beginning. They seemed to me to be friends, fellow artists. I ran into Hy at breakfast in the coffee shop just before we were to take his affidavit. He sat down with me. We talked for a while, and he got the idea, somehow, that I took exception to his position.

"You want to know why?" he asked.

"Of course not."

"Why not?"

"It's none of my business. My business is just to take it all down as accurately as I can."

"But you've got an opinion, haven't you? A point of view?"

"Certainly."

"What is it?"

"That's none of *your* business, Hy."

He laughed. "You know why I like you? One reason why? It's you're young. I love young, I always have. I'm around with the kids, it's like a transfusion. I hate rock, but I love rock concerts. That make sense?"

"No."

"It's the kids, see? Their vitality and power and excitement. But a lot of the time, I have trouble with young people. They don't know how to face reality, how to compromise, how to put first things first. Take you, for instance. Right now. You think I can't feel your disapproval?" I said nothing. He smiled and went on. "I *knew* it! Now that we have to choose up sides, you can't figure how I go with The Barracuda, right? After all, we all know he's no good. You especially. You saw how he set me up—blackmailed me—you were even *there*, for God's sake. So how come I'm with him? Is that the question? All right, here's the answer. There comes a time on every show when it's *cruel* time. Somebody out. Some arrangement made. A word has to be broken. A deal reneged on. It's all part of the game. Win some, lose some. Me? This is my business, no—my life. I have to go on in it. Money is power. You can get a show on without anything—without talent, even—but you can't get a show on without money. So money isn't always in the best hands, the right hands—but what can *I* do about it? I don't run the world. These days—you know how tough it is to raise money for a musical? A million bucks minimum —then *The New York Times* has a toothache, and you're wiped out in one night. So every year—fewer and fewer producers who want to take a chance. Right now, I figure five—next year, maybe four— so can I afford to lose a customer? This guy—if this one's a hit, and I think it *will* be—he'll go ahead with another one and another one —so he asks me a favor—what can I do?"

"Check, please," I said.

"Here—I'll take it," said Hy.

I let him.

Part of Hy's affidavit:

Q: Do you feel the show in its present state is in need of restaging?
A: Plenty.
Q: Is it being done?
A: Not to my knowledge.
Q: Why not?
A: He refused to.
Q: Who is "he"?
A: Larry Gabel.
Q: How many years have you been associated with the professional theatre, Mr. Balaban?
A: Forty years and twenty-two shows.
Q: If you were the producer of *this* show, would you retain Mr. Gabel or replace him?
A: Replace. I like the guy personally, but he's tired out and sick. So I would say *cruel* time.

Now Russ:

Q: How long have you been Mr. Gabel's assistant?
A: Five and a half years. On his last four shows.
Q: Now you said earlier that you began to be concerned about his condition and his work on *this* show.
A: Yes.
Q: Can you say exactly when you began to be troubled about the way in which he was functioning?
A: Yes. It was when he ordered the whole company to observe the color scheme.
Q: Would you explain that, please?
A: Yes. He made an announcement and put it in the bulletin that he wanted everybody to wear a certain color on certain days. Like Monday, Red; Tuesday, Blue; Wednesday, Orange—and so on.
Q: And what was the company's response to this order?
A: They thought it was crazy.
Q: They thought he was crazy?
A: Yes.
Q: Do you think he's crazy?
A: I wouldn't say "crazy." Peculiar, maybe. Or eccentric.
Q: What else did you notice?

A: A lot of daydreaming. I guess you could call it lack of concentration.

Q: What else?

A: Well, he's always been uptight about other people's ideas. A lot of us who worked with him had a kind of joke going—a routine. If you had an idea—the way to put it over was to talk to him and talk and talk and lead him to the point where *he* said the idea—or at least thought he did. But on *this* show, it was different. He started sending for me—every night, practically, and some mornings, to ask me if I had any ideas for this number or that number or a scene or a piece of staging or whatever—he seemed to have lost his drive and was like floundering a lot.

Q: And did you help him?

A: Well, of course. That's my job. I'm his assistant. I'm supposed to.

Q: But would you say you contributed more to this show than to any of the others?

A: Yes.

Q: Much more?

A: Much more.

Clay's turn. Poor Clay.

Q: Is *Shine On, Harvest Moon* ready to open?

A: No.

Q: Is it an efficiently directed show?

A: No.

Q: Could it use some help?

A: Yes.

Q: Have you noticed a diminution of effectiveness on the part of Mr. Gabel in the past six weeks?

A: Yes.

Q: Has he cooperated fully with you?

A: No.

Q: Does he appear to be, at present, ill?

A: Yes.

Q: Does he appear to possess, at present, his full faculties?

A: No.

Q: Thank you.

After transcribing all of the depositions and affidavits, I was asked to make six copies—three for Nardino, two for Art, one for the New

York file, and the original filed here. Six copies. I made seven, and after the show last night, walked Larry to The Watergate.

"May I come up?" I asked.

He looked startled.

"Up?" he repeated.

"Yes. I want to spend a little time with you."

"You're a great girl, Midge. Don't get me wrong. But I'm a sick man."

In my tense and confused state, I did not realize that my request was couched in tones and words absolutely consistent with standard-pass procedure.

"Oh, my *God!*" I said.

"What?"

"Business," I said. "Not—not *you* know. Important. *Oh*, my God!"

We laughed—he with relief, I with embarrassment.

Upstairs, he made me a drink, got himself a glass of milk and took a Demerol.

"You're not taking too many of those, are you?"

"No. At night, it's all right to. You build up a tolerance. At this point, they're more like tranquilizers than painkillers. Nothing kills this damned pain or even wounds it. But there, too—tolerance—you get used to it."

"But you are getting better, aren't you?"

"Absolutely. Not a question in the world about it."

"Great. You look *so* much better—and the swelling *is* going down."

"Business, you said."

"Yes."

"We better get on with it before I fall asleep before your very eyes —and come to think of it, they *are* very eyes. Very *very*, in fact—and when I get better, Midge—what do you think? Do you think we might try?"

What could I say?

I said, "Let's wait and see."

"It won't be long," he said.

"Larry—I don't think anything I've got to tell you is going to come as a surprise—about how they're out to get you."

"You mean '*he.*'"

"No, '*they.*'"

"Oh?"

"He's organized himself quite a cabal. Who knows why they would, but there it is."

"I'm not going to quit," he said. "No matter *what!*"

I handed him a legal envelope containing a set of the transcripts.

"I'm not going to quit," he said.

He got out the papers and began to read. I went to the sideboard and made myself another drink.

For over an hour, he read and I drank. He did not say a word in all this time, nor did he make a sound. His face was impassive; the same expression he has when reading a new scene. I was nicely mulled by the time he came to the end.

"I'm going to quit," he said.

"What?' "

"I am going to quit this show and everything about it, and all at once I feel better than I have in ten months."

"Please don't."

"What's it to *you?*"

"The show," I heard myself say. "What'll happen to the *show?* It's beautiful, and if you're not around, anything might happen—they'll *ruin* it!"

"Midge," he said, tenderly.

"Yes?"

"Fuck the show! Yes. Fuck the show and everybody connected with it. I want my blood back."

"But you once said if you quit—" I stopped.

"If I quit—what? The money? The royalties? The residuals? Sure. Money. Lots of it. But worrying about it—hanging on— Look what it's done to me. It's a good show, sure, maybe great—but it's not worth my *life,* and that's what it's on the verge of taking. If I had some support, *some*—if I—Jesus. Hy! Those two little pipsqueaks— who cares? Liars—little hookers. But Clay. *Clay!"*

"Do you think he? . . ."

"I don't think anything—I don't want to think any more—I just want to get out of here. And away from all of them! See if you can get me Art Clune on the phone."

"Wait till morning, why don't you? Sleep on it."

"Get him. *Now!"*

I saw there was no use in pursuing the matter.

I got on the phone and asked for Mr. Clune's apartment. "Should I monitor it?" I suggested. "Maybe for the record. You may need it."
"Yes."

LARRY

Mr. Clune?

ART

It's pretty late, Larry. Can this wait till morning?

LARRY

I won't be here in the morning. I'm leaving the show.

ART

Fine. Tell your agent get in touch, and we'll work out the settlement.

LARRY

No settlement. No nothing. I'm quitting. Because I loathe you.

(A long pause)

ART

Wait a second.

LARRY

What for? For you to turn on your trusty little tape recorder? You don't have to—I'm recording—I'll send you a dub.

ART

You realize—

LARRY

Oh, put a cork in it, for Christ's sweet sake! "You realize—" What I realize is that I'm free of you, you unconscionable *prick!*

ART

Watch your language!

LARRY

I *am* watching it, you despicable horror. You moneygrubbing know-nothing. You no-talent fraud.

ART

You know who's a no-talent? *You!* And I've got a stack of depositions and affidavits to prove it!

(I shudder at what may come next)

LARRY

I don't believe you. You're a congenital liar, in addition to every-thing else.

ART

You want me to bring them over?

LARRY

I would not advise you to get within twenty feet of me tonight, you slimy cocksucker. I might kill you.

ART

Ha! You *said* it! You said it! A death threat! I've got it on tape! That's a felony—a death threat.

LARRY

Rewind and play it back, you asshole! I didn't say I was going to kill you—I said I *might* kill you—you don't see the difference?

ART

No, I don't.

LARRY

Well, my lawyer's standing right here—should I put him on to explain it?

ART

You're out! That's all I care—your credit and the royalties—everything. You're *out!* I'll send you a release form for you to sign.

LARRY

Good. Make it out, sign it, initial it, notarize it, and then roll it up and stuff it up your tool—you kike!

ART

Kike?! *You* call *me* kike? You're a Jew yourself!

LARRY

That's right! I'm a Jew—but *you're* a kike!

ART

Pay your own *fare* back, too—if that's how you are.

(LARRY laughs heartily)

LARRY

My fare? My fare, you pisspot, is a gift from God. Do you know
what it means to get away from you and your disgusting ma-
chinations and your devious inanities? You're subhuman. There's
not a sensible, reasonable, respectable human being who would
do business with you from choice. You're a—you're a fucking
Barracuda!

ART

You're goddam right I am! I'm a barracuda and I'm *proud* of it.
It's got me to where I could fire you when you got to— Wait!
(He is in a panic)
I didn't say that—what I meant was—

LARRY

Oh, stop sniveling, you smelly little fart. You didn't fire me—you
didn't dare—I quit! Clear? I resign! I sever my relationship. And
as for my money—keep it and choke on it. As for my work—my
sweat and my sleepless nights and the piece of my heart that's
in this show—that's mine and always will be. And for the pain
and illness you caused me, I hope it's returned tenfold, and
something tells me it will be. Goodbye, Mr. Clune. Oh, by the
way, remind Russ—my former assistant—that we used the color
scheme idea on every one of the last three shows we did together, and he didn't think I was crazy—sorry—peculiar or eccentric.

ART

Who said? . . . Wait a second—how'd you know he? . . . Listen
a—

LARRY

No! *You* listen. You're not the only one's got spies. How about
you and Jenny? You think she balls you for joy or for her job? And
that wasn't nice what you did to Hy, even though it *did* get us
the songs in the show. And trying to set Alicia and Ivan against
each other—hell, they were laughing at you the whole time.
Goodbye, Mr. Clune.
(He hangs up)

Larry stood for a long time, looking at the phone—then he moved
slowly and resolutely to the bar. He was a changed man. The characteristic tension had gone out of his face. His posture had undergone

a transformation and he stood more erect than before. He began to pour himself a drink.

"Should you do that?" I asked.

"Shut up," he answered.

"I mean with the Demerol and all?"

"Who takes Demerol?" he asked. "Thanks for everything, good ol' Midge. But go away now. I've got to call my wife—if I can find her."

· XLIX ·

I arrived at the theatre at a quarter to ten for the ten-o'clock call, and was astonished to find a uniformed Pinkerton man at the stage door. Stu Bender was standing beside him, apparently checking everyone in.

"What's going on?" I asked Art, who was standing in the wing nearest the door.

"I don't want any dust-up with him."

He had no sooner uttered the sentence than a disturbance was heard at the stage door.

"Excuse me," said Art, and scurried across the stage to the other side.

I went to the stage door. Larry. His head was still bandaged, only one eye in use.

"Well, then," he was saying, "would you tell Mr. *Clune* I'd like to see him?"

"I can't, Larry," said Stu. "He gave strict—"

"Don't 'Larry' me, you punk—that's over."

"Sorry, Mr. Gabel, but you should, if you want to discuss anything, please call him at the hotel."

"I've got nothing to discuss with *him*—but I do have a few words for the company."

"Jesus, Larry! What can *I* do?"

He burst into tears. I began to surmise what kind of day it was going to be.

After a few more minutes of fruitless discussion, Larry left.

Onstage, Art was addressing the company.

"—and has decided that for the good of the show, he wants to withdraw and put his full attention and energy on regaining his health. Of course, his decision came very suddenly, but fortunately, Russ—who's been Mr. Gabel's main helper all these years—has agreed to take over in the interim. I know I don't have to ask all of you to give him your full cooperation and assistance. We're in very good shape, and I think we all have reason to be confident about the eventual outcome. I guess that's about all. Thank you."

The company stood or sat, confused and stony.

Now from the auditorium, the sound of one person applauding. Art turned, and the company peered off as out of the darkness came Larry, still applauding. He stopped applauding and marched up the rehearsal steps. He stood beside Art, who seemed nailed to the stage.

"Stu!" Art yelled.

Larry looked at the assembled company, but before he could speak, they began to applaud. Those who were sitting, rose. There was some whistling and rattling of chairs, and cheers. An ovation.

It was *my* turn to blub.

Larry said to Art, "I thought you knew all about *front* entrances to theatres!"

Art moved off, ostensibly in search of Stu. What would he do when he found him? Fire him? Probably.

"Thanks," said Larry. "I needed that. [*Laughter.*] I heard what Our Leader told you. I'm not going to say he lied—that would be too strong. Let me say he handled the truth a bit carelessly. I'm leaving you, yes—not entirely because I *want* to, but because I *have* to. In the circumstances, there is simply no choice. You are a splendid company—one of the best I've ever known. What with all the changes and additions and cuts—more than normal—it hasn't been easy. The fact is, we sort of did damn near *two* shows. [Applause.] But thanks to God and you and Gene Bowman and—well, you know who else—the second show is better than the first one. Wouldn't it be hell if it were the other way around? [Laughter.] I agree with Mr. Clune about one thing—you *are* in good shape and you *are* going to have a success; the degree is the only thing in question. Hit, big hit, smash? Who knows? A lot depends on discipline and precision and playing in, playing *together. Together.* In our world, believe me, nothing

· 425 ·

matters more than the show that was given *last night.* As for me—few regrets. I've enjoyed it all. To me—the doing is what counts. Success—fame or fortune—sure, those are the cherries on top. Try to find the joy in the doing. Every audience is a virgin. I'll be there opening night, so watch your step. In the meantime, goodbye and Godspeed. I may not love each and every one of you individually—there are fuckups and nasties in your number—but as a company, I adore you!" [*Another ovation.*]

Fifteen minutes of crowding about—hugs and kisses and handshaking. Finally, Larry started for the rehearsal steps, preparing to leave. Russ intercepted him.

"I really think, Larry—you might have said one word about *me.*"

"Oh? What word did you have in mind?"

"Why take it out on *me,* what happened? I mean—Jesus—so humiliating—to be totally ignored."

"Actually, Russ, I did have an idea that would have included you, but at the last minute, I changed my mind."

"Oh?"

"I was going to read them your affidavit!"

Larry looked at him until he melted away, then Larry disappeared up the aisle of the dark theatre.

My name, shouted. I responded. Art wanted me in the production office.

"Crafty bastard!" he said. "He *did* have a plant in the company. Probably *still* does. Find out who, y'hear?"

"How can I?"

"I don't care *how,* God damn it! Do it!"

"Why don't you get the Pinkertons to do it? What do *I* know? I'm no detective."

"No, but you're well connected—don't kid me—belle of the ball—Miss Popularity—find out."

"All right, I'll try."

"I'll give you a bonus if you do— What would you like? A coat? What kind? You know who I think it could be? That little Stu son-of-a-bitch. You know what somebody told me just now? That he was crying there by the door. I thought he was straight! And what about Larry himself? AC-DC? You think? Keep an eye on that little Stu son-of-a-bitch. Maybe you're right. Maybe I'll have the Pinkertons put a tail on him—see if he contacts."

"What's the difference? It's all over, isn't it? As far as Larry's concerned?"

"Y'never know," he said darkly. "Not with these talent bastards."

At the very first rehearsal, Russ erred. One could see he was determined to take charge, to show authority, but he did it so clumsily that it came out as testy petulance. Leadership is a gift, I suppose. Russ does not possess it in any measure. Bombast, yes. It was clear he was on the defensive from the start. He felt all eyes upon him. The company, onstage and in both wings. Out in the auditorium. Paul, Phil, everyone.

The first half hour was not too bad. His eye for precision (trained by Larry) is good. He caught some sloppiness and dealt with it firmly.

But when he announced: "All right, now! Hold it! On your toes, everyone. Here's a change—a big change—so pay attention. This crossover in front of the street drop—going into Delmonico's—is *out!* Right? We go right from Hotel Room into Delmonico's—no crossover—it's always been a bad tooth there. I'm glad to get it out. Let's go."

"Wait a second!" Clay.

"Yes?"

"Can't be done, Russ."

"Why not?"

"We need at least forty-five seconds for this change."

"Don't you think I know that, for Christ's sake? I put the damn thing on to *begin* with."

"What do you want, then? A forty-five–second stage wait?"

"I'll tell you what I want, Clay. I want you to do what I'm telling you to do!"

A long look exchanged.

"Certainly," said Clay, who knows how to play the game.

"We're going to do an open change. Music stet. Got it?"

"They'll see fifteen stagehands, O.K.?"

"O.K. And if you're worried about the deviation from style—don't. We're going to be doing a *lot* of open changes. It's a show-business story, isn't it? A backstage saga?"

"I don't know *what* it is," said Clay

"Let's go!" said the new director.

More open changes have indeed been going in at every perform-ance. The general reaction is affirmative. Russ is getting a lot of backslapping, especially from Star and Val. A new threesome. To-gether every night after the show.

The rest of the changes Russ is making are more subtle—in some cases, almost unnoticeable—but all have to do with framing Star. Her lights are becoming brighter; her ballad tempos more soulful; her jump tunes louder and faster. Not a single cut affects her. The restag-ing places her relentlessly center and slightly upstage. It is becoming "An Evening With . . ." Still, I must admit the show seems to be going well.

Star has redone some of her costumes—mainly in the direction of showing more cleavage, and, when possible, more leg.

Art has been in California for a week. Hy and his wife have gone to Hobe Sound. Fred is around, shaking his head quite a lot.

Star has taken to ad-libbing. It gets results, but.I doubt that "You better believe it!" and "See you later, gater," and "Out to lunch," were part of the common speech of 1908.

I phone Gene and tell him what is going on. Odd about him. When he is here or around the show, he is interested, even magnetically drawn to the excitement of it all. When he is away, any mention of it seems an irritating intrusion. It may be that I am calling him at the wrong times, but I have tried several. Is there a right time?

"Well, what about Clay?" he asks, fretfully. "Isn't it his job to see that they hold the line?"

"Yes, but right now he doesn't have the clout."

"I see. Though I don't know what I can do about it from here, do you?"

"When do you think you might come back?"

"I don't know. I'm on a big one just now, and it's complicated. Anyway, no point in me without Art and Hy. Never mind a few ad-libs. She's feeling her oats, I suppose. They'll get her back to the text in time, and if they don't, *I will.*"

"Next week, do you think?"

"Possibly. Let me ask you something," he says seriously.

"Sure."

"What do *you* think? Not of the detail—but of the show as a whole."

"I'm not sure. At first, I thought maybe it *was* getting even better than it was—it was shorter, and faster—and some of the technical deadwood was out. But I don't know—it's lósing charm—it's sort of too *insistent.*"

"I'll be there next week," he said. "Without fail."

On Friday, Russ fired Clay and replaced him with Buddy. When the blowup came, Art could not be found, so it was left to poor Henry Wadsworth to enforce the discharge.

Clay is still in town waiting for Art's return. He has a run-of-the-play contract and claims he cannot be discharged. Russ has accused him of deliberately sabotaging his ideas, making them seem wrong or impractical or impossible. Clay denies it, but secretly, I believe there is something in what Russ says.

Buddy ran the show on Friday—not too well, but it was his break-in, so everyone understood.

Saturday matinee was much better, but then Saturday night was not good at all. A number of missed light cues and two damaging sound fluffs.

Russ and Buddy had a screaming row in the alley after the show.

Sunday, a blessed day off. I spent practically the whole day—from noon on—with Clay. He is surprisingly calm. We had lunch at McDonnell's on the river. Seafood. Great. We went to The National and I took him to the Freer to see the Japanese stuff. He had never been. He hired a Hertz and we drove out to Mount Vernon.

We came back, had dinner at the Fleur de Lis in Georgetown, then walked back to The Watergate. All this time, we talked of nothing but the show. Our activity was no more than a backdrop, and an incongruous one, at that.

During the crab Maryland, he said, "You hear a piece of music and one wrong note spoils it, in the way that the greatest soufflé in the world is ruined by the presence of one little cockroach in it. That's us right now. That's our show. A beautiful soufflé full of cockroaches."

"Please!" I said. "I was looking forward to dessert."

"Sorry," he said.

Looking at the Cézannes, I had asked, "You don't think Star is aware that the show is falling apart?"

"Star's not aware of anything in or on God's green earth with the exception of Star. She's doing fine—hell, She's now got the whole damned evening to herself. But that's not a show. That wasn't *Guys and Dolls* or *Kiss Me, Kate* or *My Fair Lady* or *Annie* or *A Chorus Line*—and those are the standards we're going to be judged by."

"Do you think it can be fixed?"

"I don't know, Midge. I honestly don't know. As it stands right now, it would mean unscrambling eggs."

In the basement of the Freer, as we were studying the Hokusai wonders, he had explained:

"The reason a director is so desperately important, is that by and large, everyone looks out for Number One on a show. Hy mother-hens his score, Ivan guards his sets, Alicia her costumes, and if they play the orchestration as written, Ralph Burns thinks it's a great show. And that's all right, that's as it should be. But the *director*—he's got no special axe to grind—he's got to see it all and blend the elements. Do you think Russ can do that?"

"No, I don't," I said.

The drive to Mount Vernon was beautiful, I suppose. I have heard that it is, but I hardly saw it.

Clay said, "There was a moment there when we had it."

"Yes."

"And everyone knew it, felt it. Then it started to disintegrate."

"Clay?"

"What?"

"Do you think there's any way to get Larry back?"

"Not a chance."

"Why not?"

"Forget it. I know Art Clune. He's mean and vindictive and greedy. Getting rid of Larry was a great victory for him, *he* thinks. A lump of money saved, a challenging authority gone."

"But the *show,*" I said.

"All he sees are the statements. We're selling out."

At Mount Vernon, Clay listed every single thing that had been done since Larry's departure.

"Curious, isn't it?" he asked. "Not one of them seems to matter, but when you add them up—you've got a spoiled show."

"Gene's coming back."

"What about it?"

"He'll see it. He'll see what's happened," I said.

"And then what?"

"I don't know. He's smart."

"He's more than smart—he's brilliant, but that's not what counts now. What counts now is power—plain and simple."

"Art?"

"A dolt. He may see it, he may not. Right now he's hitched his wagon to Star—and if She's happy, *he's* happy. And She *is*—why not? —it's all hers now."

"What do you think'll happen?" I asked.

"With the show?"

"Yes."

"I think it'll fail and She'll succeed. They'll say too bad this great artist wasn't given a vehicle worthy of her. She *had* a vehicle, the silly bitch, and She drove it right off the road."

Driving back to Washington:

"Will you go back if they ask you?"

"Of course. And they will. That cream puff can't handle the job. It doesn't require talent—or even brains—but it *does* call for experience. It may turn out to have been Russ's fatal blunder."

"Anyway, haven't he and Buddy bust up?"

"Have they?"

"That's what I heard."

"Wouldn't matter. You can fake along in a so-called executive position; but something as technical as production—no. You have to hit the right buttons at the right time."

Supper at Trader Vic's:

"It all *looks* different, too," I said. "Or is it my imagination?"

"Of course it looks different, you goose. It's been relighted. She and Val like hot white light on her all the time—but the sets weren't designed for that lighting—or painted. Ivan'll have a fit."

Walking back to The Watergate, we said nothing. The long discussion of the impossible situation had drained and depressed us. But for some reason, the last thing he said stuck in my mind. Ivan.

Clay took me to my door and said, "I'll come in, for just a minute."

"Fine."

Inside, he looked at me and said, "I know about you and Gene, of course. And I'm happy for both of you."

"Thanks, Clay—but you know there's not much future there."

"Who knows?"

"*I* know."

"Hold the thought," he said.

"All right."

"Still, I *would* like to kiss you good night."

I was startled, but nodded, automatically.

He embraced me and kissed me with feeling. It was really lovely.

"Thank you," I said.

"My pleasure."

All the time I was preparing for bed, I kept trying to formulate a plan. Ivan. But what could *he* do? Did *he* have the power Clay talked about? Probably not—yet something impelled me that Sunday night at ten-thirty to call him at his country house in Newtown, Connecticut.

"Hah-*law*," he said, in that basso-profundo voice of his.

"Ivan, this is a confidential call I have no business making. I'm counting on your discretion."

"You can kont," he said.

"I think you should come down and see the show. A lot has been happening."

"I naw," he said. "Lahrry is no more. Why he quitted?"

"He didn't really. He was sort of forced out."

"Yes," he said. "Hoppens—always hoppens to directors—But me —I cannot come Vashington now—hahv new shaw. Maybe I send Nadia."

"Come yourself, Ivan. It's important."

"What means important?"

"Important to *you*. The show's in trouble."

"I heard wass good."

"*Wass*," I said. "But no more."

"Sets you cannot change, so what use?"

"You can't, but they *did.*"

"Did?!"

"Well, not the sets exactly, but the way the're used, the way they're lighted."

"I come!" he shouted. "I come *tomorrow*. With Nadia. With Millie. Goodbye!"

What makes me think Ivan can make a difference? Well, I don't think *that* exactly, but his presence here may lend some weight to the effort that has to be made to get the show back into shape.

I have noticed he is the only man connected with this enterprise never once bullied by Art. It may be his age or his eminence that has kept Art at a respectful distance. On the other hand, it may be the fact that Ivan conveys complete theatre knowledgeability. I have never heard him say one silly or careless or exaggerated thing about the show. His comments have always been perceptive and meaning-ful and profound. He possesses that rarest of all human attributes—common sense.

"Why She's acting so dignified, so like a star, in there the beginning there? When She is still the Hoor? The dignified should be for later. When She's the Hoor, She should act like the Hoor, not like the star!"

Or:

"The women—they are wearing the costumes like they are cos-tumes. They are not costumes to those people—to those people they are *clothes!* Everyday clothes. Not fonny, not strange—*clothes.* Like we're wearing these clothes *we're* wearing, so in fifty years somebody will do a show in the period nineteen seventy-nine—so the actors and the actresses will wear clothes like this, and to them it should be the same then like it is to us now!"

And:

"Too much difference, Lahrry, so far, between the scenes and songs and the nombers. Got to be in a shaw like this shaw—every song is a scene and ever scene is a song. Can't be scene song scene song. Is like two shaws in one time. Got to be *one* shaw in one time."

Also:

"What do you mean 'old-fashion'? Who cares old-fashion? Why everybody is scared the word? A *tree* is old-fashion, no? The sky! Beethoven's Fifth—that's not old-fashion? And the mawst old-fashion you know is what? Fawking! Fawking is the mawst old-fashion from everything!"

SHINE ON, HARVEST MOON
Company Bulletin
Tuesday, January 8, 1980

TONIGHT: Please make note of the running order for tonight's performance. Act I remains the same, but Act II is as follows:

ACT II

Scene 1 The Everleigh Club
""Nightfall"

Scene 2 Nora's Room
"Was It Wrong?"

Scene 3 The Everleigh Club
"Falling Star"

Scene 4 Rector's
"Skiddoo"
"Midnight Waltz"

Scene 5 Hospital
"Poor Nora"

Scene 6 Courtroom
"Cantata"

Scene 7 The Everleigh Club
"Sweetie"
"Shine On" (Reprise)
Russ Kelly

There will be a picture call immediately after the performance on Thursday, Jan. 10. Remain in costume after the call. Go to your dressing room and you will be called. *Only Act II* will be photographed so we will be following this running order working backward from Act II, Scene 7, through Act II, Scene 1. Food and beverage will be provided in the Green Room.   Russ Kelly

THE COMPANY YOU KEEP: ROGER CORMAN(Claude)
  My mother and father are both devout New Yorkers, but I was born in Denver, Colorado. Explanation: they were both touring in OKLAHOMA! My mother played right up until about 10 days before my debut. With those costumes she was able to manage, she says.
  Early on, I am on. Every kid part around, I got.

Professional Children's School. Magnificent education.

Shows too numerous to mention, but among them: CAROUSEL; THE KING AND I; DO RE MI; SUBWAYS ARE FOR SLEEPING; NO, NO, NANETTE (the revival, of course!); MACK AND MABEL; SO LONG, 174th STREET; DEAR WORLD; GANTRY—well, you get the idea. I've been around the block a few times.

P.S. Mom and Pop are still working.

OUR NORA:

> THE NEW YORK HERALD NOV. 22, 1923
>
> NORA BAYES WILL TOUR
> ONLY IN A PRIVATE CAR
>
> Court Hears Long "Jumps"
> Made Her Ill

If Nora Bayes can't have a private car when she goes on tour there won't be any touring. That was the substance of her answer to an application yesterday in the Supreme Court for an injunction restraining her from appearing under any other management than Fulcher & Behan during the next twelve weeks. If the injunction is granted the patrons of the Palace and the rest of the Keith Circuit will get along without Miss Bayes.

Miss Bayes was to get $2,500 a week and one-third of the profits from her tour and during the sixteen weeks she was under contract she was to appear at ninety theatres, make long "jumps" and play one-night stands.

Nathan Burkan, her attorney, said she would never have signed the contract if she had known she was expected to jump from place to place without her own private equipment, and she had become ill owing to the strain. She had produced a physician's certificate, he said, showing that she was unable to continue the tour. Justice Mullan, before whom the appeal came, said he would send the case to a referee.

Like those of Gallagher & Shean, Miss Bayes's services in the complaint are described as "unique and extraordinary."

QUOTE FOR TODAY:
> "Gambling diverts men faster than lechery."
> Minna Everleigh

There are now 24 days until our New York opening.

· L ·

Another crisis. Everyone turned up on Monday night. The lobby before the performance looked like the old days when we were beginning. Art and Cindy and Paul. Ivan and Nadia and Alicia. Clay hovering about. Gene, the new boy.

The performance was hardly under way when there was a violent disturbance in the theatre. The first shift—from The Everleigh Club set to the train—was made as an open change.

A shout from the audience.

"Wodihell is doing here? Stop it! *Mistake!*"

Ivan. No amount of shushing could placate him. He had to be taken out to the lobby.

IVAN
(Beside himself)
Who did that, who?

NADIA
Ivan, please. They'll *fix* it!

IVAN
They'll fix? I'll fix *them!* Who did that, who?
(Apprehensively)
They're going to do *again? Horr*-bull. Awpen change?

ME
Yes. All of them.

· 436 ·

IVAN

All??!!

ME

Russ thought it speeded up the show.

ART

Lay off, Midge. I'll handle this. . . . Now, look, Ivan—we're trying
out, after all—y'know? Trial and error?

IVAN

Mr. Clune—I naw from designing theatre—*you* naw—
I don't naw *what* you naw—you naw what *you* naw. If the director—the real director—if he has told me awpen changes—I make
a whole different conception—this conception is *not* for—*NOT!*
What you got now on the stage is *abortion! Horr*-bull and
ogly!

NADIA

Ivan, please! Remember the doctor said.

IVAN

The doctor didn't have to look this abortion—this ruination—
seven goddam months' work this goddam show, now these goddam amateurs—

RACHEL
(Where did she come from?)
I like it like this. It's interesting and also it speeds things
up.

IVAN

Who are you?
(To us)
Who is this stupid God damn it woman with the too much bad-
taste jewelry?

HY

Watch it, Ivan. She's my wife.

IVAN

So what's it her business, this idiot?

(RACHEL *slaps him, hard, with her Hermès evening bag.*
He is stunned, but not as stunned as she is a moment later
when NADIA *slaps her with such force that both her ear-*
rings fly off. She is almost at once on her hands and knees,

· 437 ·

searching for them. Meanwhile, HY *retaliates by punching* IVAN *in the stomach.* IVAN *comes back with a roundhouse swing that catches* HY *on the side of the head and sends him sprawling. His wife, intent on finding her earrings, has missed the action. Now she looks up and sees* HY *on his knees beside her)*

RACHEL
I'm looking here, you jerk! Look somewhere else!

ART
(In shock)
You're *crazy,* Ivan, you know it?

IVAN
When I have started this goddam show, I am *not* crazy. You are *making* me crazy.

ART
You hit the wrong guy.

IVAN
So tell me right guy. I hit *him,* too.

ART
Trial and error, Ivan.

IVAN
No, no. *Error* and error. Not the goddammit open changes only! Who killed the lighting? This lighting is for cabaret, not for scenery!

ART
We're workin' on it.

(HY and RACHEL, *having found the earrings, leave the theatre)*

NADIA
(To ART)
Something happens to Ivan's heart condition from all this, I swear to God I kill you.

(She leads IVAN *out)*

ART

(To me)

Call everybody. Meeting onstage right after. Jesus! Get me a
Valium.

The meeting, in the circumstances, was surprisingly calm.

Jenny announced that Buddy has resigned and returned to New
York.

"What does that do to *you*, hon?" asks Art, solicitously.

"Nothing. I replaced him with Patti two weeks ago, don't you
remember?"

"I know," says Art. "I just thought."

"But what does it do to *you?*" asked Jenny. "I doubt Stu can run
the show. Can he?"

A word, finally, from Russ. "Whether he can or not is beside the
point. He *won't.* I asked him. He refused."

"Why?" asked Art.

"He's scared."

"He *should* be," said Jenny.

Art stood up, pointed to me, and said, "Get Clay back here. Right
away. Tonight."

"Sure."

"Wait a minute," said Russ.

"Shut up!" said Art. To me: "Where is he? Do you know?"

"Six-oh-eight," I said.

"What?"

"Right here. In the hotel."

"He's still in Washington?" asked Art, astonished.

"Yes."

"How's that?"

"He says he knew you'd have to ask him to come back."

"Boy!" said Art. "Do I hate arrogant bastards like that. Get him up
here."

"Who you should get back is Lahrry," said Ivan.

"Nothing doing," said Star. "We're oil and water. I don't dig
him, he don't dig me. That idea is out, and I don't want to hear it
again."

"That's what *you* say?" asked Art.

"Definitely."

"All right, now listen to what *I* say. I would rather close this show here, right here, and burn the scenery and never mention it again, before I would have *that* louse back. I consider him an enemy. O.K.? Is that clear to everybody?"

"To the show," said Ivan, doggedly, "he's not enemy. He did it good job. Very hard. He made it stylish and good."

Star. "Next time I do a show—if there *is* a next ‧time, which I doubt—I'm going to insist that everybody connected speaks English."

Ivan studied her for a moment, and said, "When you sing is better than you talk."

"I tell you," said Star to Art, slowly, "that Larry Gabel is out and is going to *stay* out as long as I'm *in*—so what the hell is Rasputin starting in again?"

Ivan. "Because I always hope somebody is maybe going to learn something. Me, I learn something every day, and I am three times old as you."

"Well, I hope you learned something today, which is I don't do this show with Larry Gabel. In fact, with *anybody* named Larry. *Or* Gabel. I wouldn't do it with *Clark* Gable."

"Is that clear?" asked Val.

Gene. (At last!) "Very well. I suppose that's your privilege—if not your right."

"No, no," said Val. "Her right, too. Legal right. It's in her contract. Approval director."

"In the beginning," said Gene. "Yes. And she *did* approve him. I doubt her contract allows for whimsical changes of mind."

"Whimsical!" yelled Star. "What the fuck do you mean by that?"

"I mean," said Gene, "that we are all—you included—faced with a reality. The reality is a sinking ship. I have the great advantage of having been away for two weeks. I remember only too well the impression I carried away. It was simply beautiful. The show I saw tonight is not. It's lost all the qualities that made it exceptional: charm, warmth, style, humanity, fluidity, and effortless tact. So the question is: How do you get them back?" He looked at Russ. "Do you think you can?"

"Look, I haven't finished what I want to do—what I've *been* doing. Everybody's jumping on me like this is it. I don't claim this is it. For me, this is like second week of rehearsal."

"But just what is it that you 'want to do'—as you put it?" asked Gene. "Can you tell us? Can you verbalize it?"

"Of course not."

"Well," said Gene, "that's understandable."

"Second week of rehearsal," Star whispered to herself, frowning. "Jesus, God!"

There was a long silence. The sinking ship descended deeper into the morass of general disaffection. Finally, Russ rose and spoke.

"What I want to do—what I've been *trying* to do—is create a great frame for our Star. In my not-so-humble opinion, She happens to be the greatest Star in show business today. How many personalities are there—in the *world*, I'm talking—who can carry a whole show single-handed? *Name* them. We've got her, and in my not-so-humble opinion, we should present her—no, more than that—we should *flaunt* her! All right. I'll admit some of the effort looks crude now, even a little too strong—but it's easier to edit something down than drag it out—a question of dynamics. Of course, we all understand that. The open changes, Ivan, are a mistake. I see that. I apologize. I was trying for tempo—but I see now it is too high a price to pay. And Gene, to answer your question—yes, I *do* think I can get all those qualities you correctly miss back into the show—that is, if everyone will bear with me and help me—because after all, we're all in the same boat—if it goes down—we *all* go down—but we're *not* going down. This show is, potentially, a history-making smash—and I'm going to see to it that we realize that potential."

At this point, Clay walked in. Russ continued:

"And my unfortunate contretemps with Clay was another mistake on my part, for which I am deeply sorry. There is *no one* who can run this show as well as Clay, and I hope he will come back to help me. Other than that, I can only say that it is a great honor to be associated with this superlative group of creative artists, and I can assure you that your confidence in me—when we reach our goal— will not turn out to have been misplaced. Creation is discovery, and I keep discovering things every day about all of you and the show and myself: weaknesses, to be sure—but much more important— strengths. And in the end, that's what counts. So why don't we all get up and wipe off the blood and go to work?"

A smattering of applause. Gene looked at me, flabbergasted. I could hardly believe I had heard what I had heard.

(Later that night, in bed, Gene laughed and said to me, "Not since Nixon's Checkers speech—and I thought *that* was going to fail, too. Wrong twice.")

The little pipsqueak put it over. He is still in, but aware that he is walking a razor's edge. His power derives from the relationship with Star and Val, but that—considering *them*—is tenuous as can be.

If he were as talented as he is crafty, he could own Broadway. He is a lesson in out-and-out audaciousness; impressive when it works.

<u>SHINE ON, HARVEST MOON</u>
Company Bulletin
Friday, January 11, 1980

<u>INVITATION</u>: The entire company has been invited to an official tour of the White House at 9 A.M. (!) on Tuesday, January 15. We will meet at the East Gate at 8:45 A.M. Please sign up on list.

<u>TRAVEL</u>: Henry Wadsworth has all plane and train reservations in his office. You can pick them up anytime today.

<u>TRUNKS</u>: Must be ready in hotel or apartment lobbies at 9 A.M. Thursday, January 17.

<u>THE COMPANY YOU KEEP</u>: DIANA VAN RIJN(Belle)
   Portland, Maine, is my hometown and I go back to it whenever I can. Emerson College in Boston, where I earned a Master's degree in speech pathology. Nobody wanted my speech therapy but the Rockettes wanted my high kicks and had them for two long long long years. Then Broadway: FOLLIES, SMITH, COMPANY, OLIVER, and DANCIN'. I was in the National Company of APPLAUSE (Eve Harrington) and in the National Company of WHERE'S CHARLEY? (Amy). I have done specials for NBC and ABC, notably TELL IT LIKE IT IS. In resident and regional I have played leads in SUMMER AND SMOKE, BAREFOOT IN THE PARK, THE KILLING OF SISTER GEORGE, and others. Married, divorced, two adorable kids: Peter (6), Amy (5). I love life.

<u>QUOTE TO REMEMBER</u>:
        "I was never ashamed of myself. I was practically raised in a saloon, and I never had any feeling about that. I guess I knew it was better to be honest. . . . You are either something or you are not. When I came to Broadway and was meeting all those people; society people, royalty, and the like, I never thought to myself: 'Gee, kid, you really are there now. You are with the important people now.' I never said

that. I never thought it. Money never impressed me if there wasn't the person to go
with it."

Fanny Brice

There are now 20 days remaining before the New York
opening.

· LI ·

Russ is out.

The past eight days have been so jam-packed with action and work and offstage excitement that I have been unable to keep this log straight.

When I mentioned my distress about it to Gene, he laughed and said, "Don't worry. You won't forget the important things, the ones that matter. When I was a young reporter—very young—I interviewed Gene Fowler, who'd been a newspaperman before he became a marvelous writer. He asked me why I was making such copious notes, and I said it was so that I'd be able to quote him exactly. 'That would be no favor to me,' he said. 'Why don't we just talk? Then you can go off and write it up—write *your* impression of it all. There's a difference between a sketch and a snapshot. I'd rather have a sketch—how you see me—that's interesting because it's individual. A snapshot would be the same no matter *who* pressed the button on the Brownie.' That was the day I made my last note."

And need I mention that the eight days have also had nights—and that many of the hours I might have spent jotting have been spent in a far more glorious way? My feeling for this man grows in ways I had not imagined possible. I see him and I want to cry, not out of sadness but out of my overwhelming sense of wonder that such a person can exist—does exist—and that I know him and that he is in my life.

About Russ. What happened was that he slipped. After the Big

Meet, he set to work in an attempt to please everyone. The lighting went back to the old cues, except for Star's much brighter spots. He convinced Star that it was even better for her this way—that the contrasts were in her favor. Much to our surprise, he persuaded Ivan that he ought to compromise on this point because the brighter light had an affirmative psychological effect on her and helped her overall performance.

The open changes were abandoned, some of the restaging was restored, but again—most of what affected her was left as is. So almost everyone was at least partially content, and the clever fox— by means of whispers and phone calls and private dressing-room confabs—somehow succeeded in making everyone feel that every change or cut or addition was to *their* benefit.

Then, as I understand it, he tripped. With Buddy gone, he was on his own and tense and lonely. He began making his way through the boys in both the singing and dancing choruses—his position giving him a special advantage. Every chorus boy wants a line or a bit or a solo spot—*anything.* And apparently, the *quid pro quo* is anything for anything. While this was going on, Calvin Sharp began to sense that he was being more and more overshadowed by Star. Of course, he had known in advance that it would happen, was bound to happen, but as we got closer to the commitment of the New York opening, it began to trouble him. He decided to take a bold step, took Russ out to supper one night, and afterward to an out-of-town motel for the night. From that point on, they were a secret pair—they thought. The fact is there are few secrets around a theatrical company. A hint here, a remark there, a shrug or a raised eyebrow elsewhere, and information goes through the company like a flu bug.

Russ confirmed the rumors by his besotted, in-love behavior. It was not so much that he directed Calvin—in fact, at rehearsals and post-performance note sessions, he pointedly ignored him. But he became permissive and let Calvin interpolate bits of business (some good), which they had probably worked out at the motel. Calvin took new and better positions onstage and ceased being a wax dummy while She was on. His lighting was slowly and subtly improved, and—line by line—much of his part from Gene's original book was restored.

Rumors of the Calvin-Russ liaison reached Val, who immediately reported it to Star, who laughed in his face.

Bonnie told me that when Val laid it on her, She said, "You need a vacation, y'know it? You believe that, you'll believe *anything!* It's a crock!"

"How do *you* know?" he asked.

She hesitated and replied, "I know because I know, that's how I know."

She could hardly tell him She "knew" because She and Calvin had been having periodic dressing-room sessions since the show had opened in Boston.

Poor thing, living her insular life, She had never heard of "bi."

Val remained convinced. He hired an investigator (actually, a moonlighting cop) and put Calvin under surveillance. The cop stretched his assignment out to a week's work, although he had the goods on Calvin the first night. He reported back to Val, who took him at once to Star. She, needless to say, went up the wall.

It is my own opinion that She cared less about the slight stage favoritism the new situation had brought Calvin than She did about the sexual betrayal.

"Did you always know that?" She asked me once during the long postmortem period that followed Russ's departure. "That he's gay?"

"No. Is he?"

"I can prove it in writing," She said.

"What does it matter? He's sexy as can be up there on the stage with you."

"And not only there," She said. "Close the door." I did so. "Him and me. Would you believe it?"

"Yes."

"Is there anybody else?"

"What do you mean?"

"Is there anybody else in the company he's been putting the boots to? You?"

"No, not me."

"You sure? I hear you swing."

"I get my share," I said.

"But how about this minty prick romancing *me?* And scoring!"

"Life."

"God, fucking a fag, it's kinda weird, isn't it. But—like you say— as long as it looks all right from the front, so what the hell. But he's gotten into my pants for the last time, that I can promise you. In fact, I'm a nun from here till we open."

With Russ gone, the question of who to direct came up again in an intense way. Again, Ivan and Gene fought for Larry. Again, they were rebuffed. Not a single one of what Art called the "Space Cadets" was available or interested.

"They're all too rich, those slobs," he railed. "That's how these show-business clowns are. Get the wrinkles out of their bellies and they start giving you a hard time."

Two or three of the newer, younger directors came down, were examined by Star, and sent packing.

"Maybe we don't need *anybody,*" said Art. "Maybe just play it in? What does everybody think?"

Nobody thought.

"Let's watch it for a day or two," said Gene. "Then see."

I knew he had something in mind. I have come to know that dear face.

I was right. He phoned Larry and asked him to come down—as a personal favor.

I bought a single balcony seat and gave it to Larry, who got himself a beard, mustache, long-haired wig, blue jeans, turtleneck, and leather jacket. Thus disguised and attired, he saw the show.

Afterward, we met at Gene's. Larry, almost completely recovered, began to talk. I took it all down, or tried to, but did not do too well since he was talking too swiftly and excitedly and angrily, which had the effect of muffling much of what he said.

Suddenly, without warning, he burst into tears. He sat down heavily on the sofa and head in hands, let himself go.

I moved toward him, but Gene waved me off, went to the kitchen and made Larry a strong drink. Larry drank it, went out to the bathroom, returned, and sat down.

"First of those in years," he said. "Didn't know I had it in me."

"Healthy," said Gene.

"Contact with death," said Larry. "Is there anything more depressing?"

"Death?"

"You bet. What's up there is fading fast. A show has a heartbeat, and this one's stopping and skipping—and I would say the situation is just about hopeless. All the *climaxes* are wrong! And the pace—it isn't that the show is too long—it's that every *mo-*

ment in it is too long. Oh, well. Fuck it."

"That's no solution," said Gene. "It's been fucked enough."

"I don't have any children," said Larry. "It never worked out somehow. The career girls I seem to marry. Anyway, no kids. So the shows or the plays or the TV specials—*they* become the kids. This one was a real favorite, I expected so much of it, now—too soon—it's about to expire: a death in the family. Damn." Gene seemed ready to speak, but held it in, strategically. He wanted Larry to go on. Larry did. "Listen," he said. "Is *this* anything? What if I call him and offer to come back in for nothing? Free. Gratis. No credit, even. What do I care? No money, no nothing."

"But that's crazy," I said. "Why should you?"

"Because I want to."

Gene. "I don't see how he could turn that down. As long as he feels he's screwing you or anyone, he's content. It seems to be a sexual transfer, doesn't it?"

I said, "I think he'd accept a proposition like that, Larry, but—" I stopped.

"But? . . ." he asked.

"Star."

"She wouldn't?"

"She's not intelligent enough."

"Tell you what," said Gene. "No use batting it around here—by ourselves. Let's make a few calls and get a reading."

"Not too late?" I asked.

"One-fifteen," said Larry.

"Let's do it," said Gene. "Let me call Art, you call her."

"All right."

"She's in nineteen-D," I said, and went out to the bedroom to get Art. As his room phone rang, I handed the phone to Gene.

"Art? . . . Gene. Can I get you to listen without interruption for a minute or two? . . . Thanks. It's important. I just talked to Larry Gabel, and he's offered something I think you must consider. He— Now, Art, you promised two minutes, and I— Thanks. He'll come back in and straighten us out for free. No money, no credits, nothing. . . . Because he loves the show, that's why. . . . You don't? . . . Why not? . . . Try, Art. If you're going to be in this business, you'll have to try to understand creative people. Larry has a part of his life in this venture, and he can't bear to see it go down. . . . Because I *told* him it was going down, that's how! . . . O.K. What the hell can you lose? You'll be getting something for nothing. A *big* something for a little nothing. . . . Of *course,* in writing, why not? All he wants is to see the show saved, and you know and I know that it needs it. Look, Art. The stars in their courses change from night to night. Don't take fixed positions on anything, anytime. You'll fail. . . . Yes, I will. Gladly. Even *twenty* minutes. Go ahead."

Now he listened. I went out into the other room and heard Larry on the phone.

"How would I twist her arm? I'm nowhere *near* her. . . . Well, *ask* her. Or, put her on and have *her* tell me She's not interested in anything I have to say. Why not? Come on, Val. Be human, be professional. . . . Yes, I'll hold on."

He looked at me and shook his head, miserably. All at once, he brightened.

"Hello, there! How are you? . . . Hello?"

He put down the phone just as Gene bounced into the room shouting, "We're all set!"

Larry looked up. "No, we're not."

"No?"

"She hung up on me."

"Bitch!" said Gene.

"Well, that's that," said Larry.

"The hell you say," said Gene. "There's more than one way to skin a cat, as we used to say in Minnesota." To me: "Call Clay and ask him to come over right now."

A shout from Larry. "Clay?!"

"Why not?"

"No good," said Larry. "I couldn't handle it."

"Now don't *you* start hanging up on people," said Gene. "I'm having enough trouble as it is."

"But *Clay!*"

"Look, if we'd put over the other deal, you'd've been working with him, wouldn't you have?"

"I suppose so."

"All right then?"

"All right. Although I still don't know what you have in mind."

"A plot. Better than the one in the show, believe me."

I reached Clay. Woke him up, in fact, and indicated that it was of vital importance for him to join us. He seemed reluctant at first but, recognizing the urgency in my voice, he agreed.

"On his way," I reported.

"Get us some food, woman," said Gene. "All this intrigue's made me ravenous."

"Anything special?"

"Anything we've got—just so long as it's highly seasoned."

I made Spanish omelets, cottage fries, English muffins, and Irish coffee. A success. As we were finishing the feast, Clay arrived.

He went at once to Larry and offered his hand. After a split second's hesitation, Larry took it.

Clay spoke softly, ostensibly for Larry's ears only. "I'm deeply sorry, Larry. Forgive me. He said if I didn't, he'd take me off. And that I couldn't handle, not right now. I'll explain it to you someday. We all do insane things sometimes—don't we? Especially under pressure."

"Forget it, Clay."

"No, I won't forget it—I can't—but I hope *you* can."

"Sure."

Coffee. We sat close together in a sort of circled huddle.

Gene began by outlining to Clay the events of the evening just passed, right up to the unsatisfactory ending with Art and Star.

"What we must achieve now," he went on, "is Larry's eye on the show—night after night until it's right—and some method of implementing his ideas and instructions."

"Impossible," said Larry.

"Why?"

"I'd have to watch the show from mid-orchestra. And make notes. I'd be recognized eventually, no matter how many beards I wore."

Clay. "But suppose that could be overcome one way or another—even then—how do we get to make the changes in the show?"

"You," said Gene. *"You're* going to take over."

"Me?" said Clay, plainly terrified.

"Yes, of course. Didn't I mention that? You're odd man out, my boy. There's no one else. He's down to you, I can make him see that in ten seconds flat."

"Not bad," said Larry. "Now all we have to figure out is access."

Why was Gene looking at me so hard? Was he angry about something? Something I had done? Not done? No one has ever looked at me as hard or as long. Finally, I could bear it no longer.

"What is it?" I asked. "What's the matter?"

Gene, his eyes still on me, said, "Larry, as long as you're out of work, how would you like to come to work for *me*, as my secretary?"

"Best offer I've had today," said Larry.

It was not as easy to arrange as Gene thought it was going to be. Larry, although not exceptionally tall or large, is nevertheless not an easy fourteen or sixteen. Men are different, it turns out. I shopped and shopped. Woodward & Lothrop solved most of the problems in the end, except for shoes. A specialty shop in Georgetown provided those.

I helped Larry to dress and make up. He turned into a surprisingly attractive (if somewhat butch) female. He practiced walking around the apartment, sitting and rising, for one whole day.

Meanwhile, Gene, having enlisted the support of Jenny, Alicia, Ivan, and Star—talked to Art on the subject of Clay. As he predicted, it was a breeze. Art saw it at once as the practical and, of course, inexpensive solution. Ziegfeld would have been harder to convince.

Art sent for me.

"You're a major disappointment to me," he said.

"I am?"

"What happened to you? You started out so good, now you got me in a spot where you're costing me a fortune."

"In what way?"

"In the way Gene tells me he's got to bring his own secretary down from Chicago. He doesn't want you anymore."

"Why not?"

"Don't ask me. Maybe he doesn't like you. Maybe he doesn't like your work."

"Maybe his secretary is more than a secretary," I said.

"No, no. He's too square for that kinda caper."

"No one is."

"He claims you've got too much other things to do and on your mind."

"Well, that's a damn fact. He probably *does* need someone full time—now that we're in the stretch."

"Hey, y'know? I never thought of that. Him boffing his secretary. How *about* that?"

"Happens."

"Yeah, but not where I've got to pay first-class air fares and a hundred dollars a day per diem, plus salary. Just so a horny writer can get his rocks off!"

The whole conversation was not as amusing to me as I thought it was going to be.

The first two nights went well. Larry and Gene sat together, communicating—Larry making notes.

A meeting afterward at Gene's, the notes discussed.

Next day, Clay put them in. Progress—slow but unmistakable.

The third night, for some perverse reason, Art insisted on meeting Gene's secretary. He had something he wanted to give her.

Fortunately, I had put long fingernails on Larry's fingers that afternoon, given him a manicure with bright-red polish, and added false eyelashes to his makeup.

The introduction in the lobby was scary.

"Art, this is Mrs. Elizabeth Borden."

"Hi, honey! This is for you." He handed her a box containing a gold pen-light.

Larry coughed and said, "Oh, thank you!" in a hoarse whisper.

"Laryngitis," Gene explained. "From the plane."

"Don't I know!" said Art. To Larry: "Look, honey, if that's not better by tomorrow, I'm sending my doctor to see you."

Larry nodded enthusiastically.

When he and Gene had gone to their seats, Art said to me, "You were wrong. Nothing's playing there."

"How do you know?"

"How do I know? I know because I know a dyke when I see one. I've got a built-in dyke-detector."

"Don't be silly," I said. "It's *Mrs.* Borden. *Mrs.* Elizabeth Borden."

"Yeah? How much you want to bet her husband's name is *Mary?*"

But at least the game was saved.

The *modus operandi* of Larry-Gene-Clay moved into high gear. The show improved, and even Star was enjoying it more because the audiences were—and although She knows very little about the theatre, She knows *all* about audiences.

Gene was happy at last, and confident, and up, and his mood took the form of expression I most prefer. We made love. Constantly, it seemed. Not once, and then again, and later again as before—but one long continuing nonstop magical exchange.

One night—laughing, slightly stewed fucking, then blissful sleep. I am awakened by the most aphrodisiacal sensation between my legs. He tongues me awake and then to sleep. I awake again. He is asleep beside me. I move my hand to his beloved organ and fondle it. It comes alive in my hand as he wakes, slowly. He takes charge, rolls over, mounts me, and enters me powerfully, this time not to perform the act of love—but simply to be there—a reminder of what delights have been and a herald of joys yet to be. Gentle, tantalizing movement—then sudden withdrawal.

"Breakfast," he shouts, and dashes for the shower. I order an enormous breakfast and join him in the shower, where we enjoy one another's bodies. Soaping, rinsing, clinging. Drying, rubbing. A slow slow breakfast and a long long newspaper read. I get the feeling he does not read papers so much as he *consumes* them. Marking, clipping. After breakfast, we crawl back into bed and nap. The phone rings.

"No," he says, and holds me.

I am hungry for him, for the texture and taste of his stiffness in my mouth. My power over it is heady stuff. It grows and throbs and responds to my lips and to my tongue. In the ecstatic inebriation of complete let-go—it seems often to belong to me as much as to him. Gently then firmly, gently then wildly, gently then powerfully, I coax the nectar from his being. He cries out, thrashes about, lies very still. We have triumphed once again.

At first, it was difficult to understand what Larry was doing and why he was doing it—at such considerable inconvenience to himself. His name is off the show, off the house boards, and programs and publicity. Officially, he has nothing to do with it. What audiences and critics and the profession will never know is how much of this show is his —was invented and executed by him. Moreover, he has forfeited any material gain—didn't have to, could have had a settlement of some kind—why didn't he? For the moment of declaring himself free and unencumbered, I suppose. Expensive moment. Now he is back—struggling into drag night after night, going to the theatre, watching the show, making notes, getting ideas, discussing them with Gene and Clay until 2:00, sometimes 4:00 in the morning. Clay puts the stuff in, Larry checks it during the next performance. He has so often said to the company—"The *doing* is what matters." I always took that to be part of the pep talk—but now Larry is living out his own philosophy. Beyond that, I think the show means more to him than his own ego. Is that the mark of an artist? One who cares more about the piece of creative work than anything else? Probably. At any rate, that may explain Larry and what he has been doing these days and nights. The show is getting a blood transfusion and a face-lift and a Dr. Niehans treatment all at the same time. And it is responding joyfully.

The only thing they are having trouble with is getting out Star's inane interpolations. They get one out, another, another, then the first one goes back in.

"But it's not in the script, dear," Clay said one morning, close to exasperation.

"So what? It works, don't it? Gets a pisser of a laugh."

"Too expensive, that laugh."

"I'll pay, O.K.?"

"Mr. Bowman feels—"

"Hey, come on, fella. Tell Mr. Bowman he ain't Mr. Shakespeare and his show ain't exactly *Tristan and Isolde.* It's a show. For the people. So why don't we give them what they want?"

"Tell her," said Gene, a few hours later, "that audiences don't *know* what they want. It's up to us to *tell* them what they want, and they like us better if we don't tell them to like trash."

In time, Clay conveyed this message in his own way, in his own words—but it was no use.

He suggested to Gene that he himself have a shot at her. Gene did, with good, if not perfect results.

The routine was tiring Larry. It would have been so much simpler to do it in a straightforward, professional way, but given the personalities involved, it was not to be.

"It's getting better," said Gene. "There's absolutely no doubt in my mind about that. This show is getting better every night."

Larry laughed. "Oh, Gene," he said. "Oh, Gene, you lovable tyro! Getting better. Don't you know you've just enunciated the Broadway kiss of death? The theatre's illusion-delusion? Getting better. Most shows fail. What is it? Nine out of ten? Eight out of ten? Most. An investor—big—once said to me, 'I can't understand it. Good people with good track records. They start out and come up empty so much of the time. How come?' So I said, 'Well, first of all, let me ask you, who was the greatest baseball player of all time—the greatest hitter?' 'I don't know,' he said. 'Babe Ruth?' 'Right,' I said. 'That's what most people say. Babe Ruth. O.K. You know how many times he struck out? Over *three thousand.* Struck out three thousand times —to say nothing of the times he flied out or hit into double plays. So theatre people are human, too, and the theatre's full of imponderables.' And then there's that goddamned Getting Better. Look. You start a show—first days are chaotic. Nobody knows where to go, what to do, or how to do it. Days go by in agony. Now the players begin to play, put down their scripts, a scene comes to life, a song pleases. Hey! It's getting better! A cut—better. A change—better. A replacement—*much* better. And because it's getting better—not only better but better and better—we poor besotted stagestruck nuts actually believe it's getting *good!* But no. It's not getting good—it's just getting *better!* See?"

"I see," said Gene, "but I don't agree. This one *is* good—and getting better."

"Are you listening, God?" asked Larry.

Clay, still having problems with Star, comes up to see Art. Art greets him, expansively, and gives him a present. A Vuitton briefcase. Clay would prefer a less intransigent Star.

"You want me to talk to her?" asks Art. "I'll talk to her. What it'll get us, I don't promise. You know how She is. Mondays, Wednesdays, Fridays, She loves me. Tuesdays, Thursdays, Saturdays, She hates me. Sundays, She rests and changes the schedule. So I never know—but I'll try."

"We're approaching a pretty good level of precision now," said Clay. "Except for her. I have nightmares about opening night."

"It's par for the course, Clay. You learn that after a while. You want a Star, you pay the price. Like Billy Wilder said that time when somebody said to him—'Wasn't Marilyn Monroe a real pain-in-the-ass to work with—a lot of trouble?' And Billy said, 'Damn right, but let me tell you. My Aunt Ida—if I hired *her* for the part—I promise you—I'd stake my life—she would come on time and know her lines perfectly and do what I tell her with no discussion and not say a word to the cameraman or hairdresser or wardrobe or makeup persons—she would work overtime and undertime and be a perfect lady. The only trouble is—My Aunt Ida doesn't look like Marilyn Monroe and can't act like—so that's why I decided to go with Monroe—a pain-in-the-ass and plenty of trouble.' "

"Yes," said Clay. "I see what you mean."

"What's more important, Clay, is for Chrissake, why didn't you ever tell me what a good director you are?"

Instead of replying, Clay looked at me and smiled.

Art went on. "I mean it, kid. Do you *know* how good you are?"

"Yes," said Clay.

"Even Her Nibs mentioned it in her high-toned way the other day. She said to me, 'You see that, you ass-hole? Terrific director right under your nose and you don't even *know* it? Does that *prove* you're a shithead?' I took a bow, naturally."

"If She thinks I'm so terrific, why won't She listen?"

"Because She's a Star who thinks She's a *super*star, and all super-stars have invisible hearing aids that they turn on and off any time it suits them. But never mind her. Back to you. I want to talk to you, seriously. You know *Ruggles of Red Gap?*"

"Of course."

"What do you think of it as a musical?"

"Why not? With the right elements."

"The right elements to me means no Hy Balaban. He's too flaky for me—and an easy bleeder besides. You heard what Ivan did to him, didn't you? Flattened him with one roundhouse. Ivan! The man's about ninety-two."

"Hy writes excellent show music."

"Not enough," said Art. "His yenta wife comes with it. Miss Blinding Jewelry. Who needs it? Anyway, for *Ruggles,* I want an English songwriter—like Noel Coward."

"Noel Coward is dead," said Clay.

"Did I say Noel Coward? I said *like* Noel Coward. Jesus, you're as tough to talk to as every other talent shmo."

"There is no one like Noel Coward."

"But English," said Art. "Or British."

Clay looked at me, then said to Art, "I don't see why. It's an American story, with only one sequence—the opening—and one character—Ruggles—that are British. And even if there were more —what does it matter? May I remind you that *My Fair Lady* was written by Alan Jay Lerner of New York, and Frederick Loewe of Vienna?"

"You may remind me that I sure in hell don't want *you* on the goddam show. You're good, like I said, but you're a card-carrying smart-ass."

"There you are," said Clay. "Fired before hired. That must be *some* kind of a record, wouldn't you say?"

"Send it in to Guinness," said Art. "Don't tell *me.*"

"Shall we take it from the top? What did you want?"

"When?"

"Today. You sent for me."

"I did?" asked Art.

"So I was told."

To me: "I did?"

"About the credits," I reminded him.

"Oh, yeah," said Art to Clay. "I want to make a deal with you. You got an agent?"

"No."

"Better. We'll make sense. How about one percent, and a half for road companies, and credit equal to the other creative elements? Generous enough?"

"Not generous at all," said Clay. "The royalty terms you mention are the absolute minimum required by the SSDC."

Art turned to me. "Didn't I tell you a smart-ass?"

"However," said Clay, "those terms are acceptable."

"Good. Deal."

"As to the credit—no."

"No? What *do* you want?"

"No credits. No way."

Art, to me: "Smart-ass and dumb-ass in one—did you ever see such a thing?" To Clay: "If you had any brains, you'd know the credit is worth more than the money. It could be the biggest thing in your life. A show like this—directed by— How can you not want *that?*"

· 458 ·

"Of course I *want* it—but it would be a fraud. I haven't directed this show and I'm not prepared to pretend that I have."

"A dumb shot, Clay. Who knows in the end who did what on a show? The critics, the people—what it says on the program—that's what they know—and nothing else."

"That may be— But see, the trouble is—*I* know."

"You're puttin' me in a tough position, Clay. It's got to say *something*—it can't be a show with *no* director's name; it don't look good."

"Are you asking for a suggestion?"

"Go ahead."

"Say 'Larry Gabel.'"

"Are you *nuts* or what?"

"Basically, the show we're now doing is his. His casting, his concept, staging, everything."

"He hasn't been near it for weeks! What the hell are you talkin' about?"

"No matter. It's his show."

"He's off it. He's got no connection. He gets paid zip."

"Suit yourself," said Clay. "Anything else?"

"Not right now. So what's our deal?"

"One percent for New York, one-half for roads, no credit."

"Fee?"

"No fee. Let's consider my up-to-now salary my fee. And I'd like to stay with the show—for a while, anyway—if that's all right with you."

"Sure, sure."

"Thanks."

Clay left, and I had to listen to an indignant rehash of the whole meeting, told to me as if I had not been there. Then came a lecture on stupidity, followed by a long polemic on ingratitude, with a coda on the subject of this is a crazy world.

"A whackout like this Clay—what can I tell you? I don't understand him at all. Not at all."

"Of course he doesn't understand him at all," said Gene. "Clay could have been talking in Urdu so far as *he's* concerned. He doesn't understand the vocabulary of integrity or the syntax of honesty—it's another language. May I dictate something?"

"Certainly."

"I promise not to go too fast."

"Ha ha."

"My dear Mr. Clune It has come to my attention that there is some confusion as to the directorial credit on *Shine On, Harvest Moon*

Para In view of the fact that no director has made substantial contributions since my departure perhaps you would consider restoring *my* credit Para   Two conditions colon   One dash that our present arrangement of no financial obligation on your part toward me be continued   In other words comma our present understanding stands period   Two dash that I come down and see a performance to determine if what is on the stage represents my concept period   Best wishes   Sincerely yours   Space for signature then Larry Gabel in caps."

"What makes you think Larry'd go for that?"

"He'd be foolish not to."

"If he's credited, wouldn't his union make the management pay?"

"Probably. And he could kick it back. The aim is to save his credit."

"I'll be glad when this is over," I said.

"I'll be glad when we go to bed," said Gene.

SHINE ON, HARVEST MOON
Company Bulletin
Tuesday, January 15

There will be a brief rehearsal Thursday at 3:00 P.M. Then the cast is invited by Mr. Belmonte to dinner at Louisa's Restaurant. Our plan is to travel there in a group directly from rehearsal. We will provide the transportation to Georgetown. If for any reason anyone is unable to come, please tell Midge sometime during the course of the day.

I know I said earlier that we would probably not rehearse on Friday, but an important piece of restructuring has developed, which requires me to call a rehearsal at 3:00 P.M.

Mr. Balaban has canceled his Friday brush-up rehearsal of the Rector's scene.

Clay Botsford

TROUBLE SLEEPING?: Make yourself a cup of orange-flower tea. Drink it. Good night!

QUOTE TO REMEMBER:
    "I firmly believe that an actor's mental attitude is instantly conveyed to an audience. I further believe that an audience unconsciously appraises his character. It soon discovers if he is all actor or part man and its appraisal of his performance is more determined by its unconscious exploration of his unconscious than by any particular thing that he does. Invariably, the actors whom the public has loved have been people who in themselves possessed great lovable qualities. They were not people who, in their roles, assumed a lovable nature."

Arthur Hopkins

THE COMPANY YOU KEEP: GRACIE MILLS
(Minna Everleigh)
  (To the tune of "Ohio" from WONDERFUL TOWN by Bernstein, Comden and Green. My first Broadway show. 1953. Understudied Rosalind Russell.)

"Why oh why oh why—oh
Why do they want my autobio?
Why are they prying?
Should I begin lying?
My life's been a mess from the start!
Born in Alabama
Went on the stage
Big for my age
Tried not to cave in
But finally gave in
Traded it in for a part
I had to!
Thank God I still have my twat!"

There are now 16 days remaining before the New York
opening.

· LII ·

The SSDC (Society of Stage Directors and Choreographers) does indeed insist on Larry's having a contract and being paid, because he is now the accredited director of the show.

So this is how it works in The Temple of The Barracuda: Every week, Larry will be paid his royalty—a considerable amount, on these grosses. He will return it to Art. Art will give the money to Clay —who will give it to Larry!

About this last transaction, there was some argument—but Clay can be extremely firm at times, and this was one of those times. He said that unless Larry accepted the royalties—he (Clay) would give up the entire scheme.

"I don't care," said Clay, "what you do with it once you've got it. Throw it away, give it to The Actor's Fund, anything you like— but you're going to take it because it belongs to you and no one else."

Gene, ever the practical one, worried about the tax aspects of these shenanigans. He phoned a tax expert in Chicago—who got it all straight, so that any questions asked of anyone by the IRS can be handled legitimately.

"The single arm of government," said Gene, "with which I advise one and all not to horse around."

We leave for New York on Sunday. The company flies. A few will go by bus. Gene wants to drive and take all day and enjoy the country. I am looking forward to it—the trip, I mean, not New York. That scares me now. Everyone is confident (overconfident?) but as Clay says, "Anything can happen—and usually does."

But however I look at it—the whole adventure—the end is in sight.

It will take me a long time to digest it, understand it (if ever), use it.

It has been more than an experience—it has been a lifetime.

When I wrote up there "the end is in sight," I kept going because I did not want to face what it means: the end of the show—at least, as far as I am concerned—and more important—far, far more important—the end of Gene Bowman in my life.

I expect nothing of Gene and I am sure that that is exactly what I am going to get. Unlike most of the men in my life—he has no line whatsoever. He makes no promises, nor does he dangle intimations of a sweet future. He is not given to fulsome compliments, nor exaggerated statements. He is—what's the word? *Real.* That's the word. He is a real man. There are not many.

More. He is a gentleman, which means, at least to me, that he is thoughtful and considerate and sensitive. He is not in the least demanding. There have been times, of course, when lovemaking would have been something less than convenient. Most of my former partners have sulked through these times, conveying somehow that I, rather than Nature, was at fault. Gene accepts it with grace, and if anything, is even more attentive and tender and loving than usual.

I am impressed with his sense of what matters. Work comes first, yes—but he cares about food and drink and exercise and rest. He is interested in the condition of the air and earth and water. The basics. The fundamentals. He loves to make love.

He is a passionate feminist and is offended by the all-male crew and production organization.

"Sweet Jesus!" he said the other day with passion. "It turns out that the wardrobe mistress on this show is a man!"

"Yes."

"And not one woman in the crew! Don't tell me women couldn't run the electrical board or do Clay's job or Stu's or handle the follow-spots. And don't tell me that in every way, women are not more suited to the work done by property men. What's the matter with you girls? Why do you take it? Why don't you make more noise—insist on being integrated into the world's work? What was it that my illiterate grandfather used to say? 'The squeaky wheel gets the grease.' I'm afraid it's true."

"Who wants grease?" I said.

He went on, ignoring my feeble attempt at a joke. That's him. He laughs hard at good jokes, ignores bum ones.

"There are more women in our country than there are men. Why doesn't matter for the moment—but consider this: Out of nine justices on the Supreme Court bench, we have nine men. The Court, mind you, is the most powerful and important element in our structure. Frankfurter once said: 'The Constitution of the United States of America doesn't mean what *you* think it means, and it doesn't mean what *I* think it means, it means what The Supreme Court *says* it means.' So that's what we live by. All of us. You women included. But you're not represented on the Court, and you should be. Thousands of cases come up—I used to cover the Court—that involve women in a special way, that involve matters of male-female relationship. A female point of view would be valuable. Where is it? Am I to believe that out of more than a hundred million women, there's not *one* qualified for such a post? Ridiculous!"

"But what can we do? I mean, what can *I* do?"

"Raise hell! Be a squeaky wheel. What did they do up in Boston—at the Tea Party? Hell, if what I've just told you doesn't spell 'taxation without representation,' then I don't understand the English language."

Gene Gene Gene. I have been trying to fathom what it is that makes him such a superlative partner in sexual expression. I think about it a good deal, perhaps more than I should. Still, I know I am going to lose Gene and I want to have learned something from the experience. Who knows? Maybe it will be possible for me to convey some of it to someone else someday—in some way.

Partner. I suppose that's the answer, the key.

He got to talking about the problems of the show the other night while we were getting ready for bed. He undressed slowly and deliberately, one article of clothing at a time. Often he stood, transfixed, holding a shoe or trailing his tie before continuing to pace about. He would disappear into the bathroom, but keep talking even while brushing his teeth. A large part of his peroration was delivered in the buff. It may have been this event that made me relate what he was saying to the larger and, to me, more important subject of sexual life, sexual balance, sexual stimulation, sexual gratification, sexual imagination, and sexual health.

"The trouble is," he said, "that it's not a successfully organized partnership. What we have here is a struggle for power—one of the most wasteful of all human activities. It removes energy from the work at hand. Take Hy—consider what percentage of his time he spends composing and what percentage selling, scheming, promoting, pressing. And most of the rest, too. Good creative work is more likely to result from cooperation than from competition, don't you agree?"

"I do now."

"The secret of a partnership—*any* partnership—lies in equality, in perfect balance. A junior partner is no partner at all. I mean a business, a baseball team, a marriage, a friendship. Don't ever try close friendship with someone who's above you in station or status—it won't work. I suspect the Hy-Fred partnership leaves something to be desired. Hy is too strong for him, the dominant one. That's why most of the changes and adjustments in the songs are in the lyrics and not in the music."

"I've noticed that."

"You've seen marriages, haven't you, where either the husband or the wife was clearly in charge?"

"Sure."

"Well, they're no good, those marriages, because—"

He went on talking, but I stopped listening because it was all too depressing. Everything he was saying seemed to be relating directly to me and my position with him. I fought to hold back tears. Didn't he realize what he was doing to me? Or wait—was he deliberately getting me onto this track of thinking to soften the blow that surely lay ahead?

"Don't be so fucking neurotic!" I said.

"What?" asked Gene.

And I realized that what I had meant to say silently to myself, I had said aloud. I was properly embarrassed.

"Please," I said. "I was talking to myself, not to you. It just came out."

"Why do you think you're neurotic—or as you so eloquently put it—so *fucking* neurotic'?"

"Well. . . ." I hesitated.

"Come on," he urged. "Tell a pal."

"I don't know if—" I stopped again.

"Mark Twain once said, 'When in doubt, tell the truth.' It's a good rule. I've used it for years."

I took a deep breath and told him I had begun to suspect that he was saying what he was saying for my benefit, to point out that he and I were not a suitable partnership.

He laughed. "Go stand in the corner," he said. "Face to the wall. There's *nothing* in what you say. *Less* than nothing. Say! Come to think of it—you *are* neurotic, or should I say *'fucking* neurotic'? I don't mind—just so it isn't the other way about!"

"You may have to have your mouth washed out with Ivory Soap," I said.

"No," he said, studying me. "You're not neurotic. Far from it."

"Shall I tell you the truth?" I asked. "I don't even know what neurotic means. I say it, I hear it, but I really don't know."

He laughed. "Well, Mr. Freud, who invented the word, ought to know, and he once explained it this way: If an explorer and his wife are asleep in their tent in the middle of Central Africa, and she wakes him and says, 'Dear? I think there's a snake under the bed,' this woman is not necessarily neurotic. But if the same woman wakes the same man in the bedroom of their twenty-eighth-floor Park Avenue apartment, and says, 'Dear? I think there's a snake under the bed'— this woman is *definitely neurotic!*"

"Thank you," I said. "And now would you mind looking under the bed?"

He did so, and went on. "If Larry could have achieved real cooperation—say the kind Ivan and Alicia enjoy, by the way, and look at *those* results!—it would have been so much easier and better. You know what makes Solti so great with our orchestra? He gets the musicians to play *together*—he gets each one of them to serve the whole piece. Me, I love the word 'together'—it has such profundity. Some words—"

I was off again. I did not mean to be or want to be, but all at once —there was the revelation for me. There was the explanation of why the bed we shared was not so much a bed as a paradise. Gene knew how to turn the greatest of all human adventures into a true partnership. Balance. Exchange. Just. Equal. Harmony. Mated. Fated. It had never occurred to me that it could be anything like this. I had always thought of it in terms of conquest and submission. Even the language surrounding it suggests that. "I'm going to fuck you!" Someone doing something *to* someone else is different from two people doing something *together*. The others had taught me—how?—to say or whisper or shout at the appropriate moment, "Fuck me! Oh, fuck me!" And I had obliged.

"Are you listening?" I heard him say.

"Of course."

"Repeat the last sentence."

"Wait a second," I said, then recited: " 'The trouble is that it's not a successfully organized partnership.' Right?"

This time he *did* laugh. And while he was laughing, I examined his nakedness and my eyes found his private parts and marveled at the wonder that would soon be when they were transformed by love. Hold it. By love? Or by lovemaking? I love him, but are we in love? Do we share the state of love? Does he love me? I doubt it. He has never said so. I must keep all this clear in my mind. Why have we never talked about it? We have talked so much and so long about so many things—why have we never discussed love? I suppose because it is not—in Art's famous word—discussible. Words would melt it, whatever it is.

He selected a pair of those flimsy white pajamas of his that drive me wild, put the top on, came to my side of the bed, leaned over, kissed me, kissed my ears, my neck, my nipples, my lips again, said, "Hello, partner," removed his top, arranged the lights, got into bed beside me, held me, held me, and waited until I conveyed that I needed him, that I was ready to receive him. My warm—no, hot—moistures waited patiently for Nature to begin its song.

· LIII ·

A bombshell today. Hy Balaban has left Rachel.

"I don't believe it," said Art when he heard the news. "She's worth over thirty million bucks, f'Chrissake. I checked her out. A man doesn't leave thirty mil. *She* left *him*, maybe—that I can buy—but not him her. I don't believe it. Hy's a practical, sensible operator. He'd know how to square any beef. Did they say why?"

Larry to Gene. "I understand from Fred that Mrs. Balaban—the soon-to-be *ex*-Mrs. Balaban—had gotten to be more and more involved with their work. In the beginning, Fred says, she was never around. Later, they used to do the numbers for her first—before anyone else—and she'd invariably say, 'Greatest song I ever heard. By far your best.' After a while, she began to get critical—especially if she didn't think the song had a chance to be a Number One. Then on *this* show, she started making suggestions—usually for the lyrics, and that led to musical ideas. At first, Hy joked about it, then he got uptight. It led to little spats and a lot of bickering. Then, when Star started doing 'Big Town' by herself, without Sammy—Rachel raised the roof and said it was lousy and ought to come out of the show, and when finally Hy told her to mind her business, she packed up and took the Rolls and went back to New York."

"Well," said Gene, "that does sound like *she* walked out on *him*."

"No," said Larry, "Fred tells me there were a few more screamers on the phone, and finally one morning, she called him seven times and he told her not to come back—definitely—that if she did, he'd belt her. Then he heard him call The Pierre and make a reservation, and Steinway to move his piano over there, and that, he said, was like the umbilical cord."

"You wanna hear something that'll make you say '*No!!*'?" asks Sammy.
"Yes," I answered.
"Patti."
"What about her?"
"She's moved in with Hy."
"When?"
"Right now."
"Who says?"
"Frankie."
"Who's Frankie?"
"The bellhop who moved her in. I didn't even ask him. He told me. And *I'm* telling *you*. I don't know why. Enjoyable, I guess. I like it when pros stick with pros and stay off the civilians. Civilians make me nervous. 'Don't you get sick of doing the same thing night after night?' I say to them, 'Not any sicker than *you* get screwing night after night.' And how about, 'Does the makeup hurt your skin?' Or, 'Is it hard to remember all those lines?' Or, 'I didn't like it much—except you, of course—you were fantastic. They gave you a real good part, didn't they?' And how about when they complain and say, 'I don't know. It was *pretty* good. But it dragged a little in the middle of the Second Act. It definitely dragged.' Some woman once made the mistake of saying that to George S. Kaufman. He said to her, 'I know, lady, that you woke up this morning with a bang, and took an enchanting walk to the bathroom and had a thrilling pee, then a scintillating breakfast, and an exciting hour getting dressed. And then a morning filled with the pulsating, rhythmic beat of life, with ordering the groceries, and shopping, and a hilarious lunch, and a breathtaking trip to the dentist, and a bouncing cocktail party and enthralling dinner, and then the First Act not too bad until—*hell! I* provided a second act that dragged a little in the middle and *ruined* your whole God-damned day!' No, listen, Hy's better off. She was a drag, if you ask me. Although I must admit, she had a rare talent—she could say the wrong thing

· 470 ·

at the wrong time more often than anybody I've ever met."

"She thought she had a right to say *anything*—her bankroll being what it was. They're often like that, rich people."

"I don't like rich people," said Sammy. "They've got too much money."

Creamed chipped beef at The Automat with Jenny.

"The surprise to me is not that they split, but that they stuck as long as they did. What a match! An artist should never be for sale. He has to sell his work, sure—but he must never sell himself." I said absolutely nothing.

I nodded in agreement, but of course, I couldn't help thinking, Look who's talking.

"Yeah, yeah," she said, "I know. Me. Different. He's established. I still have my way to make. Anyway—a lot of us know what's right and do what's wrong. Convenience, expediency. Also, mine is as temporary as a cold sore—and just about as much fun. His was permanent —at least, that was the commitment. And I'll tell you—the years they were married, his stuff was off. I know it well—I can sing it all—I was a fan of Hy Balaban's before I even met him. In Texas, dancing school, most of the routines were built around Hy Balaban or Richard Rodgers show tunes. I admire the little screwball. But lately, the stuff's been facile and not only derivative, but repetitive—copying himself—a sure sign that a composer's getting tired. That goddam social life he's been leading—his picture in *WWD* all the time—who cares? Did you know she's employed a press agent for the two of them? But in his life—the real life—nothing mattered except what he did on the score paper. So maybe it'll turn out to be a good thing all around. Maybe he's got his balls back. Maybe we'll start to hear some Hy Balaban tunes again."

Finally, Hy himself. He came into The Lamplight after the show tonight. Patti was with him. I was there with Clay. They stopped at our table.

HY

How's everything here?

ME

You call this a rare hamburger?

(HY leans over, splits my hamburger with a fork)

HY

Absolutely not! A disgrace! Here!

(He picks up my plate and takes it right through the swinging doors into the kitchen)

PATTI

What a nut!

(HY returns)

HY

Won't be a moment, madam.

CLAY

Join us?

HY

God, I thought you'd never ask. Slide over.

(He and PATTI join us in the booth)

CLAY

Marvelous show tonight. I know one can't judge it all by the clock —but we ran six minutes shorter tonight with the same show as last night.

PATTI

And bigger laughs and longer hands.

HY

It's moving, that's all—moving.

(The waiter comes over. HY and PATTI order drinks and food)

CLAY

You're looking very well, Hy.

HY

Why not? I just lost a hundred and ten pounds.

PATTI

And that's without the jewelry.

HY

With, it's *two*-ten. Crazy, isn't it? A guy sits down somewhere and writes Act One, Scene One—and can't have any idea what

· 472 ·

that's going to cause in the way of happiness or misery or life and death or marriage and divorce—suicide, sometimes. Nine years ago, we let a dancer out of a show of mine, the most beautiful Oriental girl I've ever seen—from Thailand, I think, or Indonesia, someplace like that. We couldn't help it. She was ruining the line of girls—you couldn't look at anything but her. So stunning. So we had to let her out. She said goodbye to everybody—hugs, kisses—went home to The Rehearsal Club on Fifty-third Street, got into a tubful of warm water, and opened her veins with a razor blade. Anything can happen. Girls get knocked up—well, not so much now as they used to. Once in a while—the real thing—two people who wouldn't have met otherwise—if not for the show—they meet, they fall in love, they get married, and who knows what?

CLAY

All that's quite true. Scary and wonderful. But for me, what's even more interesting is how every company becomes a family. In time, there's a kind of father and mother, drunken uncle, backward children, precocious ones, goody-goodies, juvenile delinquents, wayward girls. Family fights, family feuds. I guess that's why closings are so sad—the death of a whole family.

HY

I take it you kids have heard my big news.

ME

Part of it.

HY

The whole story is that it was a mistake from the start. It took this show to prove it. She was my third time around, Rachel. So I guess you could say that in the marriage game, I have struck out.

ME

Isn't there a saying, "Third time, lucky"?

HY

There was. Cut it.

(More drinks are served. Who ordered them?)

PATTI
(To HY*)*

Iggy, keep an eye on me. I've got a matinee tomorrow. One more after this, and that's it.

· 473 ·

HY

Funny. Rachel never drank at all. Not even wine. She said alcohol made wrinkles.

PATTI

I don't believe it. I'd look like a prune by now.

(Food arrives. We begin to eat. Everyone is hungry)

HY

I'd like some frank talk. Everybody game?

PATTI

Wait a second. Frank talk about *what?*

HY

About the show, what else?

PATTI

Oh, the show! Fine.

HY

Question: What's still wrong with it? Never mind what's right. We all know what's right. What's wrong? Midge, you.

ME

Why me?

HY

You're the newest to the business—maybe nearest to the audience point of view.

ME

I love it.

HY

But not every minute—you *couldn't*. For years, I wondered how *Oklahoma* could have been such a hit with that "Poor Jud" number in it. Maybe nobody had the nerve to speak up and say it was no good. Bad spots in every show—*My Fair Lady, A Chorus Line*—whatever. We're so good, I wish we could be perfect.

ME

I don't think the audience hears all the words—I mean, they hear, but they don't *understand* all the words.

HY
(Annoyed)

So what? You understand everything you hear in *life*, f'Chris-sake?

CLAY

Come on, Hy—you asked her and she told you, so why get mad?

HY

I asked for constructive.

PATTI

There's a definition I heard once someplace: "A nervous person is a person who makes other persons nervous."

HY

So?

PATTI

By that definition, mister—*you* are a nervous person.

HY

You know why people can't hear, can't understand? Because they don't listen. This goddam mechanical world. Hell, when I started in the theatre, nobody ever *heard* of a mike. And we were in these same theatres. And everybody heard everything. Then comes radio and movies and TV—and everything blares, and if you want it louder even, you turn up the sound. So people used to having it belted at them with amplification get lazy in the ears. Next thing you know, they've got to have it in every legiti-mate house—even small ones.
(To me)
So don't blame us. It's *your* fault.

ME

Mine?

HY

The public's. Jesus! Look at The Met. Biggest house in New York. Over three thousand seats. Has anybody ever seen a mike there? Of course not.
(To me, again)
That understanding you talk about, I mean that *not* understand-ing—it's the goddam speakers. This chintzy cheapskate wouldn't go for the best quality—so we get distortion.

CLAY

Tell you what I'll do, Hy. I'll order a whole new set of speakers.
I promise you. They'll be in next week.

HY

He won't go for it.

CLAY

He won't *know*.

HY

Why not?

CLAY

I won't tell him. There won't be any trouble, and if there is, we'll
double-talk our way out of it.

HY

I love you.

CLAY

Now ask *me* what I think the show still needs.

HY

Go. What do *you* think our little show still needs?

CLAY

Up tunes.

(Quickly)

And don't give me a list of what we *do* have. I know. I hear the
score every night. Night after night. And I love it—but it needs
the spice and seasoning of at least two more jump-tunes, thigh-
slappers, hand-clappers. You asked me, so I'm telling you—we're
ballading them to death.

HY

By the way, I asked you because you asked me to ask you.

CLAY

I know. Otherwise, you might not have.

HY

Suppose you're right. There's no *room*—everybody's hollering
for cuts as it is.

CLAY

I know. You'd have to drop two ballads.

HY

Which two? Which *one*, even?

CLAY

From here on in, you're on your own.

HY

Thanks. You put a hole in the boat and jump out.

CLAY

No, no. But—not my job, Hy.

(HY *laughs*)

HY

The hell of it is you're right—a hundred and one percent right. I've known it all along—but I couldn't come up with what you say. Listen, now maybe I can. You know how long it is since I've felt free—or good? Or up?

(He gets up and goes to the piano)

What happened next was astonishing. Hy began to play songs of the turn of the century. I recognized some of them: "Call Me Up Some Rainy Afternoon," "Alexander's Ragtime Band," "Everybody's Doin' It Now."

"Berlin!" he called out, "all Berlin. Think of it!"

He followed this with a tune I had never heard—played it through twice, and said, "Me!"

He then went into a medley of still more period songs: "Too Much Mustard," "Get Out and Get Under," "Dardanella," but soon was interspersing these with inventions of his own. He played for an hour and a half. Patti brought him a drink now and then, kissed him, and ended up sitting on the piano bench beside him. They looked like a very happy couple indeed.

Finally, Hy left the piano, stopped by our table, and said to Clay, "I'll have something for you. I'm going to the hotel now—score paper and Fred. Here, take care of things." He dropped a $100 bill on the table, took Patti's arm, and left.

"You have just seen," said Clay, "a little history made. What a man!"

SHINE ON, HARVEST MOON
Company Bulletin
Tuesday, January 22

HALF-HOUR: Members of the company are reminded
that they are required to be in the theatre at half-
hour. In a company of this size, it is not possible
to make exceptions or allowances. Of necessity,
the half-hour rule will be strictly enforced.
Don't sign in and then leave the theatre!

TICKETS: The management is making available, with
its compliments, two pairs of seats for the first
preview performance to each member of the company.
Opening-night tickets are in your names at the Box
Office now.

REHEARSAL: "Jump for Joy" (new number) will be rehearsed in the Chorus Room at 4:00 P.M. today. You
will be dismissed promptly at 5:00 P.M.

RUNNING TIME: Act II was three minutes shorter at
Monday's preview.

THE COMPANY YOU KEEP: AKI FUKADO(Sound)
  I was born in Los Angeles. So was my father. So was
my mother. But in 1942, at the age of 14, I found myself, along with many others—interned. A Jap camp
near Scottsdale, Arizona. Had I been older, I would
have been drafted along with my two brothers. Looking back, it all seems mad. Anyway, at the camp,
very little to do so fooled around with radio and
wire recording and so on. Finally, we got permission to set up a camp radio station. FM 104.6. By the
time we were released, I was one hell of a sound man.
MIT. Went to work for Buzz Reeves in New York and was
in on the ground floor when amplification hit the
legitimate theatre. The thing I can't figure out is
—is this a success story or what?

QUOTATIONS FOR TODAY:
    "If it weren't for the married men we couldn't
have carried on at all and if it weren't for the

cheating married women we would have earned
another million."

Minna Everleigh

"I talk with each applicant myself. She must have
worked somewhere else before coming here. We do not
like amateurs. Inexperienced girls and young wid-
ows are too prone to accept offers of marriage and
leave. We always have a waiting list."

Ada Everleigh

There are now 9 days until our New York opening.

NEW YORK

· LIV ·

New York. The first preview last night. A bomb. Everyone is in a state of shock. Everything that could go wrong went wrong.

Larry came, as *himself!* All parties outwardly pleasant and cordial.

After the catastrophe, a long meeting onstage with the entire staff, except Larry.

Each one had a different theory: Wrong audience. Wrong theatre. Wrong sound equipment. Wrong lighting.

Gene and I could hardly wait to get up to Larry's place to hear what *he* thought. He was calm and unruffled.

"Nothing serious," he said. "She just got off to a bad start—stumbled and never regained her balance. It happens to prizefighters sometimes. Damn! I wish I could talk to Star."

"Why don't you?" asked Gene, coolly.

Larry smiled. "Because God won't let me."

"I think you should talk to her and to anyone else you think. And it won't surprise me one damn bit if that's what all of them want at this moment."

"Why?"

"They're terrified. Stunned. I know *I* am. Who knows *what* to do?"

"I'll talk to Clay. I think I can convey a lot through him."

"You already have, Larry. But it's different now. We're in a crisis —all of us. Sure, you can tell Clay and Clay can tell her—but I doubt She'll be able to listen. She's thrown. That audience *hated* her tonight—not right from the start, mind you. From the start, they just

· 483 ·

disliked her intensely. By the end of the evening, they hated her. Why?"

"Two reasons," said Larry. "To begin with, they were a benefit—traditionally unresponsive. She's accustomed to everything in Scene One going like wildfire, and when it didn't, She made the inexperienced player's classic error—She started pressing. Then the harder She pressed, the less they responded. That kind of effort has the effect of patronizing them—treating them like children or unintelligent adults."

"I noticed that," I said. "I couldn't figure out what She was doing —trying to do."

"It's contagious," said Larry. "So pretty soon, She had the whole company overdoing and working too hard, and everything started falling out of the window—all the charm and humor and warmth. It became a vulgar effortful slam-bang enervating evening. Someone once described the theatre as a place you go in depressed, and come out exhausted. Well, that was last night."

"Will Clay know all this?" asked Gene.

"I'll tell him."

"Idea," said Gene. "Let's go back to my place. They must be calling every three minutes. Come on. We can get some food and deal with it there. They probably think I'm on my way back to Chicago, and who could blame me?"

Why were we all so merry in the taxi on the way to the Algonquin? Did we sense that because of the unforeseen crisis, Larry would have to be put back in charge? Did we believe his analysis? Was it—at last —justice? Whatever, we were in a rollicking mood.

Gene was right. In his box at the Algonquin desk—a dozen or more messages. Call Mr. Clune. Mr. Balaban called. Clay. Clay. Call Mr. Clune. Hy. Call Mr. Clune, urgent. And so on.

Gene ignored them all and phoned Star. He got Val. "Now look, Val," he said, "we don't have time for a lot of feckless nonsense. Just put her on and don't give me a hard time. We're *all* in trouble. She more than the rest of us. After all, She's got to stand up there in front of the world and take it—the rest of us are safe in the dark. We can walk out or go home even—but not her. She's up there, so put her on before I hang up." A long wait. "Hello, Pussy. I'm sorry you had such a rough night, but all is not lost if you'll listen to me and— Look, dear, crying is not going to help. Cry next week after you've opened. Right now, I'll tell you what to do—get into a cab and come over here. I'd like to say 'alone,' but I know that's impossible, so bring him, but tell him to keep quiet—the minute *he* starts, our meeting is over. . . . All right. Algonquin. Twelve-oh-seven, eight. Bring food. We'll be here awhile, and I know there's nothing here *you'll* eat. Hurry up."

Larry was amazed.

"Well, I'll be goddamned," he said.

"*I* won't," said Gene. "I've been around more people up against the wall than you have—they share a single characteristic: helplessness. If you're going down for the third time, you don't give a damn *who* drags you out of the water. I've had guys who'd threatened to kill me appeal for help when the heat became intense. Shouldn't we get Clay, too?"

"You bet," said Larry.

Clay sent for.

We ate. Club sandwiches and red wine.

"Let's stay off the hard stuff for a couple of hours," Gene had suggested. "Later—if there *is* a later—we'll go to the Brasserie and drink properly, with real food."

"Have you got a script?" Larry asked.

"No," said Gene, "but I have seventeen."

"I've got mine," I said, and gave it to Larry, who studied it until Clay arrived.

"That audience!" he said, as he came in.

"They were matched by the company," said Larry. "Let's not waste time arguing about did the audience poison the players or the players the audience. We can't rehearse the audience—but we *can* do something about the company."

"Right," said Clay. "I think I lost eleven pounds tonight."

Star arrived. Val carried her little picnic basket. They were both flummoxed by Larry's presence.

"What're *you* doing here?" asked Val.

Gene to Star: "Didn't I tell you to tell him to hold his tongue?"

"What *is* this shit?" Val yelled. "I can't ask a simple question?"

"No, you can't," yelled Gene, outshouting him. "Now sit down and shut up and feed your baby."

Star gave Val a look. He sat down and shut up. It was awful, seeing a grown man humiliated and humbled, but I could whip up no compassion for him. I could remember only too well this sweating, grunting animal jumping on me and tearing my clothes.

Star did not look well. She never seems very delectable with her makeup off—but tonight her face was blotched and the area around her eyes red and puffed.

"Is it all right if *I* ask?" asked Star.

"Ask what?"

"What's *he* doing here? Larry Gabel?"

A silence, broken by Clay.

"I'll tell you. Under the circumstances, no reason you shouldn't know. Larry Gabel has been directing you, directing the show, for the past two and a half weeks."

Star couldn't get her mouth closed. Val couldn't get his open. It was clear he wanted to speak, but he did not dare.

"What happened tonight?" asked Star. "Or what didn't happen? Do you think you know? What a night! A *nightmare.*"

"Sit down, love." said Gene. "Relax. Give her some food, Val."

Val spent the next ten minutes serving Star her food out of the picnic basket. Plastic boxes and bottles and containers of various shapes and sizes. Odd-colored liquids and curious mélanges of chopped vegetables and nuts and fruits and mushrooms and bits of matzo. Star ate and drank and listened.

"It happens," said Larry. "Very often on a move from one theatre to another or from one city to another. Some curious change in a whole variety of imponderables. The sound, the lights, the shape of the theatre."

"No, no," She said. "This time it was the audience. They hated it. They hated me."

"Wrong," said Larry. "It didn't go as well as it's gone, but that's because you didn't play it as well."

"I certainly did."

"Missy, listen," said Larry. "This is no time for defiance. I don't *have* to do this. You may have *thought* you played it as always—but you're not in a position to know. I am. I saw it from the front. Now, let's start with a fact. This performance didn't go. Got that? This performance didn't go. And that's all it means—nothing more, nothing less. It doesn't mean that the show died or got sick. It doesn't mean that your superb talent deserted you overnight. It just means that this performance didn't go. And that's all."

"O.K., but why? *Why?*"

"Patience, baby, patience. Now look, I'm not God and I'm not infallible, and I may be wrong, but I *think* I know, and if you'll bear with me and listen and take in and digest it—maybe we'll make some progress. René Clair once said he had a theory and could prove it: The theory is that no one listens to anyone. I hope we can change that here tonight."

"I'm listening," She said.

"Fine. Now, look. There's an *enormous* difference between a Vegas performance and a performance of this show."

"I know that. So what else is new?"

Larry rose. "You're hardly in a position to be hostile, dear. And if you continue—you can take your trade elsewhere. You're like someone drowning, and beating off someone trying to save them."

"Drowning," She yelled. "Me?"

"Damn right! You *flopped* tonight—so the first thing to do is face that fact and see if you can keep from flopping again tomorrow night."

"What if I don't go on tomorrow night?"

"That's up to you—but what'll *that* prove?"

"Go ahead. What?"

"You sometimes make a basic mistake. You think the audience loves you for yourself—when the fact is that they only love you for your talent."

"Did you hear that?" asked Gene.

"Sure," She said. "I'm not deaf."

"Did you understand it?"

"Of course. What's to understand?"

"One more question. Do you believe it?"

She looked confused and troubled, then said, "I don't know. All I know is I work my ass off every night."

Larry. "No one doubts that, honey. Believe me. But effort isn't what pays off. What was wrong tonight was that there was too much you and not enough Nora. In fact, as long as we're playing the truth game, let's say it out: it was *all* you—so the scenes made no sense and there was no story to follow, no character to get involved with, no emotion, no suspense—just one number after another, each one noisier and more demanding."

"So what should I do?"

"Be Nora!" Larry yelled. "Sing like Nora, think like her, don't think of yourself or of scoring or making a hit—the hell with all that. Trust the show and the story—you had it going great toward the end there in Washington."

She began to cry again, but spoke through her tears. "I did that tonight—be Nora—and it was going for nothing. Jesus! I could feel the flop sweat oozing out all over me, so—"

"So you threw the show into the ashcan and gave 'em the ol' soft shoe."

"I what?"

"You fell back on what you thought was sure-fire—hell, it always has been. All your vocal tricks and personality traits and gimmicks and schtick—they didn't work because they didn't fit! Sweetie, listen, I feel for you—I understand you, I admire you—all this in spite of the fact that you've treated me disgracefully. But that doesn't matter now. I don't matter. You don't matter. The only thing that matters is the show. You can do it! You can do it brilliantly—but only by playing the part, not by trying to sell your dear little adorable self. The most dangerous disease an actress can contract is 'Please-love-me-itis.' It kills more actresses than alcohol. Play your part, and if the part's any good, you'll be any good. If the part's great—like this one is—*you'll* be great. The show is there; all you've got to do is *play* it. You didn't play it tonight, that's all that happened."

She had finished her food. Val came over to her to get the basket. As he did so, he said softly, "He's right. One hundred percent."

She smiled sweetly at him and said, "Fuck off!"

"Don't tell me fuck off just because I tell you he's right."

"What do *you* know about it, you pisshead? You came back and told me how *great* everything was."

"Because I wanted to cheer you up. I knew it was E-G-G!"

"Go home, Val."

"I'll go home," he said, "when I'm goddam good and ready!"

"You want to know something, Val? You're goddam good and ready right *now!* Now fuck off before I lose my temper!"

They exchanged a high-voltage look that lasted for a full minute. Val started out.

"And take the basket!" She screamed.

Moving like an automaton, Val returned, picked up the basket, and left.

"So," She said. "Less me and more Nora. And then what?"

"That should do it," said Larry.

"I can't believe it," She said. "I'll do it—I'll try—but I can't believe that's the whole thing."

"It isn't."

"What about everybody else? Christ, that creepy Calvin. What happened to *him*? He was so campy, he made me feel like a man or a dyke. He was—you know what he was?—*cute!*"

"He wasn't at his best, I'll agree to that," said Gene.

"Star, dear, listen," said Larry. "A show is a game of Follow-the-Leader. *You* set the tone, *you* set the style—when you're on the ball and have your character and your precision—the rest of the company follows and falls into place. But when it gets to be a contest as to who's going to make the biggest score—who's going to steal the show—it usually turns out there's nothing to steal."

"What can I tell you?" She said. "I'll try. Is there going to be a rehearsal, Clay?"

"I would advise against it," said Larry. "A day of rest would do you all more good."

"Fine," said Star.

"And if you like," said Larry to Star, "I'll come over to your place and we can talk some more, maybe a few specifics, not many, but mostly about Nora Bayes and her life—parts of it that aren't in the show, but ought to be in you. Gene, could you join us?"

"Sure, Larry," said Gene.

Why did his swift agreement make me so happy? It meant that I would lose him for the whole day—one of the last of our days. Yet I was excited and delighted at the planned session because I had faith that it would be good for the show, and all at once I realize how involved I am with its life and with its troubles.

· LV ·

Larry and Gene did indeed spend the whole afternoon with Star, and Gene reported to me that She had turned, overnight, into a doll baby. She listened, She repeated after Larry, She got up and performed all around the room. Gene said one could see her confidence returning like a blood transfusion.

"And what's more important than confidence?" he asked. "In any endeavor? Do you know why Adlai Stevenson lost both times? Because he *knew* he was going to—or *thought* he was going to, which amounts to the same thing. Athletes tell me that unless they are *convinced* they are going to clear the bar or make the basket or hit the homer—they don't do it. She's good because She *knows* She's good—when She gets scared and tentative, She's *gone.* In any field —I suppose in the theatre more than in any other place—a positive wrong is better than a negative right."

"How right you are," said Larry. "Wonderful actress I worked with once—Ruth Chatterton. I was the second assistant stage manager, and there was a word in her part—'scenario'—and from the first reading, she pronounced it 'shenario.' It was so positive, so confident, so convincingly correct, that no one questioned it, and the result was that the rest of the company began saying it that way. So did I, until about a year later, a brilliant girl I had—a poet—said to me, 'Why are you saying that word in such an outré fashion?' And we looked it up in twelve different dictionaries, and of course, there *is* no such pronunciation. That Ruth Chatterton!"

While Gene and Larry were with Star, I was at the session at the theatre. What a difference! Ivan was blasting the lights, Hy scream-ing about the sound system, Art blaming everyone, including the ushers. And the ideas for improvement! Jenny blamed it all on a lack of chorus precision. Clay thought the show had been rushed—mak-ing too much of it incoherent.

"Not my department, actually," said Alicia. "But at this point, I suppose it's fair game for each of us to say. And, may I say, I do think you're quite wrong, Clay. My inner clock told me that the perform-ance was dilatory in the extreme."

"Oh, shit," said Art to himself.

Alicia went on. "I mean to say, it was *leaden*—loud but leaden."

"Loud is right," said Hy. "Every note sounded like the same note."

"Benefit audience," said Fred, feeling the need to say something.

"Tonight is, too," said Art, in misery. "So what can we do about *that?*"

"It's all in Scene One," said Jenny. "If that kicks off, the show kicks off. Sets the tone, the style—gets the audience with us. Give me a rehearsal of Scene One, and I'll show you!"

"Get her a rehearsal of Scene One," said Art.

"I can't," said Clay. "The company has no call."

"*Make* a call, God damn it. Get 'em together here, those lazy bastards."

"Try, Stu," said Clay, resigned.

Two hours later, the staff had managed to round up everyone in Scene One—with the exception of Star and one girl. Patti, who is now Star's standby, went in for Nora, and the swing girl went in for the missing one. Jenny bounced around, adjusting an arm here and a leg there, showing the girls how to sit and how to rise. In an hour, she had covered the first four minutes of the scene.

I reported all this to Larry and Gene during dinner at Gallagher's.

Larry laughed. "Lord, isn't it amazing how nothing changes? It all repeats itself—the whole life process. What you just told us? Long ago, Gershwin had the most enormous success with a show called *Of Thee I Sing*. An out-and-out smash. He and Ira, Morrie Ryskind, George S. Kaufman—incredible. But even these masters made a mistake. They did a sequel, *Let 'Em Eat Cake*—and it didn't go. Notices mixed. A society lady at a dinner party once asked, 'Mr.

Kaufman, when you theatre people say "mixed notices"—what does that mean, precisely?' 'It means,' said Kaufman, 'good and lousy!' So, *Let 'Em Eat Cake*. Business poor, and got worse, and after a few weeks, the producer, Sam Harris, decided to close the show. When George Gershwin heard the news, he was furious, put an overcoat on over his pajamas, and rushed down to Harris's office.

" 'You *can't* close this show!' he yelled.

" 'George,' said Harris, 'we're doing no business. We're losing money every week.'

" 'But how can that be?' cried Gershwin. He was in pain.

" 'It can be, George, because it costs more to run the show than we're taking in, so when more goes out than comes in, that's how we lose money every week.'

"So Gershwin said, 'Let me ask you something, Sam. Isn't this book better than *Of Thee I Sing*?'

" 'In my opinion, yes.'

" 'And isn't the score better?'

" 'Yes.'

" 'And the production?'

" 'Absolutely.'

" 'Then damn it all,' said Gershwin, 'how can you close this great show?'

"Harris sighed. What could he say. 'What do you want me to do, George?'

" 'Don't close for two weeks. Give it a chance. I'll pay the losses. There are a few things wrong. I'll fix them and we'll catch on and run two years. Just give me that chance. You owe it to me.'

"So Harris said, 'All right, George. Except one thing. You don't pay the losses. I do.'

" 'Fine,' said Gershwin.

"Well, the next morning, there was a full dress rehearsal—at The Imperial—God! Right where we're suffering now. A full orchestra, scenery, lights, costumes. It must've cost a fortune.

"George Kaufman had heard about this plan. He called Morrie Ryskind, and together they went to the theatre, sneaked in, and went up to the balcony to watch.

"And the first thing Gershwin did was rehearse the orchestra for an hour and fifteen minutes on the overture. Then the opening number. 'All right, girls—listen. When you sing "Mine! Love is mine!" the word is one long syllable—not two, and not one short syllable—"Miiine!" Got it? All right, let's hear it. One! Two!' The girls sang. 'No! No no no! Here. One at a time. You.' The girl on the end sang the word. 'Fine. Next.' And so on. Sixteen girls. Finally, all together. 'Great!' he yelled—'You've got it—now keep it! Once more, but first—What's your name, honey?' 'Betty.' 'And yours? No, not you —you.' 'Frances.' 'O.K., Frances and Betty change places. Good. And what's your name? No, the blond girl.' 'Mimi.' 'And you?' 'Dolores.' 'Right. Mimi and Dolores change places. Much better. Now. From the beginning—and remember—"Mine!" One long syllable, not two and not one short. One! Two!' At this point, up in the balcony, Kaufman leaned over to Ryskind and said, 'Y'know? I don't think that's what's wrong with this show!' "

Gene and I laughed. Larry had brought that old scene to life.

We finished dinner. I felt fine, the way I usually do after one of those superlative steaks. Gene and Larry seemed up, too. And confident.

We walked down Eighth Avenue to the theatre. A big, noisy crowd. Much hugging and kissing and waving and shouting across the auditorium. A benefit audience. But happy and enthusiastic and excitedly anticipatory.

Larry said, "I guess they haven't heard about last night, huh?"

"I don't know," said Gene. "They look to me like the same people who were *here* last night!"

When the house lights began to dim, I suddenly had to go and pee. I dashed down, did, and returned just as the overture was beginning. I was nervous and light-headed. What the hell did *I* have to be nervous about? The overture had a new, crackling, sparkling sound. Some adjustments had been made. The overture got a big hand. It had gotten nothing last night. We all looked at each other happily.

Well. Now.

The early part went extremely well, and as Gene and Larry and I stood there at the back of the house, spirits were high. We smiled a lot and there was a good deal of rib-poking and even a little mutual backslapping. When "Nightfall" just about stopped the show, which was no more than twenty minutes old, Larry pantomimed, "Drink?" and the three of us went over to The Grotto to toast the remarkable change in our fortunes and the health of our splendid enterprise across the street.

"The only worry now," said Larry, "is holding on to this excellent temperature and pace."

"Not a worry in the world," said Gene. "She's on the right track now. They love her, and She knows it. So She loves them."

"Christ!" said Larry. "We're in the love business."

"Sure we are," said Gene. "That's what the theatre is—should be —a temple of love—not for Gods and idols—but for the human race."

"Let's go back," I said. "This conversation's making me horny as hell!"

"Do it again," said Gene to the bartender. "But make it Glenlivet this time."

"You got a hit, huh?" said the bartender.

"Bet your ass," said Gene.

"How's about two for next Saturday's matinee?"

"Do you serve free drinks in here?" asked Larry, bristling.

"Don't get hot," said the bartender. "I just asked."

He served the drinks and went off.

"Here's to no passes," said Larry. We clicked glasses and drank. "Why is it people think we get free tickets? They think 'house seats' mean free seats. Don't they know that someone has to pay for every ticket? Even Art. Even me. Press seats are free, and that's all."

"Jesus!" said Gene.

"What?"

"*I* thought 'house seats' meant free!"

Why this made us all laugh so hard, I can't imagine, other than the fact that we were so euphoric and that Gene was fast becoming a member of the theatre family—that tight-knit, highly charged, competitive yet admiring and appreciative, generally spirited community.

(I had never been aware of all this until Clay had taken me to a Sunday-night Actor's Fund benefit of *Annie.* The audience was made up mainly of all the other companies playing on Broadway. Never have I seen or heard such a reaction—screaming and yelling, stamping and whistling—entrances and exits applauded wildly. It was hard to tell who was having a better time—the company on the stage or the companies in the auditorium.

Out on the sidewalk during the intermission, I said to Clay, "It's a revelation! A mind-blower! Do you understand it?"

"Of course. It always happens."

"But look, I've seen this show before, and it's swell, certainly, and went well—great, even—but not like *this!* And they're all showfolk —experts—I should've thought they'd be harder to please."

"Oh, no. Wrong. Actors are the best audience, as a rule. The good ones can play anything—they can even play the part of an audience, and they love it. They do what an audience is *supposed* to do—laugh, cry, be thrilled, scared, whatever. Comics are the best laughers. Tragedians, the best criers."

"I'm getting to love them all," I said.

"When I was on *Hello, Dolly!,*" he said, "Thornton Wilder used to come around from time to time. The friendliest man in the world, he was. Loved to stay up late and pub-crawl with the players. Once, Pearl Bailey or someone brought along a dog and made a great fuss over it and talked to it and announced to us all that no one loved her as much as that little dog, and that's why she loved that little dog. And it made Mr. Wilder angry. I can remember him sitting in that little Algonquin bar and saying—not loudly, but firmly—'Now listen! That dog does *not* love you! Dogs don't love people! Dogs love other dogs!' It made *her* so mad that she took her dog and went home. When she'd gone, Mr. Wilder said to the rest of us, 'Dogs love other dogs! Dogs do not love people. . . .' Well, that's more or less what you've got here tonight. Actors love other actors. They're a breed, a race, a nationality.")

"Lordy, what a world," Gene was saying. "How do you people survive it year after year?"

"Some of us don't," said Larry.

"I always thought the newspaper business was hard—but it's a snap compared to this. This isn't only hard—this is almost *impossible!*"

"True, Gene. But for the few times in a lifetime when it all comes right—it's worth it."

"Well, this certainly begins to look like one of those times, doesn't it?"

"Fin dine moil tsu Gott's eyren," said Larry.

"Translation, please," said Gene. "My Yiddish is a bit sketchy."

"From your mouth to God's ears," said Larry.

"Let's drink to that. Moe," he said to the bartender, "if I give you two for the Saturday matinee, will you give us three drinks for right now?"

"Yes, sir!" said Moe.

"What a metamorphosis," I said. "Like a face-lift. Tonight and last night. Last night seems like last year. And I'm not sure I can see what's so different."

"The difference," said Gene, "is basic—life and death. There's no blood circulation in a corpse, and it doesn't sweat or sing. I remember the time Ali fought Joe Frazier, and I interviewed him on the day after his astonishing defeat. 'What happened?' I asked him. He shook his head and sighed, and said, 'Man, I just couldn't work up my sweat—you know? My coordination, my life.' Well, that's what we've got here. Last night, She couldn't work up a sweat—even though She was belting and trying and working. Tonight, She's dripping already, and it's only—what?—seven fifty-five."

"Let's go back," I said.

We got back to the theatre just as "Jump for Joy" was going on, and it was apparent at once that something had gone wrong.

The house had become restless. There was more than the usual amount of coughing. The whole audience, which had seemed painted on when we left, had turned into a shifting, undulating, wristwatch-watching, whispering mass. We had lost them! How? Why?

Star and Phil seemed to be having difficulty getting together. We saw her look at him and begin to snap her fingers (not in the routine), this was the worst possible sign; it meant She was taking over again and running—or trying to run—the show. She began to woo the audience with her familiar little trademarks—the hooked notes and the kooky phrasing. During the dance with Sammy, She winked at someone in the first row, pretended to trip and recover—it got a laugh and even a little hand, but the number was shot.

"Go back, Larry," said Gene. "For Christ's sake, go back and talk to her!"

"No, no," said Larry. "*Never* during a performance."

"Intermission?"

"I'll talk to Clay," he said.

I got Clay, who came out front and conferred with us in the darkness beneath the box.

"What happened?" asked Larry. "We thought it got off so well—we were out celebrating."

"She blew one laugh," said Clay, "the goldfish line—inaudible—

and panicked. Started punching everything and raising hell on and off—and well, you can see, a shambles. What can I do?"

"Tell her we're watching. Tell her to trust the show and play it. Tell her to be Nora. Tell her if She doesn't, I'll walk down the aisle and stop the show and offer the audience their money back."

"Wait a second, Larry," said Gene. "You sure?"

"God Almighty," said Larry. "We've tried everything else! Maybe rough stuff'll work. Maybe I *will* stop the show and make a speech to the audience. What the hell? Why not? What have *I* got to lose?"

The Second Act came on and proved to be as unsettling an experience as I can remember. She did not one thing wrong, but not one thing right, either. She went through the motions—said each line, sang each song, but it simply was not there. Fortunately for the evening, the rest of the company did not pick up on this dead-ass note and played, under the circumstances, quite well.

But it was hard to watch, and toward the end of the act, we drifted out to the lobby and stood silently. What was there to say?

Art appeared, wild-eyed and incensed.

"You seen it? You been in there? She's dumping on a million dollars —*my* million dollars. That son-of-a-bitch, I'll *kill* her."

Gene. "Easy, Art. She's not doing it on purpose."

"What do I care purpose or not purpose? She's doing it! I mean, She's *not* doing it! God damn amateur shit-ass!" He walked over to Larry, who was standing at the door, looking out onto 45th Street, which all at once, seemed to be the dreariest street in all the world. He touched Larry's arm. "Larry?"

Larry, without looking at him. "Yes?"

"Can you help me? Will you?"

"I don't know," said Larry. "I don't know if I can. Fact is, I'm pretty damned discouraged myself."

"If you can't, who can?"

"I don't know. Maybe nobody."

"I'll give you whatever you want. Name it."

Larry turned to him now and fixed him with a long look. "Don't try to make a hooker out of me, Art. You've damaged me enough as it is. You can't give me anything I want—because what I want is for this show to be a success. Nothing more, nothing less."

"I can so give you that!"

"How?"

"I can put you in charge, and do whatever you want."

"You won't do that."

"You want it in writing?"

"What if it meant replacing Star?"

Art swayed slightly and touched the wall for support.

"We open day after tomorrow! You talking postpone?"

"No. I'm talking going with her standby—Patti—if necessary."

"No, *no!*" cried Art, hysterically. "We can't. I couldn't."

"There you are, then," said Larry, and began to walk back into the theatre through the long, long lobby. Art ran after him.

"Wait!" he called.

We all assembled, mid-lobby.

"Jesus Christ," said Art, "I wish I was dead, I swear to God!"

"You didn't quite understand me, Art. I'd *hate* to see this show without that nemesis of ours—"

"Then what *did* you mean?"

"I meant I have to have the power of last resort. This would be a killer—for her not to open. She could claim sick, sure, but we could claim not. We've got to put it to her straight: Play or else. But—and it's a big but—if She decides to else we've got to be prepared. In other words, I won't be party to a bluff. Any threat I make, any ultimatum I lay down—I'm going to back up. My reputation—such as it is, thanks to you—is at stake."

"Take a chance, Art," said Gene. "She'll never walk."

"What if She does?" asked Art, despondently. "What happens to the million and a half advance? I can see them now lined up from here to Ninth Avenue—getting their money back."

"Not if the show gets over," said Gene.

"But if it *doesn't!* If it *doesn't!* With her, at least we got the advance, no matter what!"

"All right, Art," said Larry. "It's up to you. Just don't send me into battle with the odds against me."

"Anyway, I can't," said Art. "Not right now. Tomorrow, maybe? I got the record boys I have to talk to, and Cindy, and the lawyers."

"No good, Art," said Larry. "I'm sorry to press, but if I'm going to operate, it has to be now—in fifteen minutes."

"Fifteen!"

"We've got to hold the company—yes. Work tonight, work in the morning, maybe all day—we've got tomorrow's show and one more, and that's it before the balloon goes up."

"Or down," said Art.

"Well?" asked Gene.

"Go ahead," said Art, defeated. "Do what you have to do. I'll start phoning. That's what *I* have to do."

His retreating form was an etching of boneless misery.

Larry, conversely, looked like a man who had been given a shot of adrenalin.

He spoke to me. "Tell Clay company onstage right after. Costumes and makeup off. Clear stage. Call Gaiety. A hundred sandwiches, assorted, as soon as possible. Danish. Ice cream. Beer. Gene'll help you."

"Sure," said Gene.

"Tell Clay make it clear it's going to be a long session. No one is excused. Also, the call tomorrow will be twelve hours from whenever we finish tonight. And get *me* some coffee *right now.*"

He went back into the theatre.

"You go tell Clay," said Gene. "I'll do the food. But I'd better split it up, don't you think? Three or four delis? Who can do a hundred on the spot?"

"Whatever you say, Gene. It may surprise you to know I've never had an assignment like this before."

"Nor I, honey lamb, nor I!"

I went backstage and gave Clay the messages. The show was still on and he could not leave his spot. In between cues, he said, "O.K. Post it on the board. Big sign. Tell Wilbur on the door not to let anyone leave. They sneak out sometimes and claim they didn't get the call. Xerox it, too—and paste one on every dressing-room door. Tell the dance captain and the Equity deputy. Hurry up!"

I got going at once. Gene came in.

"Did it all on the phone," he said. "What's to do here?"

"Paste one of these on each dressing-room door. Here's the tape."

"Got it."

He went off, while I sought out Marti, the new dance captain, and Gracie, the deputy.

The word began to get around.

"What's happening, beauty?" asked Aki. "Sounds like an all-nighter to me. Who's comin' in? Gower Champion?"

"Yes," I said. "Also Hal Prince and George Balanchine and Elia Kazan and George Abbott and Billy Carter."

"That oughta do it," he said.

The minute the curtain fell on the final call, Clay was on the public-address system, announcing the assembly.

Rumors shot through the company, ranging from "postponing" through "closing" to "new director."

By 10:50, everyone had made it back to the stage—with the expected exception of Star. Perhaps She was waiting for a special invitation, once the purpose of the gathering had been made clear. At 10:55, Larry came down the aisle. As soon as the company saw him, recognized him, they burst into applause. Larry jumped up on the stage. The company went wild. The applause turned into cheers and whistling and stomping. An ovation. A riot.

Larry took it without a shred of false modesty. He just stood there, waiting for it to end. When it did, he said, "Thank you, all. As you can see, I'm back. Mr. Clune is not pleased with the way things are going, and I don't suppose you are either. I know *I'm* not. Well, let's face it. No one is." He looked around. "Where's our Nora?" he asked.

"Dressing room," said Clay.

"Ask her to join us, won't you?"

Clay went off. Larry waited. The company whispered among themselves, or conversed quietly. The atmosphere was understandably tense.

Clay returned with Val.

"She wants to see you in her dressing room," said Val.

"There isn't time," said Larry. "Her whole company's waiting for her."

"One minute," said Val.

"One minute?"

"One."

Larry to the company. "Please excuse me, ladies and gentlemen. I'll be with you in one minute."

He looked at his watch and went off with Val. I tried to resist the impulse to follow them, and failed. I followed them into her room as though I had been invited.

"What's going on?" asked Star. And before Larry could reply, added, "I mean, what the *fuck's* going on?"

"Art Clune has asked me to take over and get the show ready to open. It begins with a company meeting. Right now."

"For how long?"

"For as long as it takes."

"I just played a show, for Christ's sake!"

"I know. And not very well. I can't believe your listless performance in Act Two tired you out."

"Look, you goddam son-of-a-bitch," She said, "something crazy's happening. I don't know what, but I warn you—" She stopped.

"You warn me *what?*"

"You wouldn't *dare* come on so strong if there wasn't some goddam plot, some scheme that—What the hell do you want?"

"I want you out on the stage right now, and before you refuse to rehearse, I advise you to read your contract or have someone read it for you." He looked at his watch, then at Val. "That's one minute," he said, and walked out.

"Sorry," he said to the company. "To begin at the beginning, I can't tell you how sorry I am that—after all your diligent work for the past twenty-one weeks—you should've been subjected to the past two rocky nights. A common thing happened. You let the audience take charge of our show—instead of you taking charge of the audience. What's more—"

At this point, Star came out onto the stage, dressed for the street. Beside her was Val; just behind her, Alan Balaban (no relation), her business manager; Bernard Foley, her attorney. Bringing up the rear, Bonnie, her theatre maid; Ronnie, her hairdresser; and Bud Westman, her personal press agent. The entrance of Star and her entourage was so spectacular that the company first laughed, then applauded. This reaction so confused Star that She said nothing. She and her team found chairs at some distance from the rest of us. They seemed to be visitors—or a distant colony.

Larry continued. "What's more, you all seem to have lost confidence in yourselves and in the show. Well, your reasons for the former are your own business, but I can assure you that there is no cause for the latter. For weeks, this show—having found itself after a tortuous and torturous search—played beautifully and gave audiences pleasure. Now, for a variety of reasons—the Big Apple, new theatre, preopening nerves, unresponsive audiences—you've been thrown. Have any of you ever been to the second night of a show that got raves? Hands, please. Well, have you noticed how the company plays it like a hit, they know they're a hit, they've been told they're a hit—they're convinced! And what about the second night of a show that's been bombed? Do you notice what's happened to *that* company? They're beaten, defeated. Now look here—you people haven't been rapped, not yet. In fact, you've been highly praised. You've played this show—*this same show*—with enormous success. And you will again, as soon as you get your collective mind on one thing, and that is: tell the *story*—play your *parts,* not yourselves—mean what you say when you say it." He moved a step toward Star. "Most of it depends on you, dear. Do you remember—it seems a long time ago —we were all on this stage, sitting around like this, and I told the company what I thought of you, how tremendous you were and how we were counting on you to carry this whole show on those beautiful little shoulders? Do you?"

"Yes," She said, and began to cry softly.

"You're rattled," said Larry. "And fatigued. I won't keep you long, just long enough to—"

Star pitched forward out of her chair and lay stiff on the floor in a dead faint. Larry was at her side in an instant. Val and Alan moved toward her.

"Get away!" Larry yelled. "Stay away! I'll do this."

Clay came running in with a first-aid kit. He handed Larry two ammonia capsules. Larry broke one of them under her nose. She jerked her head away and moaned. She began to get to her feet.

"Not yet," said Larry. "Lie still."

"Don't tell *me* what to do, you show-off jerkoff. Lemme out of here."

"The girl is sick!" Val shouted to the company. "You all saw her faint."

Alan. "We're taking her to Doctors Hospital for the night."

Bud. "Please don't anyone say anything to *anyone!* It could have a very bad box-office effect."

All at once, Larry laughed out loud. "Holy Jesus!" he said. "What needs rehearsal is *your* act—not this show! If there's one thing in the world I can't abide, it's amateur acting." To Star: "And that faint, Missy, was a mess. One of the phoniest I've ever seen!"

She took a step toward him, slapped him a hard crack!—and stalked off, followed by her gang in disarray.

At this point, the food began to arrive, adding to the confusion, and a few minutes later, Art, with an armful of those inevitable *presents!*

"Have a bite, people," said Larry. "We'll reassemble in a short while."

Art came over to Larry, handed him a small long box, and said, "Welcome home, Larry."

"Thank you."

"What's going on? Did She leave, or what?"

"You missed a great show," said Larry. "Fake fainting and everything."

"What's their game?"

"Protection. In case She wants to threaten to skip a show or two —She's protected."

"Oh, my God!"

"So we don't have to worry anymore about do we maybe replace her. She may replace herself."

"Oh, my God!"

"My guess is yes. My guess is She's going to punish you and stay off tomorrow night."

"Oh, my God!"

"So the practical thing to do is get Patti ready."

A mini-conference in Star's dressing room. Patti, Larry, Clay, and Maurice. Could Patti wear these clothes? Fortunately, yes. Wigs, with a little adjustment. Shoes, no—but she can wear her own show shoes.

Back to the stage. The company, for the most part, had finished with the too-much food.

"All right, now," Larry called out. "All together now. Anything left take home for your dogs or cats or canaries." The company applauded. "Here's the situation. Our Star is not feeling well—as you all observed. I'm sure She'll have recovered by showtime tomorrow —but just in case, we're getting Patti ready. That means a call at twelve noon tomorrow. And we'll be running Nora stuff only—from the top, each scene or number twice—so you can time your arrivals accordingly. Here she is, here's Patti." The company applauded. Patti looked as though she were sleepwalking. "Just a few more general notes and comments, and we'll dismiss, except for staff, Patti, Calvin—if you don't mind."

"Delighted," said Calvin.

"The rest of you who are concerned with Nora's material—we'll deal with tomorrow. For now, just a few things to think about tonight —in your sleep. Those of you who've worked with me before know that I'm not in the habit of deceiving myself or the company. Insofar as possible, I always try to face the facts, even when they're unpleasant. But the facts about *Shine On, Harvest Moon* are pleasant indeed. A strong, literate book—with a moving story and a powerful theme. A lovely, authentically period score—with variety and a haunting melodic line. Everything else: sets, costumes, orchestrations, choreography, lighting—plus plus plus. And a nonesuch company—*you*. What's wrong, then? Simply this: the elements haven't yet fused in this house. Why? A good question, and I wish I had a good answer, but I don't. No matter. I'm convinced that they will, that you'll *make* them. You can and you will. What I said earlier, about playing the show, and in addition— Listen, the missing ingredient is rhythm. R-H-Y-T-H-M. Every single one of you individually possesses that marvelous and ineffable quality—what we haven't yet achieved is a *communal* rhythm. I went out to Ivan's house in the country one weekend, and found him doing a painting of that same copper beech tree that he's done dozens of times in every season and from every angle. I said to him, 'Ivan, tell me—what's so fascinating about that particular tree?' And he said, 'You don't see it? That tree has rhythm!' I confess I didn't know what he meant at the time, but later, it occurred to me. There are many, many words for rhythm—for the idea of rhythm. Think of some between now and noon tomorrow— write them down. Here, let me start you off. Rhythm, form, balance, tempo, equilibrium, beat, cadence, rhyme, meter, poetry, form, swing, pace, momentum, timing, shape, structure, routine, organization, symmetry, harmony, accord, control, arrangement, proportion, agreement, equality, regularity, precision—"

"Good God!" said Gene.

And the company—for some reason—applauded.

"I'm sure you can think of many others."

The company laughed.

"But it's the *idea* that matters. When this show finds and hits its own rhythm, stays with it—is carried along by it—the audience will be, too. When I was with *Hello, Dolly!*, I used to go out front regularly to check the show, and often, I'd see Irving Berlin standing at the back of the house. He used to drop in from time to time—always at eight-fifty, when the 'Hello, Dolly!' number went on. One night he turned to me in the middle of it and said, 'My God! How did they ever find that rhythm?' Think of it—here was one of the incomparable masters of the popular song—still involved with the magical question. Well, then, that's the bedtime story. Clay—everyone dismissed, except as previously discussed. Thank you all. Get some sleep. Leave the carousing for next week, right?"

Clay. "Scene One, please. From Nora's entrance!"

The company has begun to disperse. Patti takes her position onstage, ready to make her entrance. Larry, Gene, Art, and I go out front through the pass door. As we take our seats in the fifth row, we notice something strange. Very few of the players have left. All the girls in the first scene with Nora are on.

"I guess they didn't understand, huh?" I say. "Aren't they dismissed?"

"They understood all right," says Larry. He turns to me. Tears have welled up in his eyes. "Actors!" he says. "Actors and actresses!"

The scene begins. Patti seems a bit subdued, but there is no question that she has mastered the material. She knows every word, every note, every move.

Art sits slumped across the aisle from us, completely dejected.

Phil is at his place on the podium, conducting Buzz at the piano as though he were the full orchestra.

When Patti finishes "Nightfall" with Calvin, he embraces her, kisses her, and the company applauds from both wings. We join in. Not Art.

Skip to Scene Two. Patti has gained confidence and is warming up. (Working up a sweat?) At the end of Scene Two, Larry goes down to the pit and says to Patti: "Good, sweetie. Real good. Now enjoy yourself more. Have a good time. Come on. You're a star!"

Jump to where Nora comes in in Scene Three. Larry walks up the aisle to the back of the house. We follow him. Art joins us.

"She's no star," he says glumly.

"Who said she was?" asks Larry.

"*You* did. Just now. I heard you."

"I said it to *her*, Art. Not to the world. She needs the confidence. We've got to treat her like a star if we want her to behave and perform like one."

"One thing, sure," says Art, "I don't want to be around here if somebody's going to go out and announce the bad news. I can take only so much. I can see a stampede for the refunds now."

"Now, now, Art. Take it easy. There are ways and ways. Techniques. I'll show you how to do it when the time comes."

Art is startled. "What do you mean 'when'? You mean 'if,' don't you?"

"Who knows?"

Art turns to Gene, pleadingly. "What do you think, Gene? Is She gonna blow it?"

"I wish I knew."

"I know you don't *know*, for Chrissake! I'm askin' you what you *think!*"

"I'm new to all this, remember? I've had no experience with people like Star and Val and her Brains Trust. I can't get a handle on it."

"I think She's bluffing," said Larry.

"But if they put her in the hospital, like they said?"

"Not so easy," said Larry. "According to Equity—you'd have a right to have *our* doctor examine her."

"I would?"

"Of course."

"But what if they *made* her sick? Gave her something. I wouldn't put it past those shits!"

"Come on, Art. If *you* owned the Golden Goose—would you take a chance on killing it? Or even damaging it?"

"So what's going to happen?"

"My best guess," said Larry, "is that She may stay off tomorrow night—"

"Oh, my God!" said Art. "What makes you think?"

"First, it's only a preview—so what? Second—and this is the big one—She would like to prove to you that you've got no show without her."

"We *haven't!*"

"I'm not so sure. Show-business history is full of stories of losing a star and gaining a show."

"Not this one!" cried Art. "I'm sure not! I wouldn't've *done* it without her."

"So what it comes down to," said Gene, thoughtfully, "is this: if She goes on tomorrow night, well and good—"

Larry. "*If* She plays the show."

"Right. If She *doesn't* go on—it's in the balance. If it looks like a show without her—She has to come back and behave. If it falls off the stage and proves to be a nothing without her, She's got us by the balls."

"Exactly," said Larry. "And that adds up to quite a few balls. So I better go back and see what's doing with Patti—just in case."

"I can't look at it," said Art. "I can't face it. She's *got* to go on, that cunt. I bet a million bucks on her. How can She do this to me? Why? What'd I ever do to her except put a great show around her?"

"Listen, Art," said Larry, heatedly. "Those are questions you should be asking *her,* not us."

"God damn right," said Art. "And that's what I'm going to do. Right now! You go ahead and do what you think you have to do—I'm going to see that She gets her dumb ass up on that stage tomorrow night!"

"Good luck," said Larry.

"I don't need luck," said Art. "I'm a power! I'm a barracuda!" He had worked himself up into a considerable frenzy, and added, "You want to bet She goes on? I'll bet you anything! I'll give you odds!"

"No bet," said Larry. "We all *hope* She goes on. Why would I bet against it?"

"Don't underestimate me, buddy. I've still got a trick or two!"

Gene was about to say something, but Art was gone.

We went back into the theatre and stayed there with Patti and some of the company until 2:15 A.M.

Then Gene took us all to The Brasserie. It turned out to be a rather tired and somewhat worried party. But the food was good, and welcome.

· LVI ·

What was it Art said last night? "I've still got a trick or two!" Well, he could have used three.

Thank God for Larry and his experience.

The rehearsal began at noon—Patti in costume, wigs, and shoes, the rest of the company in street clothes. Sets. Lights. No orchestra, which worried Phil. He was afraid that the full sound might jar her in performance, but Art would not approve the expense of an orchestra rehearsal. Gene offered to pay for it, but Art got stubborn and intractable and hysterical. Still Gene did not give up until Patti assured him it was not important to her. All was going well, the major problem turning out to be the costume changes. Larry suspected that Star's maid, Bonnie, was not providing full cooperation, and sent her home. He substituted two dressers. But the difficulty was solved ultimately by Calvin—who had watched the changes from the beginning and was able to assist most efficiently.

"Isn't it lucky for all of you that I'm a devout voyeur?" he said. "Truth is, the most fun I've had on this show has been watching those changes night after night."

At about 1:00 P.M., Val turned up with two hampers of food, which he slowly and systematically unpacked and placed in Star's dressing-room refrigerators.

A jubilant Art came in half an hour later.

"You can stop," he said to Larry. "We're all set. She'll be in. Didn't I tell you?"

"I think I'd like to finish," said Larry. "Just to be sure."

"I'm *tellin'* you sure, you stubborn bastard. You get your jollies out of spending my money? This is costing me a fortune! Call it off!"

"Not a chance," said Larry. "And stop griping. Send me the bill."

"Don't think I won't!"

"Not the whole bill—just what it costs from now till we finish."

"I will!"

"You see, Art, I'm not sure I believe this ploy. This could be their way of getting us off-balance—and leaving us unprepared."

"Jesus Christ!" said Art. "How can you enjoy life with a mind like that?"

"I don't very much, if you want the truth. But 'Be prepared' is my motto—ever since I was an Eagle Scout."

"Yeah? Well, right now you're an Eagle Asshole! And you'll get the bill, all right."

"Fine."

"He was just here—I think he's *still* here—putting all that garbage She eats in her room."

"I know."

"How do you know? You're out here."

"Midge told me. Midge tells me *everything.*"

"So?"

"An act maybe? Like her phony faint?"

"Jesus!"

"Midge, go ask the doorman if Val usually stocks the fridge at this hour. And ask Stu—Clay—anybody who might know."

Art began to laugh as I went off.

The doorman. No, he'd never *seen* Mr. Belmonte around the theatre at this hour. Stu? No, never. Out of town? "No, not that I can recall." Clay? "Of course not." The standbys? One by one. "No." "No." "No."

I return to Larry with the information.

"Figures," he said. To Art: "Now I'll tell you what I think. They're going to keep you going until half-hour—and then not show. And *now,* if you want to make a bet, I will."

"How much?" said Art.

"The cost of this rehearsal."

"You got it! You're a witness, Midge. O.K.?"

"O.K. I hate bets and betting."

"So what's it your business?" he yelled at me. "Mind your business. *Shut up!*"

Larry looked at Art. "You know what makes you a king-sized prick, Mr. Clune? I'll tell you. You scream at Midge. At the kids. At Stu. At waiters. But not at stars or bigshots or the ones you *think* are bigshots —and you're usually wrong, by the way. You've never said 'Shut up' to me, have you?"

"No," said Art," but *you* said it to *me*— and it cost you, didn't it?"

"What it cost me, I can spare. And by the way, if my name isn't up on the house boards by six o'clock tonight—I'm leaving for Saint-Jean-Cap Ferrat."

"Where's that?"

"Where my wife is."

"What am I? A sign painter? They told me yesterday—so what can *I* do?"

"As you so often have said to me and to other members of my staff, 'That's *your* problem!' Now get away and let me do my work—"

"Don't tell me—"

"And *shut up!*" yelled Larry.

Art stormed up the aisle—clearly on his way to give someone a bad time with reference to the delay on the house boards.

At 5:30, Bonnie came in and began to get the dressing room ready for Star.

At 6:30, noise backstage. Bonnie refuses to let Patti into Star's dressing room.

"You got a dressing room, lady. Get up there in it! Way up! This here one is ourn!"

Larry takes charge.

"Go downstairs, Bonnie, and wait. As soon as your lady turns up— *if* She turns up—you can come back. I'll let you know."

"You don't push *me* around, Mr. Charlie. I got a *union!*"

"Move!" said Larry.

Bonnie pointed at Patti. "Don't you touch nothin'! Not one damn thing!"

"If you don't move," said Larry, "I'm going to touch *you!*"

"Fuck you, honky!" yelled Bonnie. "Motherfucker!"

She went off.

"Not a word of truth," said Larry, "in that accusation."

Patti went in and began to get ready, Gloria acting as her maid.

Larry and I went out onto the stage.

"I'm getting a bad feeling," I said. "Or is it a good feeling?"

"What?"

"I think She *is* going to turn up."

"Why?"

"Bonnie. She's no kind of an actress. And she really expects her. That's why she got so excited."

"Yuh," said Larry, "I thought of that, too. But on the other hand —they could have this plan and not let *Bonnie* in on it. They could be bullshitting *her* the way they are Art. It's still my guess She's going to stay off. And, by the way, Hy agrees with me. *He's* been to a few of these fires before, too. In fact, he's so sure, he's bringing Dick Zanuck and David Brown to the show tonight."

"He is?"

"Yes, he figures if it's Star—fine—so they've seen a preview. But if not—which he hopes—they'll see Patti. Hy's doing a picture for them—and there's a part."

"I'm upside down," I said. "Now I hope it *is* Patti."

Three minutes before half-hour. Stu dashes in.

"She's here!" he shouts. "Limo just drove up."

We all move to the stage door. In marches that redoubtable single file: Val Belmonte, Alan Balaban, Foley, Westman.

By the fourth man, we know what the situation is. No Star. She would never, under any circumstances, be in the vanguard. They troop onto the stage. We notice two new faces. A semicircle.

"Where's Art?" asks Val. "Get Art!"

Art is summoned. We join the group.

"This here," says Val, "is Doctor Timothy Franklin, the diagnostician. And this here is Doctor Joseph B. Wakefield, the neurologist. I'm sorry, Art, but they say She can't go on tonight. Doctors' orders. Two doctors. Here it is in writing. They both signed it. She's in Doctors Hospital right now. That's the name of it."

Art exploded. "Don't give me that horseshit! You fuckin' snake! You promised! You told me six o'clock She was going to make it! You *told* me! You promised, you dirty bastard!"

"Doctors' orders," Val repeated.

"Doctors' shit! You get her back here in thirty minutes—forty, the most—we'll hold the curtain."

"Impossible," said Dr. Franklin. "The woman is—"

"The woman! The *cunt,* you mean."

Dr. Franklin left.

"I would not advise—" began Dr. Wakefield.

"I *would!* I would advise you to watch your step, you quack! I'll report you! I'll report you to the AMA for full of shit. She's gonna be examined by two other doctors in the next ten minutes—they're right there right now—at Doctors Hospital!" He pulled a paper out of his breast pocket and read: "Doctor Burness and Doctor Hataki— You know 'em? Ever hear of 'em?"

"Of course," said Dr. Wakefield, shaken. He looked at Val with considerable apprehension.

"Equity says! That's the rule—the law!"

Val. "What makes you think we're going to allow you to—"

"*Allow*, you shithead?! Allow? I've got a court order—you wanna see it?"

"Yes," said Dr. Wakefield.

"Here's a *copy,*" said Art. "The doctors've got the original. Signed this afternoon. See it? Judge Kupferberg?"

The doctor handed the document to Val, who read it with difficulty. His hands were trembling.

"This is nothing," he mumbled.

"*Nothing?* You pisspot! You may have yourself a lawsuit that'll keep you broke forever—and her too, the phony little bitch!"

"Exhaustion," said Dr. Wakefield. "She's suffering from complete exhaustion. I'm sure my colleagues will concur."

And Christ Almighty! Damned if they *didn't!* The report came back from the hospital just as the overture struck up.

A moment before—Larry had walked out onto the stage and said: "Ladies and gentlemen. I'm Larry Gabel, the director of *Shine On, Harvest Moon*—and I'm afraid I have bad news. [A groan from the audience.] Yes. You've guessed it. Our Star is indisposed. In fact, hospitalized. Please keep your seats until I have finished. The performance will go on. The part of Nora will be played by a remarkably talented young player—Miss Patti Rolph. Now I know that many of you, perhaps most of you, came especially to see our Star—so here is our offer. Please stay for Act One: if at that time you wish to make an exchange for a later date or get a refund, the box office will be open to accommodate you—or you can make arrangements by mail or through your broker. Just be sure you keep your stubs. Ladies and gentlemen—who knows? This may turn out to be a memorable evening in the theatre. Thank you."

A surprisingly big hand. About eight or ten people left. No more.

The performance began. Patti, having been given a rousing pep talk in the dressing room a few minutes earlier, came on in high. There was nothing tentative or shy about her attack—which so relieved the audience, that her first number damn near brought down the house. I suspect that Larry's skillful curtain speech did a good deal toward smoothing the way, too.

In any case, she went from strength to strength throughout the evening.

I stood between Larry and Gene at the back of the house, watching. We said little, but it was clear we each had thoughts.

Toward the end of Act One, Gene said, "Here they are, The Star Mafia."

We looked across the rear of the auditorium, and indeed, there they were: Val, Alan, Bud, and the rest. They left just before the end of Act One, and returned a few minutes after Act Two began. They looked grim.

I have no way of knowing what they thought, nor what Larry or Gene thought—my own feeling was that the show needed Star. Patti was good and game and talented—but that added dimension, that "star quality" was absent. Of course, I had seen dozens of performances *with* Star, some of them excellent. Suppose I put it this way: Patti was better than Star at her worst, but nowhere near as good as Star at her even less than best.

The audience, on the other hand, had no such frame of reference. They loved Patti, they loved the show. They felt they were in on a happening. At the intermission, with the Star Mafia watching—only four tickets were exchanged. Four out of 1860—not bad.

At the curtain, a definite ovation for Patti and the show, and when she took her solo call—a standing ovation. The cast applauded, she wept. It was something. And I prayed that Star would stop malingering or that She would recover—because more than anything, I wanted to see that dirty, no-good, stuck-up, stinking, rotten bitch as Nora once again.

We went back to see Patti, who looked as though she had lost fifteen pounds. She looked old and exhausted. I wondered if *she* would next be put into Doctors Hospital.

"Super!" said Larry.

"Congratulations," said Gene.

And I knew they thought what I thought.

"I'll be better tomorrow," said Patti. "You'll see."

At which Larry and Gene exchanged a meaningful look.

Art jumped into the room—I said jumped—yelling, "Four returns! Two pair! Seventy bucks out of thirty-two thousand five hundred and fifty. Holy Jesus! You know what that means? It means every performance She misses, we make more money. Holy Jesus!"

He was gone.

"Get a good night's rest, Patti," said Larry.

"Thanks for everything," she said.

As we left, Hy was bringing in Dick Zanuck and Brown—all three beaming.

"A star is born," said Hy. "Hey! Song title! The fellows are mad about her—aren't you, fellows?"

"Mad's the word," said Zanuck.

"Ditto," said Brown.

"Jesus," said Hy, "history repeats. This is Shirley MacLaine and Hal Wallis all over again! Remember that one?"

"And this girl's got youth!" said Zanuck.

"So did Shirley," said Larry, "when Wallis signed her."

"That's right!" said Brown. "You know he's perfectly *right?*"

It was cold, but we walked uptown anyway.

"What'd you think, Midge?"

I told him.

"That's about me, too," said Gene. "Seems ungracious in view of the fact that she kept the curtain up, kept the show alive. But what the hell—fact's a fact. What's your guess, Larry?"

"Fifty-fifty chance for tomorrow. If She misses, we'd better postpone."

"But you think She'll open sometime?"

"I'm sure of it. Just as soon as She's eaten everyone's nerves to the bone."

In the lobby of The Plaza, Gene asked, "Oak Bar?"

"Not me, thanks," said Larry. "I'm still beat from *last* night."

He got into the elevator.

"What about *you*, partner?" asked Gene.

"Algonquin," I said.

"Good."

We walked there, had a slow drink, went upstairs and spent a quiet reflective time as we prepared for bed. Once there, I clung to Gene —my life raft. We slept for half an hour or so, then awoke and made love, a new kind—gentle and comforting—a quintessential expression of friendship. Glorious.

A lazy, crazy day. The suspense began early, directly after breakfast. A call from Larry.

"She's going on!" I called in to Gene in the bathroom.

"Great!" he called back.

Half an hour later, Art.

"She's not," I reported.

Gene put his newspaper down and put on his jacket.

"Come on, love," he said. "We're going to be unfindable all day today."

"Wait," I said. I phoned Art and told him I wouldn't be in.

"Why not?" he asked.

"I'm sick," I said. "Just like Star!"

Gene and I went to a morning movie, the highly praised Russian film, *A Slave of Love*. Overwhelming. Then by taxi to the World Trade Center and lunched in the sky at Windows on the World, and discussed the picture thoroughly. We looked out and down, and thought we could see The Imperial Theatre.

"It doesn't seem all that important from up here, does it?" asked Gene.

We walked through the downtown area to Fraunces Tavern, went in, looked around. Taxi to the Frick, walked to the Guggenheim, down to The Plaza, a slow carriage ride to Tavern on the Green. Shared a bottle of Dom Pérignon. Back to our carriage, and soon the Algonquin. Showers. Made raucous, laughing love. Changed. Six-o'clock dinner at La Grenouille—only four others at that unfashionable hour—then to the theatre for the final preview, happily ready for anything.

Star arrived. Patti wept again.

Curtain up, and in the first ten minutes, we knew our troubles were over. Saul, standing beside us, resplendent in his new dinner jacket, began to sob and could not stop. In the confusion, he somehow got the idea that this was opening night. Well, in a way it was.

She took hold, played the show, related to the company, led the audience, and what is most important, became and remained Nora Bayes—with all her gifts and hopes and troubles and triumphs. I had the feeling that I had never before seen *Shine On, Harvest Moon. This* was the memorable evening.

Backstage after the show was a madhouse. Everyone connected with the enterprise showed up. Ivan and Nadia. Alicia. The record boys, beaming. (I didn't know they *could!*) Cindy Sapiro. Neysa, kissing everyone. Millie. Hy, high on something. Fred, glassy-eyed. Art, hysterical. Jenny, drunk. Absolute unshakable confidence in the air.

Onstage, Larry talks to the company—very briefly. "That's it," he says. "You've done it. Now all you've got to do is do it again and again and again and again, ad infinitum. Fred Astaire in *The Gay Divorce* at The Shubert Theatre did the greatest single dance number ever. 'Night and Day.' Dancing on the furniture, on the mantelpiece, all over the room. It was so spectacular, so dangerous— In later years, when I got to know him, I asked him how he had done it. 'Well,' he said, in that diffident way of his, 'I used to get to the theatre at about six-thirty and go out on the stage and do it. Then, once I'd done it —I knew I could do it again.' So that's it. Hang on to it. I promise you it's worth hanging on to—and we want to hang on to *you*, each and every one—as long as we can. One we've lost already, as you know —Patti. She's off to Lotus Land. Take our thanks and love with you, Patti. That's all. See you after the show tomorrow night. Forget it's an opening. Just play another great show."

Hugs and kisses—Patti and Star, a notable coupling.

Art invites the staff to supper at "21."

"Fine," says Gene. "See you there."

We walk to Fifth and start uptown. Gene is thinking, so I let him. We reach 52nd Street, but he keeps walking. Another two blocks, and I say, "We've passed it, love."

"I know," he says, turning back, but continuing downtown and to the Algonquin.

"You didn't think I was going to spend our last evening together with that hellhound, did you?" he asks.

"But you said—"

"Easier."

"And what do you mean, 'last evening'? For God's sake. *Please!*"

"This is it, love. Back to life tomorrow. It's time."

"—the opening?" I say, stunned.

"Nothing I can do about that now, is there?"

"No, I guess not."

"It's been a tremendous adventure—one of the best and most stimulating of my life. It'll take me months to sort it out, maybe years. And whatever happens tomorrow, I'm—"

"Whatever? You *know*, don't you?"

"Certainly not. Anything can happen— She may revert—She has before—and we know what that means. No matter, I've done what I can do."

"Please stay."

"Can't."

"Why not?"

"I don't want to. For the first time, Midge—darling Midge—I'm panicked. Scared out of my wits. I've *got* to get out of here. I feel like London in the Blitz. Ridiculous, I know."

"Wait till morning, then decide. Please?"

"All right."

We went to bed and lay apart for a long time, sharing sadness. It seemed years before he reached out and touched me. When he did, I moved to him at once and we kissed.

Inside I was screaming, "Don't go! For Christ's sweet sake, don't go! One more day! Night! Don't go!"

Where had I read it? What sage had pronounced it? "The way to get a man is to be sexually attractive. The way to hold on to a man is to be sexually satisfactory."

Well, we'll see. I was determined—in mind, body, and cunt, to see if there was any truth in this admonition. Where would he find love like mine? Who was waiting for him in Chicago? Fuck her! No. Fuck *him*. Yes.

In all our miraculous time together, there had been no such exchange. It was a farewell, all right, and we made it into a long long occasion. It would have to be enough to last me into infinity—I could not imagine sharing myself with anyone else ever. Was it possible? What we were doing? Or was all this taking place in imagination? I shall write no more about it, other than to record that it was the pre-eminent, surpassing, transcendent lovemaking of all time.

<u>SHINE ON, HARVEST MOON</u>

Company Bulletin

Friday, February 1

<u>OPENING-NIGHT AUDIENCES</u>: New York opening-night audiences are traditionally unpredictable. They may respond too much, or not enough. They seldom hit the norm of a regular audience. We are in good shape. Sing out. Play confidently.

<u>SECOND NIGHT</u>: Having not yet played our first night, any discussion of the second night may appear to be gratuitous, but we feel it is worth reminding you that the second night is just as important as the first night.

<u>HEALTH AND WELFARE</u>: For God's sake take care in the next several hours. Don't play with knives, and don't eat funny foods, and, from its knees, the Management implores the members of the company to dispense with any alcoholic refreshment until the final curtain has fallen.

<u>ROAD COMPANY?</u>:
    "Girls came of their own volition and when the quota was filled the equivalent of the No Casting Today sign of the theatrical office was posted in the outer hall. There usually was a waiting list. In jest, Minna and Ada often discussed the feasibility of putting out a road company, but never got around to it.
    "The Everleigh Club was, in the lingo of Broadway ticket brokers, a 'hot ticket.' The show was a bona fide hit, running twice as long as 'Abie's Irish Rose' and exhibiting to four times the gross. As in the case of 'Abie,' many came more than once. It also had the same Romeo-and-Juliet quality that motivated 'Abie.' It must have been the neighborhood."

                                        Washburn

<u>QUOTATION FOR TODAY</u>:
        "We are a part of all we have met, and we've met
        them all."

                                        Ada Everleigh
<u>OPENING NIGHT</u>: GODSPEED.

· LVII ·

I awoke feeling bereft. In a moment, I was to know why. It was noon, and he was gone. On the bedtable beside me, a handwritten letter.

> Midge, dear girl, dear friend, dear person, dear love: My business is words and now when I need them, they fail me.
>
> I sit here, writing as quietly as I can so as not to awaken you.
>
> You gave me back my youth, for which I thank you—but now, as I take my leave of you—I feel old again.
>
> If only you had had the wit to be born some twenty years earlier —or is it my fault? Should I have waited?
>
> Still, we had the Heaven of meeting in a demented, artificial world—where you befriended me beyond any dream of amity I have ever cherished.
>
> For more things and kindnesses and generosities and help than my bewildered brain can summon at this wretched moment— my undying gratitude, my everlasting love.
>
> I do love you. And the fact that I must not, should not—makes it all the more poignant.
>
> To be real for an instant—let me hear from you. Surely there is a measure of harmony we can share. You have a life before you, mine is becoming largely memory.

I suppose I will be coming to New York one day when the smoke has cleared. Business, you know. In that happy event, may I call you? Perhaps we can go somewhere high up and look down on the silly world down there again.

The short life you permitted me to share with you was anything *but* silly—it was a soaring, unforgettable dream.

My hand in yours.

Gene

It took me an hour and two and a half breakfasts to decide what to do, then I did it.

I checked out of the Algonquin and went home to 55th Street. I packed. I packed what I would need immediately and I packed what I would need permanently. I arranged to have UPS pick up everything. Key with the super. I called Mr. Kritzman at Douglas Elliman about the sublease. I left a temporary forwarding address: The Whitehall, 105 East Delaware Place, Chicago, Illinois 60611. I called The Whitehall and made a reservation for two days, beginning tonight. I called Vartan.

"I thought you were dead," he said.

"Just the opposite, darling. Listen. I'm leaving New York."

"Show finished?"

"Opens tonight. Looks good."

"Aren't you supposed to be there?" he asked.

"Yes—but that's why."

"You sound loopy."

"Oh, I am! I am!"

"What?"

"Vartan—dear—brother! Will you tell a lie for me?"

"Why not?"

"Call Art Clune's office—say Pop is sick and I have to come right home."

"Certainly not!"

"Why not?" I asked.

"Terrible idea. Bad luck."

"Jesus, you're not going to go fucking superstitious on me, are you?"

"Mariam!! Is that you?"

"Will you do it? It's life or death!"

"I'll tell you what," he said. "I'll say *I'm* sick."

"How can you phone if you're sick?"

"I mean, my secretary will say—"

"All right, but right *now.* Judson six, one one five five—got it? Area code two one two. I'll call you. I'll write you. I love you. I love you like a brother."

All this took all day. The phone rang incessantly during those times when I was in the apartment, but I paid no attention. My mind was on my future. The egg of my life was hatching.

I made the last plane to Chicago. Nine fifty-five P.M., United. Slept all the way. To The Whitehall by 11:45, Chicago time. Twelve forty-five in New York. I phone Sardi's—Belasco Room. It takes twenty minutes to get Clay to the phone—I don't want to talk to anyone else. At last, Clay.

"How is he?" he asks.

"I'm not there yet. Layover in Chicago."

"Oh."

"What happened?" I ask.

"Smash."

"Say it again."

"Smash!"

"What's in?"

"All the TV—raveroo. Radio same. *Times* and *News* over the moon. Don't know *Post* yet, but hear great. *Time, Newsweek*—everything."

"Wow!"

"That seems to be the word of the hour, honey. Wow. When will you be back?"

"I don't know. Anyway—thanks. See y'."

Too late to call what I came for. Sleep unthinkable. I get into a comfortable chair by the window and look out at Chicago—at the night, at the lake—and I think of the past six and a half months. I try to do it as chronologically as possible—remembering it all—step by step. Now and then, I doze. When I wake, I pick up from where I left off. In the end, as the sun comes up, I am happy for all of them: Art, Hy, Fred, Star, Ivan, Alicia (Alicia!), Clay, Jenny, Phil, Patti, Gloria, Calvin—everyone. Gene. Gene! What am I waiting for?

Seven-forty-five. I dialed. One ring. Two. Three. Oh, God! Four.

· 521 ·

"Yes?"

"Yes!" I said.

"How are you?"

"Fine. Have you heard?"

"*God,* yes! Phone hasn't stopped all night. Isn't it grand?"

"Yes."

"Unbelievable."

"No, it's not," I said. "It's believable. What's *un*believable is that I'm here."

"Where?"

"In Chicago."

"What?"

"Here."

"Where?"

"In Chicago. *I'm in Chicago!*"

"What are you doing in Chicago?"

"I live here," I said.